£4.9

RADIATION RISK, RISK PERCEPTION AND SOCIAL CONSTRUCTIONS

Proceedings of a Workshop,
Oslo, Norway, October 19–20 1995

Co-organised by:

The Norwegian Radiation Protection Authority
The Swedish Radiation Protection Institute, and
The European Commission

Proceedings Editors:

J.B. Reitan
U. Bäverstam
G.N. Kelly

ISBN 1 870965 44 2
CONF 9510147
EUR 16518 EN
RADIATION PROTECTION DOSIMETRY Vol. 68 Nos. 3/4 1996
Published by Nuclear Technology Publishing

RADIATION RISK, RISK PERCEPTION
AND
SOCIAL CONSTRUCTIONS

Proceedings of a Workshop,
Oslo, Norway, October 19–20 1995

British Library Cataloguing in Publication Data

A catalogue record of this book is available at the British Library

© ECSC-EEC-EAEC Brussels-Luxembourg (1996)
Publication No EUR 16518 EN of the Commission of the European Communities,
Dissemination of Scientific and Technical Knowledge Unit
Directorate-General Telecommunications
Information Industries and Exploitation Research, Luxembourg

RADIATION RISK, RISK PERCEPTION
AND
SOCIAL CONSTRUCTIONS

Proceedings of a Workshop,
Oslo, Norway, October 19–20 1995

SCIENTIFIC COMMITTEE

J. Brenot	IPSN, Fontenay-aux-Roses, France
G.N. Kelly	CEC, DGXII, Brussels, Belgium
B. Mårdberg	Swedish War College, Stockholm, Sweden
J.B. Reitan (Chairman)	NRPA, Østerås, Norway
L. Sjøberg	Stockholm School of Economics, Sweden
L. Weisæth	University of Oslo, Norway

ORGANISING COMMITTEE

U. Bäverstam	SSI, Stockholm, Sweden
G.N. Kelly	CEC, DGXII, Brussels, Belgium
P. Strand (Chairman)	NRPA, Østerås, Norway
A. Tønnessen	NRPA, Østerås, Norway
H. Velle	NRPA, Østerås, Norway,
R. Waldahl	University of Oslo, Norway

SESSION CHAIRMEN AND PANEL

J. Brenot	IPSN, Fontenay-aux-Roses, France
G.N. Kelly	CEC, DGXII, Brussels, Belgium
L. Sjøberg	Stockholm School of Economics, Sweden
L. Weisæth	University of Oslo, Norway
L. Weisæth	University of Oslo, Norway

Acknowledgements

The professional work by Hans Velle in dealing with all the main practical organisational details and the excellent secretarial contribution by Mrs Marianne Jarnøy in preparing papers for submission to the publishers are very gratefully acknowledged.

Radiation Protection Dosimetry

ISSN 0144-8420

Editor-in-Chief:
Dr J.A. Dennis, UK

Executive Editor:
Mr E.P. Goldfinch, UK

Staff Editor:
Mrs M.E. Calcraft, UK

Consultant Editors:
Prof. Dr G. Dietze, Germany
Prof. Y. Horowitz, Israel
Dr J. Stather, UK
Dr G.A. Swedjemark, Sweden

Editorial Board Members
Dr R.M. Alexakhin, Russia
Prof. Dr K. Becker, Germany
Dr M.A. Bender, USA
Dr A. Birchall, UK
Prof. Dr J. Böhm, Germany
Dr A.J.J. Bos, The Netherlands
Dr L. Bötter-Jensen, Denmark
Dr G. Busuoli, Italy
Mr M.W. Carter, Australia
Dr M.W. Charles, UK
Mr G. Cowper, Canada
Dr W.G. Cross, Canada
Dr A. Delgado, Spain
Dr Li Deping, People's Republic of China
Prof. Dr B. Dörschel, Germany
Prof. Dr K. Duftschmid, Austria
Miss F.A. Fry, UK
Mr J.A.B. Gibson, UK
Mr R.V. Griffith, USA
Dr K. Harrison, UK
Mr J.R. Harvey, UK
Dr H. Ing, Canada

Dr K. Irlweck, Austria
Prof. Dr W. Jacobi, Germany
Dr R.L. Kathren, USA
Dr E. Kunz, Czech Republic
Dr D.C. Lloyd, UK
Dr H.F. Macdonald, UK
Mr T.O. Marshall, UK
Dr J.C. McDonald, USA
Dr M. Moscovitch, USA
Prof. Y. Nishiwaki, Japan
Mr K. O'Brien, USA
Dr P. Pihet, France
Dr G. Portal, France
Dr A.S. Pradhan, India
Dr D.F. Regulla, Germany
Prof. Dr A.R. Scharmann, Germany
Mr J.M. Selby, USA
Dr F. Spurný, Czech Republic
Dr R.H. Thomas, USA
Mr I.M.G. Thompson, UK
Dr L. Tommasino, Italy
Mr J.W.N. Tuyn, Switzerland

Published by Nuclear Technology Publishing, P.O. Box 7, Ashford, Kent, TN23 1YW, England.

Advertising office: Mrs L. Richmond   Subscription office: Mrs M.L. Mears

Subscription rates,   1996: Vols. 63–68 inclusive, UK £590.00 p.a.; outside UK US$ 1270.00 p.a.
1997: Vols. 69–74 inclusive, UK £620.00 p.a.; outside UK US$ 1330.00 p.a.

Orders and remittance should be sent to:

Subscription Department, Nuclear Technology Publishing, P.O. Box No 7, Ashford, Kent, TN23 1YW, England
Telephone (01233) 641683   Facsimile (01233) 610021

COPYRIGHT ©1996 Nuclear Technology Publishing

Legal disclaimer: The publisher, the editors and the Editorial Board accept no responsibility for the content of the papers, the use which may be made of the information or the views expressed by the authors.

Typeset by Photographics, Vine Yard, Vine Passage, Honiton, Devon, England
Printed by Geerings of Ashford Ltd., Cobbs Wood House, Chart Road, Ashford, Kent, England

Radiation Protection Dosimetry
Vol. 68, No. 3/4, pp. v – vi (1996)
Nuclear Technology Publishing

Contents

CONTENTS

Radiation Protection Dosimetry is abstracted or indexed in APPLIED HEALTH PHYSICS ABSTRACTS
AND NOTES, Chemical Abstracts, CURRENT CONTENTS, Energy Information Abstracts (Cambridge),
EXCERPTA MEDICA (EMBASE), Health and Safety Science Abstracts (Cambridge), INIS ATOMINDEX (hard
copy and CD ROM), INSPEC, Nuclear Energy (Czech Republic), QUEST and Referativmaja Zhurnal.

Radiation Protection Dosimetry
Vol. 68, No. 3/4, p. 155 (1996)
Nuclear Technology Publishing

Editorial

Radiation Risk, Risk Perception and Social Constructions

In October 1995 an international workshop on Radiation Risk, Risk Perception and Social Constructions was convened in Oslo, Norway, co-organised by the Norwegian and Swedish radiation protection authorities and the European Commission. Radiation protection authorities are concerned with measurements and evaluation of radiation doses to the population in their daily work, considering questions about whether or not these doses have harmful effects on man, and trying to minimise unnecessary doses. The agencies issue regulations to industry, institutions, health professionals and the public, on the basis of recommendations from, for example, the International Commission on Radiological Protection (ICRP). This activity is a form of applied natural science, and, of course, a vital base for radiation protection and the workshop.

Many of us have been struck by the fact that worries in the population about radiation do not parallel the assessment of the statistical risks in question. The public is concerned about nuclear industry and waste problems, as well as more general nuclear pollution such as in the Urals or the Kola peninsula. They seem less concerned about increasing radiation doses due to new technologies in medical radiology, or radon in homes. The Chernobyl accident highlighted these issues. The enormous efforts in mitigating the nuclear pollution from the accident fallout and the engagement by politicians and people in public life in general have been questioned by several institutions, national and international, because the mean doses to the population in most countries outside the former Soviet Union, and even for most groups within it was, in general, quite low. However, people experienced the contamination of water, soil and air in a highly charged context of uncertainty and in some areas people experienced alienation and felt rejected as contagious. Many felt influenced beyond their control and comprehension. What followed was a loss of trust in institutions trying to help them in time of need, and they might view the authorities as able but unwilling to act. When national agencies finally found there was sufficient cause to issue public warnings, groups in the community were already convinced that they had been poisoned. On the other hand, government authorities in many countries saw only a range of hyperactive citizens and a sensationalist press, and they urged the public to behave in a more 'responsible and rational manner', towards a crisis which might well prove to be no threat at all.

Such considerations should turn us towards questions of ethics and democracy. In fact, authorities and civil servants are expected to act on behalf of and in the interests of the public. Members of the public are within their rights to make demands of an administration in accordance with their own political preferences. There are apparently qualitative issues and values which are not regularly taken into account in radiation protection. We are obviously observing the problems within different frameworks, no one more true than another. Some consider risk to be a quantifiable attribute of technologies and a basis for decisions. For others, risk has a meaning in its wide social and political context only, as a subjective feeling which can be felt by anyone, expert or not. As a parallel, the growing population in the world may be considered within a reproduction context, and the solution may be different types of contraception. Alternatively, it can be framed within a social context of securing the life for old people by having many children, and the solution is combating poverty and famine. Both viewpoints may be right, and are not mutually exclusive. Moreover, the ultimate goal is to work for a better society, where people feel secure in the sense of their human rights. This is also true in radiation protection. The award of the 1995 Nobel Peace Prize to the Pugwash movement and Dr Rotblat highlighted the fact that nuclear science has moral aspects.

The proceedings volume contains nearly all of the communications at the workshop, as well as a few papers which were intended for presentation, but where the author was prevented from attending for differing reasons. The workshop was aimed at bringing together scientists from different disciplines to report results, discuss common problems, and meet in a cross-discipline milieu. It apparently reached its aim, was a stimulating event for all participants, made new friends, and hopefully opened the way for cross-discipline research in the future.

J.B. Reitan, U. Bäverstam and G.N. Kelly

Previous Proceedings published in **Radiation Protection Dosimetry** on behalf of the Commission for the European Communities

EXOELECTRON EMISSION AND ITS APPLICATIONS 166 pp, Softback, Proceedings of the VIIth International Symposium, Strasbourg, March 1983, Price US$66.50

INDOOR EXPOSURE TO NATURAL RADIATION AND ASSOCIATED RISK ASSESSMENT 440 pp, Softback, Proceedings of an International Seminar, Anacapri, October 1983, Price US$133.00

MICRODOSIMETRIC COUNTERS IN RADIATION PROTECTION 120 pp, Softback, Proceedings of a Workshop, Hamburg/Saar, May 1984, Price US$47.50

RADIATION PROTECTION QUANTITIES FOR EXTERNAL EXPOSURE 166 pp, Softback, Proceedings of a Seminar, Braunschweig, March 1985, Price US$66.50

MICRODOSIMETRY 400 pp, Softback, Proceedings of the Ninth Symposium on Microdosimetry, Toulouse, May 1985, Price US$133.00

DOSIMETRY OF BETA PARTICLES AND LOW ENERGY X RAYS 134 pp, Softback, Proceedings of a Workshop, Saclay, October 1985, Price US$57.00

ENVIRONMENTAL AND HUMAN RISKS OF TRITIUM 192 pp, Softback, Proceedings of a Workshop, Karlsruhe, February 1986, Price US$76.00

ETCHED TRACK NEUTRON DOSIMETRY 130 pp, Softback, Proceedings of a Workshop, Harwell, May 1987, Price US$47.50

ACCIDENTAL URBAN CONTAMINATION 192 pp, Softback, Proceedings of a Workshop, Roskilde, June 1987, Price US$76.00

NEUTRON DOSIMETRY 498 pp, Softback, Proceedings of the Sixth Symposium on Neutron Dosimetry, Neuherberg, October 1987, Price US$142.50

NATURAL RADIOACTIVITY 560 pp, Softback, Proceedings of the Fourth International Symposium on the Natural Radiation Environment, Lisbon, December 1987, Price US$161.50

BIOLOGICAL ASSESSMENT OF OCCUPATIONAL EXPOSURE TO ACTINIDES 400 pp, Softback, Proceedings of a Workshop, Versailles, May 1988, Price US$123.50

IMPLEMENTATION OF DOSE-EQUIVALENT QUANTITIES INTO RADIATION PROTECTION PRACTICE (ISBN 1 870965 03 5) 166 pp, Softback, Proceedings of a Seminar, Braunschweig, June 1988, Price US$66.50

IMPLEMENTATION OF DOSE-EQUIVALENT METERS BASED ON MICRODOSIMETRIC TECHNIQUES (ISBN 1 870965 04 1) 156 pp, Softback, Proceedings of a Seminar, Schloss Elmau, October 1988, Price US$57.00

MICRODOSIMETRY (ISBN 1 870965 05 X) 460 pp, Softback, Proceedings of the Tenth Symposium on Microdosimetry, Rome, May 1989, Price US$152.00

STATISTICS OF HUMAN EXPOSURE TO IONISING RADIATION (ISBN 1 870965 08 6) 280 pp, Hardback, Proceedings of a Workshop, Oxford, April 1990, Price US$114.00

RESPIRATORY TRACT DOSIMETRY (ISBN 1 870965 09 4) 268 pp, Hardback, Proceedings of a Workshop, Albuquerque, July 1990, Price US$114.00

SKIN DOSIMETRY - RADIOLOGICAL PROTECTION ASPECTS OF SKIN IRRADIATION (ISBN 1 870965 12 4) 212 pp, Hardback, Proceedings of a Workshop, Dublin, May 1991, Price US$114.00

DOSIMETRY IN DIAGNOSTIC RADIOLOGY (ISBN 1 870965 11 6) 316 pp, Hardback, Proceedings of a Seminar, Luxembourg, March 1991, Price US$152.00

AGE DEPENDENT FACTORS IN THE BIOKINETICS AND DOSIMETRY OF RADIONUCLIDES (ISBN 1 870965 15 9) 254 pp, Hardback, Proceedings of a Workshop, Schloss Elmau, November 1991, Price US$114.00

GUIDEBOOK FOR THE TREATMENT OF ACCIDENTAL INTERNAL CONTAMINATION OF WORKERS (ISBN 1 870965 22 1) 50 pp, 'Softback, A Joint Publication for the CEC and the USDOE, Price US$38.00

NEUTRON DOSIMETRY (ISBN 1 870965 16 7) 486 pp, Hardback, Proceedings of the Seventh Symposium on Neutron Dosimetry, Berlin, October 1991, Price US$152.00

THE NATURAL RADIATION ENVIRONMENT (ISBN 1 870965 14 0) 800 pp, Hardback, Proceedings of the Fifth International Symposium, Salzburg, September 1991, Price US$228.00

RADIATION EXPOSURE OF CIVIL AIRCREW (ISBN 1 870965 13 2) 140 pp, Hardback, Proceedings of a Workshop, Luxembourg, June 1991, Price US$57.00

TEST PHANTOMS AND OPTIMISATION IN DIAGNOSTIC RADIOLOGY AND NUCLEAR MEDICINE (ISBN 1 870965 26 4) 416 pp, Hardback, Proceedings of a Workshop, Wurzburg, June 1992, Price US$152.00

MICRODOSIMETRY (ISBN 1 870965 21 3) 500 pp, Hardback, Proceedings of the Eleventh Symposium on Microdosimetry, Gatlinburg, September 1992, Price US$171.00

DECISION MAKING SUPPORT FOR OFF-SITE EMERGENCY MANAGEMENT (ISBN 1 870965 25 6) 320 pp, Hardback, Proceedings of a Workshop, Schloss Elmau, October 1992, Price US$114.00

INTAKES OF RADIONUCLIDES - DETECTION, ASSESSMENT AND LIMITATION OF OCCUPATIONAL EXPOSURE (ISBN 1 870965 28 0) 370 pp, Hardback, Proceedings of a Workshop, Bath, September 1993, Price US$152.00

INDIVIDUAL MONITORING OF IONISING RADIATION - THE IMPACT OF RECENT ICRP AND ICRU PUBLICATIONS. (ISBN 1 870965 29 9) 232 pp, Hardback, Proceedings of a Workshop, Villigen, May 1993, Price US$85.50

INDOOR RADON REMEDIAL ACTIONS -THE SCIENTIFIC AND PRACTICAL IMPLICATIONS. (ISBN 1 870965 30 2) 400 pp, Hardback, Proceedings of a Workshop, Rimini, Italy, June 27 to July 2 1993, Price US$171.00

QUALITY CONTROL AND RADIATION PROTECTION OF THE PATIENT IN DIAGNOSTIC RADIOLOGY AND NUCLEAR MEDICINE. (ISBN 1 870965 37 X) 512 pp, Hardback. Proceedings of a Workshop, Grado, Italy, September 29−October 1 1993, Price US$171.00

ADVANCES IN RADIATION MEASUREMENTS: APPLICATIONS AND RESEARCH NEEDS IN HEALTH PHYSICS AND DOSIMETRY. (ISBN 1 870965 33 7), 310 pp, Hardback. Proceedings of an International Workshop, Chalk River, Ontario, Canada, October 3-6, 1994 Price US$142.50

FUTURE PUBLICATIONS:

NEUTRON DOSIMETRY, (ISBN 1 870965 43 4) 152 pp, Hardback. Proceedings of the Eighth Symposium, Paris, November 13−17 1995 Price US$184.30

REAL TIME COMPUTING OF THE ENVIRONMENTAL CONSEQUENCES OF AN ACCIDENTAL RELEASE FROM A NUCLEAR INSTALLATION. (ISBN 1 870965 49 3), Proceedings of the Fourth International Workshop, Aronsborg, October 6−11 1996. Price not yet known.

Radiation Protection Dosimetry
Vol. 68, No. 3/4, pp. 157–163 (1996)
Nuclear Technology Publishing

THE RISK PHILOSOPHY OF RADIATION PROTECTION

B. Lindell
Swedish Radiation Protection Institute
S-171 16 Stockholm, Sweden

INVITED PAPER

Abstract — After a discussion of the meaning of 'risk', the processes of risk assessment and risk evaluation are described. The assumptions behind current radiation risk assessments, which are focussed on the probability of attributable death from radiation-induced cancer, are reviewed. These assessments involve projection models to take account of future cancer death in irradiated populations, the transfer of risk estimates between populations and the assumptions necessary to derive risk assessments for low radiation doses from actual observations at high doses. The paper ends with a presentation of the basic radiation protection recommendations of the International Commission on Radiological Protection (ICRP) in the context of a risk philosophy.

THE CONCEPT OF RISK

Risk definitions

There is no universal definition of 'risk'. To the layman, 'risk' is often a diffuse threat, an uncomfortable possibility that something dreadful will happen. In professional terms, we speak about a possible *consequence* and of the *probability* that it will actually occur. If we wish to describe a situation involving risk, therefore, we must refer to both the consequence and the probability of its occurrence. In most cases, there is also not just one possible consequence but a multitude of consequences, each one with its probability. If risk is seen as a quantity, it is therefore a *multidimensional* quantity and cannot be unambiguously represented by a single number[1].

Acceptable risk

It is not meaningful to ask whether a risk, as defined above, is acceptable. Such a question would be similar to asking whether a stone is too heavy. Neither the weight of a stone, nor the magnitude of a risk can be judged out of context. The acceptability of a risk depends on the associated benefit of the decision, practice or situation that causes the risk. It is not the risk but the situation or practice that we accept or reject. We may not necessarily accept something which brings us no benefit and is of no interest to us just because the risk is trivial[2].

Unacceptable risks

There is no risk-free society and this fact is usually well recognised. To quote the International Commission on Radiological Protection (ICRP): 'There seems to be an unspoken convention that we are willing to accept certain levels of risk in order to enjoy the benefits of a modern society, provided that the risks are not un-

necessary or easily avoided.'[3] These risks are accepted by implication, but if unusually high risks are encountered, the acceptance of the situation will depend on many factors as will be described in the following section. There are levels of risk (usually levels of the associated probability of individual death) which most people would find unacceptable if they arise from other than voluntary actions. The concept of unacceptable risks under normal life conditions is behind the choice of individual dose limits in radiation protection. Voluntarily, people are willing to take much higher risks (smoking being one example) and sometimes voluntary risk taking seems to have an attractiveness of its own.

ATTITUDES TO RISK

Risk perception

It is the author's opinion that 'risk perception' often relates to the situation or practice that causes the risk, rather than to the risk itself. It is a semantic question whether the word 'risk' should be reserved for what has above been called risk or have a wider meaning covering other aspects. For this presentation, the meaning is limited to the complex of event probabilities and consequences as described above. Some authors, e.g. Sandman[4], use 'hazard' rather than 'risk' for this concept, but this has the disadvantage that this word already has other connotations (e.g. that which causes the risk).

With this limited definition of risk, two types of risk perception may be identified, although there is no distinct borderline. A simple — perhaps too simple — classification will be used where the first type relates to the identification, quantification and description of the risk (risk assessment) and the second to the attitude towards the risk situation (risk evaluation).

Risk assessment

With 'risk' defined as a set of event probabilities and

consequences, risk assessment essentially consists in quantification of event probabilities and description of the associated consequences. The result is sometimes referred to as the 'objective risk', in contrast to a perceived or subjective risk. In reality, however, there is no distinct difference, because any risk assessment is by necessity subjective. This perhaps unexpected statement will be supported by the following discussion.

Assessing probabilities

Probability is a concept which is often misunderstood. Its main use is as a tool to predict future frequencies of events. If experience says that 83 out of 100,000 individuals of a certain age died within a year, we can say that the probability of death was 0.083% and that, under similar conditions, we would expect about 25 (namely $0.00083 \times 30,000$) to die in a future year in a population of 30,000 individuals of the same age. But what does this probability of 0.083% mean in the case of only one identified individual?

To apply this probability meaningfully to any one given individual we must make two assumptions, namely (1) that the individual is an average individual in the population from which we have drawn our experience, and (2) that there has been no significant change in any of the conditions which prevailed when we obtained our experience.

All probabilities are conditional to assumptions based on some degree of knowledge and experience[5]. In orderto know whether a person's odds of surviving are better or worse than for the average person we need some knowledge, and our use of a probability value is therefore subjective, depending upon that knowledge. It is not helpful to state that a probability is one in a million if we do not feel very convinced that our assumptions are correct. It is not the uncertainty in the probability assessment which is the weak point, it is the uncertainty of the validity of the assumptions.

As regards radiation risks, the ICRP has stated a nominal probability coefficient of 5% per sievert for attributable death from cancer in an average individual[3]. We might say that this is the ICRP perception of cancer death probability and it is based on a number of assumptions which are more or less likely to be true. Some experts have different views and feel (i.e. perceive) that the probability is higher or lower. Laymen without capacity of their own of assessing the probability may perceive the probability as yet higher or might not believe in any risk at all.

In addition to risks composed of probabilities of harm to radiation-exposed individuals, there are risks involving events which may cause great societal harm, both economic, political and by death of many individuals from one single event such as a major reactor accident. In this case the meaning of the event probability is even more obscure. Such events are necessarily rare (or the practice would be discontinued). Any event probability

derived from an event frequency is of little use in the case of identified installations which are likely to deviate from the (non-existing) average. The assumption that the experienced frequency was obtained under conditions relevant for the particular installation can hardly be made. Probability assessments based on probabilistic methods (event trees, fault trees) are valid only on the assumption that no significant event chain has been overlooked, and little can be said about the validity of that assumption. Any probability statement, therefore, is rather meaningless if it is low, but highly suggestive if it is high.

Describing consequences

All probability statements are subjective because they depend on assumptions which in their turn depend on knowledge and experience. The description of consequences is equally or more subjective because consequences can be described in so many ways and the descriptions may be more or less complete. In assessing individual risks, ICRP to a large extent deals with the probability of death. However, there is a significant difference between death from cancer at the age of 80 or immediate death from an accident in childhood. The detriment of death has therefore been taken to depend on the expected number of years of life lost. In addition, there is a detriment also from curable cancer. This has been taken to be in proportion to the lethality fraction for each type of cancer, i.e. near 100 per cent for lung cancer and less than 1 per cent for skin cancer[3]. These assumptions involve judgements and there is no objective way of quantifying consequences.

This is even more obvious for societal consequences of a major catastrophe. There is no objective way of representing a number of deaths, the corresponding grief, associated economic losses, political agitation and social disrupture by one single member.

It therefore follows that, if different individuals are asked to rank risks according to magnitude, their rankings will differ. Some would give higher weight to the event probability, others would primarily see the consequence, and others again would combine probabilities and consequences[6]. The ranking will differ even if those making it have the best intentions of being objective and even if they are not told what causes the risk so that attitudes towards the actual risk situation do not enter into the picture.

Risk evaluation

If the actual risk situation is described this might change the result of the risk assessment but above all the circumstances will influence the attitude to the cause of the risk. Usually this is described as if there is a different risk perception[7,8]. My belief, without having any evidence for its truth, is that it would be better to talk about the attitude, not just to the risk but to its source. Smokers do not necessarily perceive their risk as small. It is true that badly informed smokers may underestimate the risk by orders of magnitude, but today many smokers know that their risk is high. It is not necessarily because of a perception of a low risk that they continue smoking (although some feel that 'this will not happen to me') but because they see a benefit in the practice and therefore have a positive attitude, you may say to the risk, I would prefer to say to the risk situation.

Sandman wants to combine the risk with what he calls an 'outrage factor'[(4)]. What he refers to is the same type of factors which other authors refer to as influencing risk perception. I would prefer to say that these factors influence the attitude to the situation or practice that causes the risk. If Sandman's outrage factors work in the outrage direction, the attitude becomes hostile. If in the other direction, the attitude becomes sympathetic.

The two dominating factors are the existence of some benefit and the feeling of control (as in the vase of voluntary actions), but there are many other factors listed, such as trust and ability to comprehend the situation. The result is that the acceptance of a situation (and its associated risk) does not merely depend on the magnitude of the risk. Some accept smoking in spite of the high risk, while the same individuals may not accept a situation where a much smaller risk arises from something which is not perceived as bringing any benefit and seems to be beyond control. This turns out to be entirely logical as long as we understand that it is the situation and not merely the risk that is evaluated (or, alternatively, that the risk is evaluated in the context of the situation). We do not evaluate 'naked' risks.

ASSUMPTIONS BEHIND CURRENT RADIATION RISK ASSESSMENTS

The ICRP concept of radiation risk

The ICRP protection policy is based on the assumption that, with the exception of accidents, doses encountered in radiation protection are not large enough to cause deterministic effects. Such effects are usually the effect of cell death, and in order to cause observable harm, the radiation dose must be large enough to kill a sufficient number of cells. For deterministic effects there is therefore a dose threshold, below which the effect cannot arise and the risk is zero. Effects such as cancer and hereditary harm are called stochastic effects, and their dose–response relation is assumed to show no threshold. The ICRP protection policy is based on the assumption that radiation doses not caused by accidents are kept so low that only stochastic effects occur[(3)].

In many other areas of health protection, deterministic effects dominate or cannot be ruled out even if no accidents occur. Therefore, in contrast to the radiation case, the possibility of zero risk is then often not seen as unrealistic. The assumed absence of a dose threshold,

and the lack of deterministic harm which makes cause–effect relations obvious, cause big communication problems about radiation risks. For stochastic effects, cause–effect relations can only be established on probabilistic grounds.

As already mentioned, ICRP essentially bases its radiation protection recommendations on the exposed individual's probability of death, i.e. seeing death as the dominating consequence. This simplifies the quantification of radiation risk, since, with the consequence kept constant, the probability of attributable death can be taken as the measure of the risk. However, ICRP recognises that the risk of death can be expressed in many different ways (e.g. by the age-dependent relative increase in the age-specific mortality rate, or by a combination of the death probability and the related life shortening). ICRP also tries to include the individual's detriment from non-lethal cancer and hereditary disease in descendants including all future generations, so that the probability of death becomes the probability of death-equivalent harm, a procedure which by necessity involves a lot of subjective assumptions and judgements. On this basis, ICRP has arrived at a 'nominal detriment coefficient' of which about two thirds consists of a 'nominal probability coefficient' of 5% per sievert for attributable cancer death of an average individual in the main population[(3)].

Major assumptions behind the derivation of the ICRP probability coefficient

For the magnitudes of radiation dose encountered in radiation protection under normal circumstances, the probability of cancer and hereditary harm is so small that the effects, due to statistical uncertainties, cannot be detected against the normal background of the same types of harm. The probability per unit dose at low doses (effective doses less than about 100 mSv) must therefore be inferred from observations at higher doses on assumptions about the biological mechanisms behind the causation of stochastic effects.

Sources of information

The basic source of information is the result of epidemiological studies of radiation-exposed populations. Such populations are, for example, groups of radiation workers, patients exposed to radiation during medical diagnostic or therapeutic procedures, and populations surviving major radiation accidents or irradiation from nuclear weapons as in Hiroshima and Nagasaki.

The atomic bomb survivors in Japan offer the best conditions for epidemiological studies. The studied group is large (some 80,000 individuals), it contains both sexes and all age groups in normal proportions, and the whole body was exposed. In other groups subject to epidemiological studies some of these conditions are not met. Most of the information on the carcinogenic risk at high doses is therefore derived from observations on the Japanese survivors. No hereditary harm has been observed, but from the experience of animal studies, it was not expected that the collective dose was high enough to cause observable hereditary harm[9].

Observations at high doses: projection models

Not even at high doses can the lifetime probability of attributable cancer be assessed without some assumptions, because a major fraction of the exposed population is still alive. If most of the radiation-induced cancer will come at high ages, some guess has to be made on how the age-specific probability rate of induced cancer varies with time. For this purpose, *projection models* have been used. The *additive model* was the first in use. It was based on the assumption that the annual probability of radiation-induced cancer is proportional to the radiation dose but constant over age after a minimum latency period.

When it was found that the rate of radiation-induced cancer seems to increase with age, other projection models were proposed. The simplest one, which has been used by ICRP, is based on the assumption that the age-specific probability rate of radiation-induced cancer is proportional, not only to the radiation dose but also to the normal age-specific cancer rate. This is called the *simple multiplicative model*. There are also other, more complicated models. Only time will show which one best described the actual situation.

With the multiplicative model, the lifetime probability of attributable cancer is twice as large as with the additive model, because more cancer will be expected at high ages. For the same reason, however, the expectation of loss of lifetime will be approximately the same. This illustrates how a risk can be described in several different ways[10].

Transfer of risk estimates between populations

Hereditary susceptibility and different promotive factors make it possible that the probability of radiation-induced cancer per unit dose differs between populations and between sub-groups within populations. Accumulating information on the requirement of a number of different DNA changes for cancer to be initiated indicates that this probability will depend of the degree of changes already obtained or expected because of other agents than radiation. If the multiplicative model holds approximately true it reflects this dependence on other agents and therefore on the overall cancer risk.

For specific cancer sites the difference in the overall cancer risk is substantial, e.g. stomach cancer in Japan compared with the western world, and lung cancer between smokers and non-smokers. However, ICRP has shown that, with all cancer sites taken together, the variation between national populations seems to be less pronounced. Nevertheless, a necessary assumption behind radiation risk estimates is that the population at risk must be representative of the population for which the risk was first assessed. If not, assumptions must be made on the basis for transferring the risk estimates, considering the differences in the total cancer risk for particular sites[3,10].

Possible dose–response for significant DNA modifications

DNA changes due to radiation may be either single or double strand breaks and associated base destruction. In the case of single strand breaks, repair is likely, and if there is base damage in a single strand this is also likely to be repaired because the crucial information has not been lost and may be used as a template. However, if there is also destruction of the other base before repair has occurred, there is no template for reconstruction, and there may be a cell death, gene deletion or a point mutation with consequences for cancer development. This would only happen if the dose or dose rate is sufficiently high for the second damage to occur before the first has been repaired, or if the other base is destroyed by causes other than radiation before repair of the first damage. If the first is the case, the necessity of both a first and a second hit by radiation would imply a quadratic dose response for each DNA modification necessary for cancer induction. At low doses, the modification would be caused by the first hit if the repair fails or if the second base is destroyed by other causes, which implies a linear relation to radiation dose at low doses and, for the same reason, at low dose rates. Densely ionising radiation could destroy the two bases already by one single track, and in this case a linear dose response would always be expected.

On this basis, it is generally assumed that the dose response for each significant DNA modification by sparsely ionising radiation, such as X rays and gamma rays, is linear-quadratic and always linear if the absorbed dose rate is less than 0.1 Gy.h^{-1} or the absorbed dose less than 0.2 Gy[3].

The assumption of 'linearity'

In the previous section we dealt with the possible dose–response relation for each significant DNA modification. We must now consider the dose–response relation for initiation of cancer, i.e. for causing all the necessary modifications for initiation of cancer[11].

Most cases of cancer are caused by agents other than radiation. We could devise a dose concept also for the exposure to such agents, not on the basis of absorbed energy, but on the power of causing changes in the DNA. If we accept that more than one modification is necessary in the DNA for initiation of cancer, say n changes, then the relation between the non-radiation 'dose' and the probability of all n changes would be in proportion to the nth power of the dose, i.e. increase rapidly with the accumulated 'dose' (just as we see that the cancer rate actually increases steeply with age). However, since this increase cannot exceed a probability of 100%, the 'dose'–response relation at high doses has to bend to make the curve sigmoid.

Since our life-time probability of cancer is quite high, it seems likely that the non-radiation exposure corresponds to some point near the middle of this sigmoid curve, i.e. in the approximately linear section of the curve. This means that any small increment of dose, such as from radiation, would be expected to cause a proportional increment of cancer probability.

It is unlikely that radiation, in the presence of much stronger other agents, would cause more than one of the necessary DNA changes. At low doses, the probability of that change, according to the discussion earlier, would be proportional to the dose. In the presence of strong competition, radiation would (a) be more effective than without that competition (a number of cells are already near completion of the n changes), and (b) be expected to cause a response in proportion to the radiation dose (since it only has to cause one more change)[11].

So far, we have discussed the dose–response of the initiation of cancer, i.e. of completing all the necessary n DNA modifications. There is still a long way to go before the cell actually succeeds in giving rise to a clone of cancer cells. However, this does not modify the shape of the dose–response curve but merely introduces a further probability factor influencing the overall likelihood of a cancer actually arising.

'Linearity' is interpreted in more than one way. In line with the discussion above, ICRP has assumed a linear-quadratic dose–response relation and therefore not a straight line between zero and the points of observation. However, what is essential for radiation protection is the assumption of direct proportionality between dose and probability of harm at low doses, i.e. linearity in the low dose region. Only if this can be assumed would it be appropriate to make use of collective doses for radiation protection purposes.

The cancer probability per unit dose, i.e. the slope of the straight line, at low doses is believed to be less than the quotient P/D, where P is the cancer probability observed at a high dose D. The ratio between P/D and the slope of the assumed straight line at low doses is called DDREF (Dose-Dose Rate Effectiveness Factor). In its Publication 60, ICRP assumes that this factor is 2. UNSCEAR, in 1994, reported a likely interval of 1–3.6 for solid tumours.

Applicability of ICRP probability coefficients

The ICRP nominal probability coefficient of 5% per sievert at low doses for the lifetime probability of attributable cancer deaths relates to the average member in a normal population. This means that the product of this coefficient and the collective dose for a population of normal age and sex distribution would indicate the expectation of the number of cancer deaths if all individuals received one and the same dose. It is on this basis that the collective dose may be taken as a measure of the total health detriment.

However, there is a large individual variability in susceptibility to radiation-induced cancer, for reasons already discussed. The nominal probability coefficient is therefore not relevant to any particular individual unless 'it' happens to represent the average, but then also the average sex. The probability coefficient is therefore not an appropriate tool for calculating the risk to actual individuals or, for that matter, the expected number of cancers in exposed population groups which deviate from the characteristics assumed in the assessment of the probability coefficient. It was not designed for that purpose but for radiation protection administration.

THE BASIC PROTECTION PHILOSOPHY OF ICRP

Practices and intervention

In the Commission's most recent general recommendations (ICRP Publication 60), ICRP makes a distinction between practices (which add radiation exposures when they are introduced) and intervention (which is intended to reduce exposures which would otherwise have occurred, e.g. from radioactive contamination due to an accident)[3].

The basic protection principles recommended by ICRP for practices

Since 1977, the ICRP has recommended three basic protection principles for practices causing radiation exposures. The essence of these principles is[3]:

(1) No practice involving exposure to radiation should be adopted unless it produces a sufficient benefit to the exposed individuals or to society to offset the radiation detriment it causes (the justification of a practice).
(2) In relation to any particular source within a practice, the magnitude of radiation doses, the number of people exposed, and the probability of accidental exposures should all be kept as low as reasonably achievable, economic and social factors taken into account (the optimisation of protection).
(3) The exposure of individuals resulting from the combination of all the relevant practices should be subject to dose limits, or to some control of risk in the case of potential exposures (individual dose and risk limits).

Justification of a practice

The adoption of a new practice as well as the continuation of an existing one usually involves a choice between a number of options and the final question is whether the existing situation should be changed by the introduction of a new practice. The change would only be justified if it produces a positive net benefit, the net benefit being the difference between the change in benefit and the change in detriment going into the new situation. Usually the radiation detriment is only a small part of any total detriment and the justification of a practice, therefore, goes far beyond radiation protection considerations.

Optimisation of protection

In dealing with justified practices the question arises how available resources should best be used for risk reduction. The more risks are reduced, the higher is the cost of further significant risk reduction, and a point is reached where the resources would be better used for risk reduction elsewhere. At that point radiation protection is said to be optimised in the sense of the second basic principle of ICRP, a principle sometimes referred to by the acronym ALARA. Since the radiation risk (considering both the probability of death of the exposed individuals and their number) may be described by the expected number of deaths it may be taken to be proportional to the collective dose (the product of the number of people and their average dose). In the case of non-accidental exposure, therefore, optimisation of protection is tantamount to reducing the collective dose as far as reasonable achievable.

This kind of optimisation keeps the societal detriment at the lowest reasonable level. However, there are cases where this may only be achieved by measures which cause a rather high dose to a few individuals. This means a conflict between the two main ethical principles, utilitarian ethics (maximising the total benefit) and deontological ethics (recognising individual rights). The conflict would not exist if detriment and benefit were equally distributed over the exposed population, but in many cases those who run the highest risk do not enjoy any benefit of the practice. For equity reasons, and following deontological ethics, ICRP therefore recommends the introduction of a source-related restriction of the individual dose in each case of optimisation of protection. This restriction used to be called 'source-related upper bound' but is now called *source-related constraint* by ICRP[3].

'ALARA' and 'optimisation of protection' are identical concepts. Optimisation of protection may be carried out by various means, the most common being *differential cost-benefit analysis* (CBA). By this method radiation doses or collective doses are converted into monetary terms by the multiplication by a conversion coefficient often referred to as 'alpha' (α). Collective doses may then be seen as costs representing the radiation detriment, which has to be balanced against the actual cost of radiation protection. The collective dose for which the sum of the two costs has a minimum then represents optimised protection[12].

The value of α is related to the sum of money that society is prepared to pay per human life that is 'saved' (in a statistical sense) by protection measures. This has nothing to do with the 'value of life' but merely reflects the available resources for lifesaving. 'Saving' a life on the average means saving perhaps 15 years of life if the risk is dying from radiation-induced cancer. A lower limit for α may be derived from the annual BNP per caput. Society would, for pure economic reasons, wish to pay at least that much per year of life statistically saved. An upper limit is inevitably set by the largest fraction of BNP that can be alotted to statistical lifesaving without jeopardising society's ability to sustain the necessary resources.

Individual dose and risk limits

If practices causing radiation exposure are justified and the protection in each case is optimised for every source (subject to dose constraints), the situation might seem acceptable. However, although unlikely, it cannot be ruled out that the exposure from many optimised sources might result in unacceptable risks (in the meaning described previously). For that reason, and to give some guidance for the selection of constraints, ICRP recommends an overall dose limit for individual exposures irrespective of source. This limit, which applies to the sum of all doses an individual will receive from all sources except in medical exposure of patients and (for public exposures) from natural sources of radiation, is intended to indicate the borderline to unacceptable risk under normal conditions. The source-related constraints must be so selected (by national authorities) that the individual's total dose does not exceed the limit. Since no individual constraint, nor the combined exposures, is permitted to exceed the dose limit, this guarantees that no justified practice will cause radiation risks not usually envisaged under normal circumstances. This ensures that a justification on the basis of utilitarian ethics (in the best interest of society as a whole) also, from the point of view of radiation risk, satisfies deontological ethics (i.e. the interest of sub-groups who see no justification)[13].

When ICRP selected its present dose limits for occupational and public exposures as indicating the borderline to unacceptable risk, 'risk' was treated as a multifactorial concept and the Commission looked at various ways of presenting the risk (composed of probabilities and consequences), avoiding the temptation to express risks by single numbers[3].

The ICRP protection principles in the case of intervention

The first two of the basic principles for protection in the case of practices also apply in the case of intervention, but the justification principle now relates to the intervention. Any intervention must be justified in the sense that it must do more good than harm. The benefit of the detriment reduction due to the intervention must be sufficient to justify the intervention costs, including social costs.

Once an intervention has been judged justified, its form, scale and duration should be optimised, just as any radiation protection measures should be optimised.

The third basic principle, dose and risk limitation, is not relevant in the case of interventions, since it is superseded by the first principle of more good than harm. However, on the basis of the first principle and for specified conditions, action levels may be derived indicating when remedial actions are likely to be justified[3].

Protection against potential exposures

For practices, one must not only consider radiation doses that are actually caused by the practice but also the risk that doses may be caused by events which are not certain to happen. This is referred to as 'potential exposures'. It is the recommendation of ICRP that the annual probability of death from potential exposures should not exceed the probability of attributable death annually committed by exposure at the dose limits. For the average individual, the latter may be calculated as the product of the ICRP nominal detriment coefficient and the annual dose limit. For potential exposure the annually committed probability of death is the product of the probability of the potential event (accident etc.) and the probability of death given that the event occurs.

Optimisation of protection against potential exposure is more difficult, because there is no collective dose on which a cost-benefit analysis may be based, but only a mathematical expectation of collective dose. At low probabilities, the expectation value has a large uncertainty (the most likely outcome is no event and hence no collective dose, but in the unlikely case that there is an event, the collective dose will greatly exceed the expectation value). There is also the fact that the situation is differently perceived if, for a given expectation of collective dose, the expectation is due to a large collective dose with a low probability or a small collective dose with a high probability[14].

REFERENCES

1. Hansson, S. O. *Dimensions of Risk*. Risk Analysis **9**(1), 107–112 (1989).

2. Lindell, B. and Malmfors, T. *Comprehending Radiation Risks*. In: Radiation and Society: Comprehending radiation risk. Papers prepared by the Swedish Risk Academy for an IAEA Conference in Paris 1994. Conference Proceedings, Vol. 1, pp. 7–18 (1994).

3. International Commission on Radiological Protection. *1990 Recommendations of the International Commission on Radiological Protection*. ICRP Publication 60 (Oxford: Pergamon Press) (1991).

4. Sandman, P. *Hazard versus Outrage in the Public Perception of Risk*. In: Effective Risk Communication. Ed. V. T. Covello (New York: Putnam Press) pp. 45–49 (1989).

5. Beninson, D. *The Concept of Probability*. In: Radiation and Society: Comprehending Radiation Risk. Papers prepared by the Swedish Risk Academy for an IAEA Conference in Paris 1994. Conference Proceedings, Vol. 1 pp. 19–27 (1994).

6. Drottz-Sjöberg, B.-M. *Perception of Risk. Studies of Risk Attitudes, Perceptions and Definitions*. Centre for Risk Research, Stockholm School of Economics (1991).

7. Sjöberg, L. and Drottz-Sjöberg, B-M. *Risk Perception*. In: Radiation and Society: Comprehending Radiation Risk. Papers prepared by the Swedish Risk Academy for an IAEA Conference in Paris 1994. Conference Proceedings, Vol. 1, pp. 29–59 (1994).

8. Slovic, P. *Perception of Risk*. Science **236**, 280–285 (1987).

9. United Nations Scientific Committee on the Effects of Atomic Radiation (UNSCEAR). *Sources and Effects of Ionizing Radiation*. Report to the General Assembly (New York: United Nations) (1993).

10. Clarke, R. H. *Problems in Radiation Risk Assessment*. In: Radiation and Society: Comprehending Radiation Risk. Papers prepared by the Swedish Risk Academy for an IAEA Conference in Paris 1994. Conference Proceedings, Vol. 1, pp. 75–95 (1994).

11. Lindell, B. *The Case of Linearity*. SSI-News **4**(1) (Swedish Radiation Protection Institute) (1996).

12. International Commission on Radiological Protection. *Optimization and Decisionmaking in Radiological Protection*. ICRP Publication 55 (Oxford: Pergamon Press) (1989).

13. Shrader-Frechette, K. *Risk and Ethics*. In: Radiation and Society. Comprehending Radiation Risk. Papers prepared by the Swedish Risk Academy for an IAEA Conference in Paris 1994. Conference Proceedings, Vol. 1, pp. 167–182 (1994).

14. International Commission on Radiological Protection. *Protection from Potential Exposure: A Conceptual Framework*. ICRP Publication 64 (Oxford: Pergamon Press) (1993).

Radiation Protection Dosimetry
Vol. 68, No. 3/4, pp. 165–180 (1996)
Nuclear Technology Publishing

PERCEPTION OF RISK FROM RADIATION

P. Slovic
Decision Research
1201 Oak Street
Eugene, Oregon 97401, USA

INVITED PAPER

Abstract — Perceptions of risk from radiation have been studied systematically for about 20 years. This paper summarises the key findings and conclusions from this research with regard to the nature of risk perceptions, the impacts of these perceptions, and the need for communication about radiological hazards. Perhaps the most important generalisation from research in this area is that there is no uniform or consistent perception of radiation risks. Public perception and acceptance is determined by the context in which the radiation is used — and the very different reactions to different uses provide insight into the nature of perception and the determinants of acceptable risk.

INTRODUCTION

How does the public perceive the risks associated with exposure to radiation? Perhaps the most important generalisation from research in this domain is that there is no uniform or consistent perception of radiation risks. This is what makes this topic so fascinating to study. Public perception and acceptance is determined by the context in which the radiation is used — and the very different reactions to different uses provide insight into the nature of perception and the determinants of acceptable risk.

A second generalisation, and a disturbing one, is that in every context of use, with the exception of nuclear weapons, public perceptions of radiation risk differ from the assessments of the majority of experts on radiation and its effects. In some cases, members of the public see far greater risks associated with radiation technology than do technical experts — in others the public is much less concerned than the experts believe they should be. Although differences between perceptions of laypersons and those of experts cannot be attributed in any simple way to degree of knowledge, it is clear that better information and education about radiation and its consequences is needed. With the exception of studies that have designed brochures to help people understand their risk from radon, there has been little effort or progress made on the communication side.

There is a particularly urgent need to develop plans and materials for communicating with the public in the event of a radiological disaster. This point is driven home by the difficulties observed in Europe after Chernobyl, and in the chaos and disruption that reigned in Goiania, Brazil, after two scavengers unwittingly sawed open a capsule containing caesium that had been used for cancer therapy.

The remainder of this article will attempt to elaborate these points by highlighting some key results and conclusions pertaining to

(i) the nature of risk perceptions,
(ii) the impacts of perceptions, and
(iii) the need for communication about radiological hazards.

THE PSYCHOMETRIC PARADIGM

One broad strategy for studying perceived risk is to develop a taxonomy for hazards that can be used to understand and predict responses to their risks. A taxonomic scheme might explain, for example, people's extreme aversion to some hazards, their indifference to others, and the discrepancies between these reactions and experts' opinions. One approach to this goal has employed the psychometric paradigm[1] which uses psychophysical scaling and multivariate analysis techniques to produce quantitative representations or 'cognitive maps' of risk attitudes and perceptions.

Within the psychometric paradigm, people make quantitative judgments about the current and desired riskiness of diverse hazards and the desired level of regulation of each. In one of the earliest psychometric studies, four different groups of people were asked to rate 30 activities (e.g. smoking, fire fighting), substances (e.g. food colouring), and technologies (e.g. railroads, aviation) according to the present risk of death from each[2,3]. Three groups were from Eugene, Oregon; they included 30 college students, 40 members of the League of Women Voters (LOWV), and 25 business and professional members of the 'Active Club'. The fourth group was composed of 15 persons selected nationwide for their professional involvement in risk assessment. This 'expert' group included a geographer, an environmental policy analyst, an economist, a lawyer, a biologist, a biochemist, and a government regulator of hazardous materials.

Each was asked, for each of the 30 items, 'to consider the risk of dying (across US society as a whole) as a consequence of this activity or technology'. To make the evaluation task easier, each activity appeared on a 3' × 5' card. Respondents were told first to study the items individually, thinking of all the possible ways someone might die from each (e.g. fatalities from non-nuclear electricity were to include deaths resulting from the mining of coal and other energy production activities as well as electrocution; motor vehicle fatalities were to include collisions with bicycles and pedestrians). Next, they were to order the items from least to most risky and, finally, to assign numerical risk values by giving a rating of 10 to the least risky item and making the other ratings accordingly. They were also given additional suggestions, clarifications, and encouragement to do as accurate a job as possible.

Table 1 shows how the various groups ranked these 30 activities and technologies according to riskiness. There were many similarities between the three groups of laypeople. For example, each group believed that motorcycles, motor vehicles, and handguns were highly risky, while vaccinations, home appliances, power mowers, and football posed relatively little risk. However, there were strong differences as well. Active Club members viewed pesticides and spray cans as relatively much safer than did the other groups. Nuclear power was rated as highest in risk by the LOWV and student groups, but only eighth by the Active Club. The students viewed contraceptives as riskier and mountain climbing as safer than did the other lay groups. Experts' judgments of risk differed markedly from the judgments of laypeople. The experts viewed electric power, surgery, swimming, and X rays as more risky than did the other groups, and they judged nuclear power, police work, and mountain climbing to be much less risky.

In an attempt to understand why some hazards were rated more risky than others, Fischhoff *et al*[2] borrowed a technique from personality theorists and tried to assess what might be called the 'personality' of hazards. They asked people, in addition to estimating the perception of risk, to evaluate each hazard item or activity on a

Table 1. Ordering of perceived risk for 30 activities and technologies.

	Experts	League of Women Voters	College students	Active Club members
Nuclear power	20	1	1	8
Motor vehicles	1	2	5	3
Handguns	4	3	2	1
Smoking	2	4	3	4
Motorcycles	6	5	6	2
Alcoholic beverages	3	6	7	5
General (private) aviation	12	7	15	11
Police work	17	8	8	7
Pesticides	8	9	4	15
Surgery	5	10	11	9
Fire fighting	18	11	10	6
Large construction	13	12	14	13
Hunting	23	13	18	10
Spray cans	26	14	13	23
Mountain climbing	29	15	22	12
Bicycles	15	16	24	14
Commercial aviation	16	17	16	18
Electric power (non-nuclear)	9	18	19	19
Swimming	10	19	30	17
Contraceptives	11	20	9	22
Skiing	30	21	25	16
X rays	7	22	17	24
High school and college football	27	23	26	21
Railroads	19	24	23	20
Food preservatives	14	25	12	28
Food colouring	21	26	20	30
Power mowers	28	27	28	25
Prescription antibiotics	24	28	21	26
Home appliances	22	29	27	27
Vaccinations	25	30	29	29

Note. The ordering is based on the geometric mean risk ratings within each group. Rank 1 represents the most risky activity or technology.

variety of scales that were hypothesised to be related to the perception and acceptance of risk — such as whether exposure to the activity is voluntary or not, whether it has the potential to be catastrophic, whether it evokes an emotional reaction, whether it can kill people or not, how well known it is to those exposed or to science, whether its effects are immediate rather than delayed, whether it is controllable or non-controllable, whether the technology involved is new or old, and whether the risk situation is equitable or not equitable. (Equity is a concept whereby people who bear the risk also get the benefit. If a risk situation is not equitable, then one person gets the benefit, and someone else gets the risk.) From these ratings, profiles emerged (see Figure 1) much like personality profiles. They showed that not only do nuclear power and X rays, for example, have a very different stature on perception of risk, they also have very different profiles. The quality of their risks was judged to be different. Nuclear power was seen as less voluntary, more catastrophic, higher in dread, more likely to be fatal, less controllable, newer, and so forth. They also found that these qualities were not independent across hazards. They tended to be associated across the domain of hazards. If something was judged to be voluntary, it tended also to be seen as controllable. If something was judged to be catastrophic, it also tended to be judged as fatal, and so forth.

Fischhoff et al[2] performed a factor analysis on the relationships among these variables, which yielded two very strong factors that we called 'dread' risk and 'unknown' risk. The 'dread' risk factor was combined from three scales which loaded on that factor — dread, catastrophic potential, and fatal. The 'unknown' risk factor combined judgments on the scales unknown, unfamiliar, and delayed consequences.

Slovic et al[4] conducted a new study with a much larger number of scales, and a larger number of items, some 90 hazards rated on 15 scales. Again, factor analysis yielded a two-factor representation, with the factors designated as 'dread' and 'unknown'. However, in this case, the dread factor loaded on uncontrollable, catastrophic, fatal, not equitable, high risk to future generations, not easily reduced, and involuntary. The 'unknown' factor loaded on unobservable, delayed effects, and so forth. The factor space, shown in Figure 2, was very revealing. Nuclear energy hazards and chemical hazards were located in the unknown and dread quadrant of the space. Medicines tended to fall in the upper left quadrant, everyday hazards in the lower left quadrant, and common catastrophic hazards in the lower right quadrant.

Additional research has shown that laypeople's risk perceptions and attitudes are closely related to the position of a hazard within the factor space shown in Figure 2. Most important is the factor Dread Risk. The higher a hazard's score on this factor (i.e. the further to the right it appears in the space), the higher its perceived risk, the more people want to see its current risks reduced, and the more they want to see strict regulation employed to achieve the desired reduction in risk. In contrast, experts' perceptions of risk are not closely related to any of the various risk characteristics or factors derived from these characteristics. Instead, as noted earlier, experts appear to see riskiness as synonymous with expected annual mortality. As a result, some conflicts over 'risk' may result from experts and laypeople having different definitions of the concept.

PERCEPTION OF RADIATION RISK

Numerous psychometric surveys conducted during the past decade have examined perceptions of risk and benefit from various radiation technologies. This work shows that there is no general pattern of perception for radiation. Different sources of radiation exposure are perceived in different ways. This was evident in the first psychometric study, summarised in Table 1. There we see that three groups of laypersons perceived nuclear power as having very high risk (rank 1, 1, and 8 out of 30 hazards), whereas a group of risk-assessment experts had a mean risk rating that put nuclear power 20th in the hierarchy. Note also that the three groups of laypersons judged medical X rays relatively low in risk (ranks 22, 17, and 24), whereas the experts placed it 7th. Thus we see that two radiation technologies were perceived differently from one another and differently from the views of experts.

Figure 2 further illustrates the differences in percep-

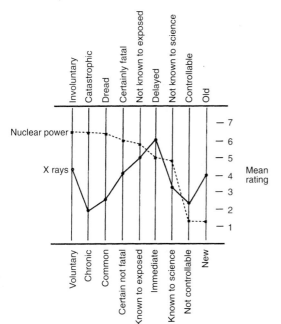

Figure 1. Profiles for nuclear power and X rays across nine risk characteristics. Source: Slovic et al[3].

tion of various radiation hazards. Note that nuclear reactor accidents, radioactive waste, and fallout from nuclear weapons testing are located in the upper right quadrant of the factor space, reflecting people's perceptions that these technologies are uncontrollable, dread, catastrophic, lethal, and inequitable in their distribution of risks and benefits. Diagnostic X rays are perceived much more favourably on these scales, hence they fall in the upper left quadrant of the space. Nuclear weapons fall in the lower right quadrant, separating from nuclear reactor accidents, nuclear waste, and fallout on the scales measuring knowledge, immediacy of effects and observability of effects.

Although Table 1 and Figure 2 represent data from small and non-representative samples collected a decade or more ago, recent surveys of the general public in the US, Sweden, and Canada show consistently that nuclear power and nuclear waste are perceived as extremely

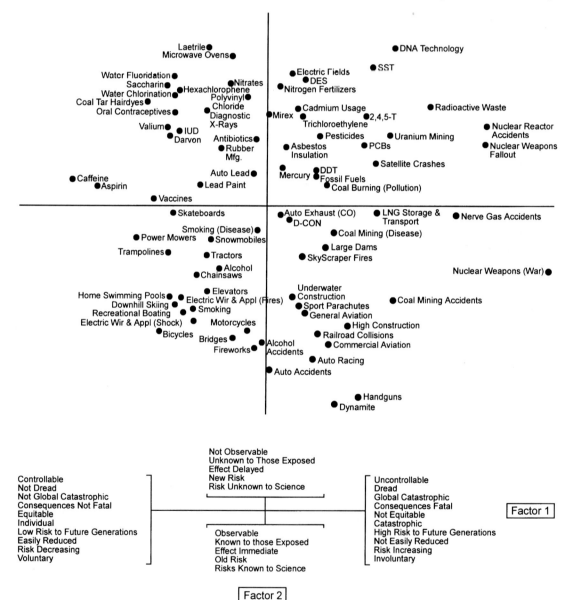

Figure 2. Location of 31 hazards on factors 1 and 2 derived from the interrelationships among 15 risk characteristics. Each factor is made up of a combination of characteristics, as indicated by the lower diagram. (Factor 1 is labelled 'dread' risk; factor 2 is labelled 'unknown' risk.) Source: redrawn from Slovic[1].

high in risk and low in benefit to society, whereas medical X rays are perceived as very beneficial and low in risk[5-7]. Smaller studies in Norway and Hungary have also obtained these results[8,9].

Perceptions of risk associated with nuclear waste are even more negative than perceptions of nuclear power[5,10-14]. When asked to state whatever images or associations came to mind when they heard the words 'underground nuclear waste storage facility', a representative sample of Phoenix, Arizona, residents could hardly think of anything that was not frightening or problematic (see Table 2). The disposal of nuclear wastes is a technology that experts believe can be managed safely and effectively. The discrepancy between this view and the images shown in Table 2 is indeed startling.

The perception of nuclear power as a catastrophic technology was studied in depth by Slovic et al[15]. They found that, before the TMI accident, people expected nuclear power accidents to lead to disasters of immense proportions. Scenarios of reactor accidents were found to resemble scenarios of the aftermath of nuclear war. Replication of these studies after the TMI event found even more extreme 'images of disaster'.

The powerful negative imagery evoked by nuclear power and radiation is discussed from a historical perspective by Weart[16]. Weart argues that modern thinking about radioactivity employs beliefs and symbols that have been associated for centuries with the concept of transmutation — the passage through destruction to rebirth. In the early decades of the 20th century, transmutation images became centered on radioactivity, which was associated with

'uncanny rays that brought hideous death or miraculous new life; with mad scientists and their ambiguous monsters; with cosmic secrets of life and death; . . . and with weapons great enough to destroy the world. . .' (Ref. 16, p. 42).

But this concept of transmutation has a duality that is hardly evident in the imagery associated with nuclear power and nuclear wastes. Why has the evil overwhelmed the good? The answer undoubtedly involves the bombing of Hiroshima and Nagasaki, which linked the dread images to reality. The sprouting of nuclear power in the aftermath of the atomic bombing has led Smith[17] (p. 62) to observe:

'Nuclear energy was conceived in secrecy, born in war, and first revealed to the world in horror. No matter how much proponents try to separate the peaceful from the weapons atom, the connection is firmly embedded in the minds of the public.'

Additional insights into the special quality of nuclear fear are provided by Erikson[18,19], who draws attention to the broad, emerging theme of toxicity, both radioactive and chemical, that characterises a 'whole new species of trouble' associated with modern technological disasters. Erikson describes the exceptionally dread quality

Table 2. Hierarchy of images associated with an 'Underground Nuclear Waste Storage Facility'.

Category	Frequency	Images included in category
1. Dangerous	179	dangerous, danger, hazardous, toxic, unsafe, harmful, disaster
2. Death/disease	107	death, sickness, dying, destruction, lethal, cancer, deformities
3. Negative	99	negative, wrong, bad, unpleasant, terrible, gross, undesirable, awful, dislike, ugly, horrible
4. Pollution	97	pollution, contamination, leakage, spills, Love Canal
5. War	62	war, bombs, nuclear war, holocaust
6. Radiation	59	radiation, nuclear, radioactive, glowing
7. Scary	55	scary, frightening, concern, worried, fear, horror
8. Somewhere else	49	wouldn't want to live near one, not where I live, far away as possible
9. Unnecessary	44	unnecessary, bad idea, waste of land
10. Problems	39	problems, trouble
11. Desert	37	desert, barren, desolate
12. Non-Nevada locations	35	Utah, Arizona, Denver
13. Storage location	32	caverns, underground salt mine
14. Government/industry	23	government, politics, big business

Source: Slovic et al. Survey of 400 residents of Phoenix, Arizona (1989).

of technological accidents that expose people to radiation and chemicals in ways that

> 'contaminate rather than merely damage; . . . pollute, befoul, and taint rather than just create wreckage; . . . penetrate human tissue indirectly rather than wound the surface by assaults of a more straightforward kind' (p. 120).

Unlike natural disasters, these accidents are unbounded. Unlike conventional disaster plots, they have no end.

> 'Invisible contaminants remain a part of the surroundings — absorbed into the grain of the landscape, the tissues of the body, and, worst of all, into the genetic material of the survivors. An 'all clear' is never sounded. The book of accounts is never closed' (p. 121).

Erikson's 'contamination model' may explain, in part, the reaction of the public to exposures to carcinogens. Numerous studies have found that a high percentage (60–75%) of people believe that if a person is exposed to a chemical that can cause cancer, that person will probably get cancer some day[20,21]. A similarly high percentage believe that 'exposure to radiation will probably lead to cancer some day'[21]. The belief that any exposure to a carcinogen is likely to lead to cancer tends to coincide with the belief that it can never be too expensive to reduce such risks[20]. Therefore, it is not surprising to find in an analysis of more than 500 life-saving interventions by Tengs *et al*[22] that radiation controls in industry were associated with the highest costs per year of life saved.

The deep fears and anxieties associated with radiation and with nuclear power make the cases in which radiation is responded to rather casually of particular interest. For example, Sandman, *et al*[23] surveyed residents in the Reading Prong area of New Jersey, a region characterised by very high radon levels in many homes. They found that residents there were basically apathetic about the risk. Few had bothered to monitor their homes for radon. Most believed that, although radon might be a problem for their neighbours, their own homes did not have any problem.

A striking contrast to the apathy regarding radon in homes is the strong public reaction that developed in many New Jersey cities when the state attempted to develop a landfill in which to place 14,000 barrels of mildly radioactive soil. The soil had been excavated from the former site of a radium watch-dial factory that had operated at the turn of the century. Over a period of several years, the state tried in vain to find a community that would accept the soil[24].

Table 3 summarises the status of perceived risk for six radiation technologies, contrasting the views of technical experts with the views of the general public. In addition to nuclear power, nuclear waste, X rays, radon, and nuclear weapons, food irradiation[25] and a source of non-ionising radiation, electric and magnetic fields (EMF), are included in the table, although there is relatively less information about perceptions of these two sources. We see that there is typically disagreement between the experts and the public regarding the level of risk and its acceptability. To my knowledge there have been only two published studies thus far of perceptions of risk from electric and magnetic fields. Both of these studies, by Morgan *et al*[26] and MacGregor *et al*[27], found that perceived risks associated with fields from home appliances and electric blankets were relatively low, and that perceived risks associated with large power lines were relatively high. Both studies also

Table 3. Summary of perception and acceptance of risks from diverse sources of radiation exposure.

	Perceived risk	
	Technical experts	Public
Nuclear power/nuclear waste	Moderate risk Acceptable	Extreme risk Unacceptable
X rays	Low/moderate risk Acceptable	Very low risk Acceptable
Radon	Moderate risk Needs action	Very low risk Apathy
Nuclear weapons	Moderate to extreme risk Tolerance	Extreme risk Tolerance
Food irradiation	Low risk Acceptable	Moderate to high risk Acceptability questioned
Electric and magnetic fields	Low risk Acceptable	Significant concerns beginning to develop Acceptability questioned

showed that, when the respondents were given a briefing about research on health effects of electric fields (which said that many studies had been done but no adverse human health effects had yet been reliably demonstrated), their perceptions on subsequent retest shifted toward greater perceived risk. MacGregor *et al* found that this briefing (in the form of a brochure) also lead to greater dread (particularly regarding power-line risks) less perceived equity, and greater concern regarding effects of EMF on the nervous system, the immune system, cell growth and reproduction, chronic depression, and cancer. These results imply that, as concerns (and reports of research) about the risks from electric and magnetic fields continue to be publicised, public fears will increase. The significance of the public's uneasiness about these fields is documented by Florig[28], who estimated that the utility industry spends more than one billion dollars annually attempting to mitigate public concerns.

Conspicuously missing from Table 3 is exposure from radiation medicine. An extensive search of Medline and six other data bases using key words such as radiation, risk perception, fear, and nuclear medicine failed to uncover any studies of perception of risk regarding the use of radionuclides in medicine.

It is instructive to compare perceptions of risk and benefit for various radiation technologies with perceptions of various chemical technologies. Concerns about chemical risks have risen dramatically in the past decade, spurred by well publicised crises at Love Canal, New York, Times Beach, Missouri, and many other waste sites; by major accidents at Seveso, Italy, Bhopal, India, and Prince William Sound, Alaska; and by numerous other problems such as the contamination of ground water and flour with the pesticide ethylene dibromide (EDB) and the controversy regarding the use of Alar, a growth regulator, in apples. The image of chemical technologies is so negative that when you ask members of the general public to tell you what first comes to mind when they hear the word 'chemicals', by far the most frequent response is 'dangerous' or some synonym (e.g. toxic, hazardous, poison, deadly). Chemicals in general and agricultural and industrial chemicals in particular are seen as very high risk and very low benefit, as are nuclear power and nuclear waste technologies. However, just as medical uses of radiation (such as X rays) are perceived in a very favourable way, differently from other radiation technologies, so are prescription drugs, which are a very potent and toxic category of chemicals to which we are often exposed at high doses. Figure 3, taken from a study in Canada[7] illustrates the parallels between nuclear power and non-medical chemicals (pesticides) seen as high in risk and low in benefit and between X rays and prescription drugs (high benefit/low to moderate risk). A national survey in Sweden has shown much the same results[6].

LESSONS

What does this research tell us about the acceptance of risk from radiation? There seem to be several lessons.

First, although many technical experts have labelled public reactions as irrational or phobic, such accusations are clearly unjustified[29]. There is a logic to public perceptions and behaviours that has become apparent through research. For example, the acceptance afforded X rays and prescription drugs suggests that acceptance of risk is conditioned by perceptions of direct benefits and by trust in the managers of the technology, in this case the medical and pharmaceutical professions. The managers of nuclear power and non-medical chemical technologies are clearly less trusted and the benefits of these technologies are not highly appreciated, hence their risks are less acceptable. High risks from nuclear weapons are tolerated because of their perceived necessity (and probably also because people lack knowledge about how to intervene in military security issues; they do have such knowledge and opportunities to intervene in the management of nuclear power).

The apathetic response to the risk from radon appears to result from the fact that it is of natural origin, occurring in a comfortable, familiar setting, with no one to blame. Moreover, it can never be totally eliminated. Opposition to the burial of radioactive soil, on the other hand, likely derives from the fact that this hazard is imported, technological in origin and industry and the

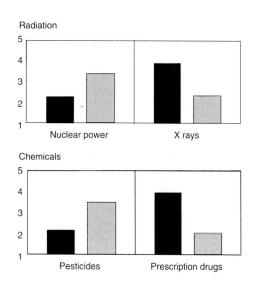

Figure 3. Mean perceived risk (light) and perceived benefit (dark) for medical and non-medical sources of exposure to radiation and chemicals. Each item was rated on a scale of perceived risk ranging from 1 (very low risk) to 7 (very high risk) and a scale of perceived benefit ranging from 1 (very low benefit) to 7 (very high benefit). Note that medical sources of exposure have more favourable benefit/risk ratings than do the non-medical sources. Data are from a national survey in Canada by Slovic *et al*[7].

state are blameworthy. In addition, it is involuntary, has a visible focus (the barrels or the landfill), and can be totally eliminated by preventing the deposition in the landfill[23].

THE IMPACTS OF PERCEPTIONS

It has become quite clear that, whether or not one agrees with public risk perceptions, they form a reality that cannot be ignored in risk management. The impact of public perceptions on regulatory agencies is illustrated by the report of a task force assembled by the Environmental Protection Agency to evaluate the Agency's priorities[30]. The task force concluded that EPA's actual priorities and legislative authorities corresponded more closely with public opinion than they did with the task force's estimates of the relative risks.

Ripple effects

During the past decade, research has also shown that individual risk perceptions and cognitions, interacting with social and institutional forces, can trigger massive social, political, and economic impacts. Early theories equated the magnitude of impact to the number of people killed or injured, or to the amount of property damaged. The accident at TMI, however, provided a dramatic demonstration that factors besides injury, death, and property damage impose serious costs. Despite the fact that not a single person died at TMI, and few if any latent cancer fatalities were expected, no other accident in our history has produced such costly societal impacts[31,32]. In addition to its impact on the utility that owned and operated the plant, this accident also imposed enormous costs on the nuclear industry and on society. These came from stricter regulation, reduced operation of reactors worldwide, greater public opposition to nuclear power, reliance on more expensive energy sources, and increased costs of reactor construction and operation.

A theory aimed at describing how psychological, social, cultural, and political factors interact to 'amplify risk' and produce ripple effects has been presented by Kasperson et al[33]. An important element of this theory is the assumption that the perceived seriousness of an accident or other unfortunate event, the media coverage it gets, and the long-range costs and other higher order impacts on the responsible company, industry, or agency, are determined, in part, by what the event signals or portends. 'Signal value' reflects the perception that the event provides new information about the likelihood of similar or more destructive future mishaps.

The informativeness or signal value of an event, and thus its potential social impact, appears to be systematically related to the characteristics of the hazard. An accident that takes many lives may produce relatively little social disturbance (beyond that caused to the victims' families and friends) if it occurs as part of a familiar and well understood system (e.g. a train wreck). However, a small accident in an unfamiliar system (or one perceived as poorly understood), such as a nuclear reactor, may have immense social consequences if it is perceived as a harbinger of further (and possible catastrophic) mishaps.

The concept of accidents as signals helps explain our society's strong response to problems involving nuclear power and nuclear wastes. Because these nuclear hazards are seen as poorly understood and catastrophic, accidents anywhere may be seen as omens of future disasters everywhere, thus producing large socioeconomic and political impacts.

Stigma

Substantial socioeconomic impacts may also result from the stigma associated with radiation contamination. The word stigma was used by the ancient Greeks to refer to bodily marks or brands that were designed to expose infamy or disgrace — to show, for example, that the bearer was a slave or criminal. As used today, the word denotes someone 'marked' as deviant, flawed, spoiled, or generally undesirable in the view of some observer. When the stigmatising characteristic is observed, the person is denigrated or avoided. Prime targets for stigmatisation are members of minority groups, the aged, homosexuals, drug addicts, alcoholics, and persons afflicted with physical or mental disabilities and deformities.

A dramatic example of stigmatisation involving radiation occurred in September, 1987, in Goiania, Brazil, where two men searching for scrap metal dismantled a cancer therapy device in an abandoned clinic. In doing so, they sawed open a capsule containing 28 grams of caesium chloride. Children and workers nearby were attracted to the glowing material and began playing with it. Before the danger was realised, several hundred people became contaminated and four persons eventually died from acute radiation poisoning. Publicity about the incident led to stigmatisation of the region and its residents[34]. Hotels in other parts of the country refused to allow Goiania residents to register, airline pilots refused to fly with Goiania residents on board, automobiles driven by Goianians were stoned, hotel occupancy in the region dropped 60% for six weeks following the incident, and virtually all conventions were cancelled during this period. The sale prices of products manufactured in Goiania dropped by 40% after the first news reports and remained depressed for a period of 30–45 days despite the fact that no items were ever found to have been contaminated.

RISK COMMUNICATION: PLACING RADIATION RISKS IN PERSPECTIVE

Given the importance of risk perceptions and the extraordinary divergence between perceptions of experts and laypersons in the domains of chemical and radiation technologies, it is not surprising that there has been a burgeoning interest in the topic of 'risk communication'. Much has been written about the need to inform and educate people about risk and the difficulties of doing so[35-43]. As many writers have observed, doing an adequate job of communicating about risk means finding comprehensible ways of presenting complex technical material that is clouded by uncertainty and is inherently difficult to understand.

The crux of the communication problem is providing information that puts risk into perspective in a way that facilitates decision making. One important lesson emerged from the 1983–1984 controversy over ethylene dibromide, a widely used pesticide that was detected at very low levels in packaged foods. The Environmental Protection Agency, which was responsible for regulating ethylene dibromide, disseminated information about the aggregate risk of this chemical to the exposed population. Although the media accurately transmitted EPA's 'macro' analysis, newspaper editorials and public reaction clearly indicated an inability to translate this into a 'micro' perspective on the risk to an exposed individual. What the newspaper reader or TV viewer wanted to know, and had trouble learning, was the answer to the question 'Should I eat the bread?'[44].

Risk comparisons

One of the few 'principles' in this field that seems to be useful is the assertion that comparisons are more meaningful than absolute numbers or probabilities, especially when these absolute values are quite small. Sowby[45] argued that to decide whether or not we are responding adequately to radiation risks we need to compare them to 'some of the other risks of life'. Rothschild[46] observed 'There is no point in getting into a panic about the risks of life until you have compared the risks which worry you with those that don't, but perhaps should'.

Typically, such exhortations are followed by elaborate tables and even 'catalogs of risk' in which diverse indices of death or disability are displayed for a broad spectrum of life's hazards. Thus Sowby[45] provided extensive data on risks per hour of exposure, showing, for example, that an hour riding a motorcycle is as risky as an hour of being 75 years old. Wilson[47] developed a table of activities (e.g. flying 1000 miles by jet, having one chest X ray), each of which is estimated to increase one's annual change of death by 1 in one million. Cohen and Lee[48] rank ordered many hazards in terms of their reduction in life expectancy on the assumption that

'to some approximation, the ordering should be society's order of priorities. However, we see several very major problems that have received very little attention . . . whereas some of the items near the bottom of the list, especially those involving radiation, receive a great deal of attention' (p. 720).

A related exercise by Reissland and Harries[49] compared loss of life expectancy in the nuclear industry with that in other occupations.

Although such risk comparisons may provide some aid to intuition, they do not educate as effectively as their proponents have assumed. For example, although some people may feel enlightened on learning that a single takeoff or landing in a commercial airliner takes an average of 15 minutes off one's life expectancy, others may find themselves completely bewildered by such information. When landing or taking off, one will either die prematurely (almost certainly by more than 15 minutes) or one will not. From the standpoint of the individual, averages do not adequately capture the essence of such risks.

Furthermore, the research on risk perception described earlier shows that perception and acceptance of risk are determined not only by accident probabilities, annual mortality rates, and losses of life expectancy, but also by numerous other characteristics of hazards such as benefits, uncertainty, controllability, catastrophic potential, equity, and threat to future generations. Therefore, the fact that a particular risk is smaller, by comparison, than other risks that are considered acceptable, does not necessarily imply that it, too, should be acceptable. Moreover, within the perceptual space defined by the various characteristics of risks, each hazard is unique. A statement such as 'the annual risk from living near a nuclear power plant is equivalent to the risk of riding an extra 3 miles in an automobile' fails to consider how these two technologies differ on the many qualities that people believe to be important. As a result, such statements are likely to produce anger rather than enlightenment, and they are not likely to be convincing in the face of criticism[50,51].

In sum, comparisons across diverse hazards may be useful tools for educating the public. Yet the facts do not speak for themselves. Comparative analyses must be performed with great care to be worthwhile.

Fortunately, radiation risks can be compared in a number of useful and defensible ways. Radiation emissions can be measured and comparisons can be made between actual or potential exposure levels of concern and familiar, everyday exposures from natural sources of radiation or medical X rays and treatments. By making comparisons from one source of radiation to another, one avoids the apples vs oranges comparisons that befuddle and anger people.

Wilson[52] used comparisons with natural sources of radiation to put the risks from the Chernobyl accident into perspective for the 2 million people living downwind from the reactor in Byelorussia. He noted that the estimated increased lifetime dose was 0.7 rem for each of these persons and that this is considerably less than the difference in the lifetime external dose a person receives on moving from New York to Denver. It is also less than the difference in the dose a person receives from inhaled radon if he or she moves from an average New England house to an average Pennsylvania house.

When radiation from Chernobyl reached the United States, the Inter-Agency Task Force, chaired by EPA administrator Lee Thomas, used similar comparisons to illustrate the low level of risk involved. Media stories pointed out that exposures in the US were a small fraction of the exposure from a chest X ray. A news story from Portland, Oregon, indicated that readings of 2.9 for ^{131}I per cubic metre of air were insignificant compared to the 2700 pCi level that would trigger concern.

This discussion is not meant to imply that we already know how to communicate radiation risks effectively. Communication about Chernobyl was dreadful in Europe[53–57]. Information messages were peppered with different terms (roentgens, curies, bequerels, rads, rems, sieverts, grays) which were explained poorly or not at all. Public anxiety was high and not always related to actual threat. Public officials were at odds with one another and inconsistent in their evaluations of risks from consuming various kinds of food or milk. Comparisons with exposure to natural radiation from familiar activities were not well received because the media and the public did not trust the sources of such information. Other comparisons (e.g. with background cancer rates) fared even worse. Many of the statements made by officials to calm the public confused and angered them instead. Although communications in the US effectively maintained a calm perspective, one could say that US officials had a relatively easy job. All they had to do was convince people that minuscule levels of radiation were not a threat. Had there been higher levels and 'hot spots' as in the Soviet Union and western Europe, the job of communicating would have been far tougher and it is not clear that proper perspectives on risk would have been achieved.

The good news is that enough is known about radiation and about risk communication to enable us to craft useful risk comparisons, if we devote proper attention and resources to doing so (see, e.g., the effort by Johnson et al[58] to inform homeowners about their risks from radon; and the recommendations by Adelstein[59]).

Mental models

An important new development is the use of mental models to guide risk communication efforts[60,61]. Mental models are detailed representations of a person's knowledge and beliefs about a hazard and its consequences. These models are elicited by means of an interview procedure, beginning with open-ended questions (e.g. 'what do you know about radon?') and proceeding to more specific questions about exposure, effects, and mitigation issues. Ultimately, the person's valid knowledge and misconceptions are identified and risk communication is designed to fill knowledge gaps and correct misconceptions. This technique has been applied,

with some success, in the design of brochures to inform people about the risks of radon[60,61].

Framing effects

It would be comforting to believe that risk attitudes and perceptions, if erroneous, would respond to informational and educational programmes. Unfortunately, psychological research demonstrates that people's beliefs change slowly and are extraordinarily persistent in the face of contrary evidence[62]. Once formed, initial impressions tend to structure the way that subsequent evidence is interpreted. New evidence appears reliable and informative if it is consistent with one's initial beliefs; contrary evidence is dismissed as unreliable, erroneous, or unrepresentative.

When people lack strong prior opinions, the opposite situation exists — they are at the mercy of the way that the information is presented. Subtle changes in the way that risks are 'framed' or expressed can have a major impact on perceptions and decisions. One dramatic example of framing in the context of medical decision making comes from a study by McNeil et al[63] who asked people to imagine that they had lung cancer and had to choose between surgery or radiation therapy. The two treatments were described in some detail. Then, some respondents were presented with the cumulative probabilities of surviving for varying lengths of time after the treatment. Other respondents received the same cumulative probabilities framed in terms of dying rather than surviving (e.g. instead of being told that 68% of those having surgery will have survived after one year, they were told that 32% will have died — see Table 4). Framing the statistics in terms of dying dropped the percentage of respondents choosing radiation therapy over surgery from 44% to 18%. The effect was as strong for physicians as for laypersons.

Numerous other examples of 'framing effects' have been demonstrated by Tversky and Kahneman[64] and others. The fact that subtle differences in how risks are

Table 4. A framing effect: surgery or radiation therapy.

	Mortality rates		Survival rates	
	Surgery	Radiation	Surgery	Radiation
Treatment	10%	0%	90%	100%
1 year	32	23	68	77
•				
•				
•				
5 years	66	78	34	22
Percent choice of radiation therapy		44%		18%

Source. McNeil et al[63].

presented can have such marked effects suggests that those responsible for information programmes have considerable ability to manipulate perceptions and behaviour. This possibility raises ethical problems that must be addressed by any responsible risk information programme.

Risk communication and trust

Social relationships of all types, including risk management, rely heavily on trust. Indeed, much of the contentiousness that has been observed in the risk management arena has been attributed to a climate of distrust that exists between the public, industry, and risk management professionals[65,66].

Also, as noted earlier, greater public acceptance of medical technologies based on chemicals and radiation, as opposed to industrial technologies, can be explained by the relatively high degree of trust in physicians and other health-care workers. Typical of the research findings are the conclusions of Bord and O'Connor[25] regarding their survey of public acceptance of food irradiation:

'The most consistent, dramatic finding ... is the impact of trust on acceptability: trust in industry in general, in the food irradiation industry specifically, in government regulatory agencies, and in science itself' (p. 505).

The limited effectiveness of risk communication efforts in many circumstances can be attributed to the lack of trust. If you trust the risk manager, communication is relatively easy. If trust is lacking, no form or process of communication will be satisfactory[54,67]. Thus trust is more fundamental to conflict resolution than is risk communication.

One of the most fundamental qualities of trust has been known for ages. Trust is fragile. It is typically created rather slowly, but it can be destroyed in an instant — by a single mishap or mistake. Thus, once trust is lost, it may take a long time to rebuild it to its former state. In some instances, lost trust may never be regained. Abraham Lincoln understood this quality. In a letter to Alexander McClure he observed: 'If you *once* forfeit the confidence of your fellow citizens, you can *never* regain their respect and esteem' (italics added).

The fact that trust is easier to destroy than to create reflects certain fundamental mechanisms of human psychology called here 'the asymmetry principle'. When it comes to winning trust, the playing field is not level. It is tilted toward distrust, for each of the following four reasons:

(1) Negative (trust-destroying) events are more visible or noticeable than positive (trust-building) events. Negative events often take the form of specific, well defined incidents such as accidents, lies, discoveries of errors, or other mismanagement. Positive events, while sometimes visible, more often are fuzzy or indistinct. For example, how many positive events are represented by the safe operation of a nuclear power plant for one day? Is this one event? Dozens of events? Hundreds? There is no precise answer. When events are invisible or poorly defined, they carry little or no weight in shaping our attitudes and opinions.

(2) When events do come to our attention, negative (trust-destroying) events carry much greater weight than positive events. This important psychological tendency is illustrated by a study in which 103 college students rated the impact on trust of 45 hypothetical news events pertaining to the management of a large nuclear power plant in their community[65]. Some of these events were designed to be trust increasing, such as:
(i) There have been no reported safety problems at the plant during the past year.
(ii) There is careful selection and training of employees at the plant.
(iii) Plant managers live nearby the plant.
(iv) The county medical examiner reports that the health of people living near the plant is better than the average for the region.

Other events were designed to be trust decreasing, such as:

(i) A potential safety problem was found to have been covered up by plant officials.
(ii) Plant safety inspections are delayed in order to meet the electricity production quota for the month.
(iii) A nuclear power plant in another state has had a serious accident.
(iv) The county medical examiner reports that the health of people living near the plant is worse than the average for the region.

The respondents were asked to indicate, for each event, whether their trust in the management of the plant would be increased or decreased on learning of that event. After doing this, they rated how strongly their trust would be affected by the event on a scale ranging from 1 (very small impact on trust) to 7 (very powerful impact on trust).

The percentages of Category 7 ratings, shown in Figure 4, dramatically demonstrate that negative events are seen as far more likely to have a powerful effect on trust than are positive events.

There was only one event perceived to have any substantial impact on increasing trust. This event stated that:

'An advisory board of local citizens and environmentalists is established to monitor the plant and is given legal authority to shut the plant down if they believe it to be unsafe.'

This strong delegation of authority to the local public was rated 6 or 7 on the impact scale by 38.4%

of the respondents. Although this was a far stronger showing than for any other positive event, it would have been a rather average performance in the distribution of impacts for negative events.

The importance of an event is at least in part related to its frequency (or rarity). An accident in a nuclear plant is more informative with regard to risk, than is a day (or even a large number of days) without an accident. Thus, in systems where we are concerned about low probability/high consequence events, problematic events will increase our perceptions of risk to a much greater degree than favorable events will decrease them.

(3) Adding fuel to the fire of asymmetry is yet another idiosyncracy of human psychology — sources of bad (trust-destroying) news tend to be seen as more credible than sources of good news. For example,

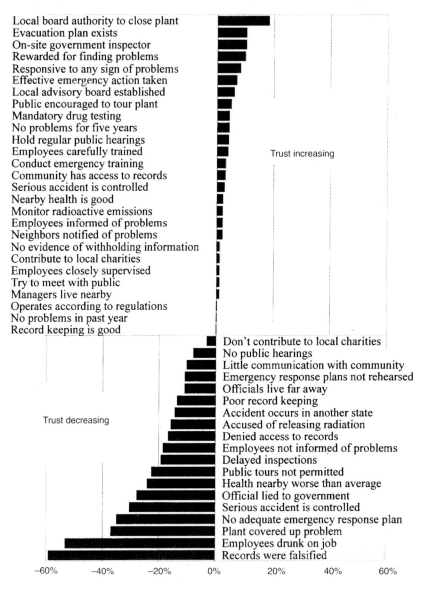

Figure 4. Differential impact of trust-increasing and trust-decreasing events. Each event was rated on a scale ranging from 1 (very little impact on trust) to 7 (very powerful impact on trust). Only the percentage of respondents giving Category 7 ratings (very powerful impact) are shown here. Source: Slovic[65].

in several studies of what they called 'intuitive toxicology', Kraus *et al*[20] examined people's confidence in the ability of animal studies to predict human health effects from chemicals. In general, confidence in the validity of animal studies was not particularly high. However, when told that a study has found that a chemical is carcinogenic in animals, people expressed considerable confidence in the validity of this study for predicting health effects in humans. Regulators respond like the public. Positive (bad news) evidence from animal bioassays is presumptive evidence of risk to humans; negative evidence (e.g. the chemical was not found to be harmful) carries little weight[68].

(4) Another important psychological tendency is that distrust, once initiated, tends to reinforce and perpetuate distrust. This occurs in two ways. First, distrust tends to inhibit the kinds of personal contacts and experiences that are necessary to overcome distrust. By avoiding others whose motives or actions we distrust, we never get to see that these people are competent, well-meaning, and trustworthy. Second, initial trust or distrust colours our interpretation of events, thus reinforcing our prior beliefs. Persons who trusted the nuclear power industry saw the events at Three Mile Island as demonstrating the soundness of the 'defence in depth' principle, noting that the multiple safety systems shut the plant down and contained most of its radiation. Persons who distrusted nuclear power prior to the accident took an entirely different message from the same events, perceiving that those in charge did not understand what was wrong or how to fix it and that catastrophe was averted only by sheer luck.

Appreciation of those psychological tendencies that create and reinforce distrust leads us toward a new perspective on risk perception and conflict. Conflicts and controversies surrounding risk management are not due to public irrationality or ignorance but, instead, can be seen as expected side effects of these psychological tendencies, interacting with a highly participatory democratic system of government, and amplified by certain powerful technological and social changes in society. The technological change has given the electronic and print media the capability (effectively utilised) of informing us of news from all over the world — often right as it happens. Moreover, just as individuals give greater weight and attention to negative events, so do the news media. Much of what the media reports is bad (trust-destroying) news[69]. This is convincingly demonstrated by Koren and Klein[70], who compared the rates of newspaper reporting of two studies, one providing bad news and one good news, published back to back in the 20 March 1991 issue of the *Journal of the American Medical Association*. Both studies examined the link between radiation exposure and cancer. The bad news study showed an increased risk of leukaemia in white

men working at the Oak Ridge National Laboratory. The good news study failed to show an increased risk of cancer in people residing near nuclear facilities. Koren and Klein found that subsequent newspaper coverage was far greater for the study showing increased risk.

The social change is the rise of powerful special interest groups — well funded (by a fearful public) and sophisticated in using their own experts and the media to communicate their concerns and their distrust to the public in order to influence risk policy debates and decisions[71]. The social problem is compounded by the fact that we tend to manage our risks within an adversarial legal system that pits expert against expert, contradicting each other's risk assessments and further destroying the public trust.

The young science of risk assessment is too fragile, too indirect, to prevail in such a hostile atmosphere. Scientific analysis of risks cannot allay our fears of low probability catastrophes or delayed cancers unless we trust the system. In the absence of trust, science (and risk assessment) can only feed distrust, by uncovering more bad news. A single study demonstrating an association between exposure to chemicals or radiation and some adverse health effect cannot easily be offset by numerous studies failing to find such an association. Thus, for example, the more studies that are conducted looking for effects of electric and magnetic fields or other difficult to evaluate hazards, the more likely it is that these studies will increase public concerns, even if the majority of these studies fail to find any association with ill health[26,27]. In short, risk assessment studies may tend to increase perceived risk.

IMPLICATIONS FOR RADIATION MEDICINE

In 20 years of research on perception and acceptance of technological risks, there has been remarkably little attention given to the medical uses of radiation — quite a contrast to the hundred or more studies of perceptions of nuclear power and nuclear waste. This lack of attention is surprising, given the importance of radiation medicine and the fact that some procedures such as mammography screening for younger women have been the source of much concern and controversy.

In the absence of studies specifically directed to radiation medicine, one can only speculate about public views, based on more general findings. The use of radiation for diagnosis and therapy will likely stand apart from other radiation technologies because people see great benefits from medical radiation and they have relatively high trust in the medical profession. Where the need is particularly evident (e.g. cancer therapy), tolerance of risk will be quite high, as shown by the strong desire of AIDS patients to have access to new, potentially dangerous medicines[72]. But acceptance of radiation exposures will undoubtedly come with anxieties, due to the association of such exposures with the cause of cancer as well as the cure. Moreover, the public will likely support strict controls over radiation medicine regardless of costs and they will react strongly to incidents of improper or incompetent administration. Research on the 'social amplification of risk' shows that even 'small incidents' can produce massive 'ripple effects' if they are perceived to be caused by managerial incompetence or other blameworthy factors[73]. Such ripple effects could include loss of public confidence, reluctance of patients to undergo necessary examinations and treatments, extensive litigation against physicians, hospitals, and manufacturers, and demand for stricter regulatory control.

Ultimately, the best way to understand the public's view of radiation medicine is to ask people directly — by means of one-on-one interviews, focus groups, and structured surveys. In this way we can obtain a 'clear image' of people's mental models pertaining to various diagnostic and therapeutic procedures, including their knowledge and misconceptions, their perceptions of risk and benefit, and their attitudes toward the use and regulation of these procedures.

Such data are really quite easy to collect. The methods are developed and the costs are reasonable. In the past, focused surveys have rarely failed to provide insights that are useful for education and policy.

REFERENCES

1. Slovic, P. *Perception of Risk*. Science **236**, 280–285 (1987).
2. Fischhoff, B., Slovic, P., Lichtenstein, S., Read, S. and Combs, B. *How Safe is Safe Enough? A Psychometric Study of Attitudes Towards Technological Risks and Benefits*. Polit. Sci. **9**, 127–152 (1978).
3. Slovic, P., Fischhoff, B. and Lichtenstein, S. *Rating the Risks*. Environment **21**(3), 14–20, 36–39 (1979).
4. Slovic, P., Fischhoff, B. and Lichtenstein, S. *Facts and Fears: Understanding Perceived Risk*. In: Societal Risk Assessment: How Safe is Safe Enough? Eds. R. Schwing and W. A. Alberts Jr (New York: Plenum) pp. 181–214 (1980).
5. Kunreuther, H., Desvousges, W. H. and Slovic, P. *Nevada's Predicament: Public Perceptions of Risk from the Proposed Nuclear Waste Repository*. Environment **30**(8), 16–20, 30–33 (1988).
6. Slovic, P., Kraus, N. N., Lappe, H., Letzel, H. and Malmfors, T. *Risk Perception of Prescription Drugs: Report on a Survey in Sweden*. Pharm. Med. **4**, 43–65 (1989).
7. Slovic, P., Kraus, N. N., Lappe, H. and Major, M. *Risk Perception of Prescription Drugs: Report on a Survey in Canada*. Can. J. Public Health **82**, S15–S20 (1991).
8. Englander, T., Farago, K., Slovic, P. and Fischhoff, B. *A Comparative Analysis of Risk Perception in Hungary and the United States*. Social Behaviour: Int. J. Appl. Social Psychol. **1**, 55–66 (1986).
9. Teigen, K. H., Brun, W. and Slovic, P. *Societal Risks as Seen by a Norwegian Public*. J. Behav. Decis. Making **1**, 111–130 (1988).
10. Flynn, J. H., Slovic, P., Mertz, C. K. and Toma, J. *Evaluations of Yucca Mountain*. Technical Report (Carson City, NV, Nuclear Waste Project Office) (1990).
11. Sjöberg, L. and Drottz-Sjöberg, B. *Risk Perception*. In: Radiation and Society: Comprehending Radiation Risk. Swedish Risk Academy. Vol. 1, pp. 29–60 (Vienna: International Atomic Energy Agency) (1994).
12. Sjöberg, L. and Drottz-Sjöberg, B. *Risk Perception of Nuclear Waste: Experts and the Public*. Rhizikon Risk Research Report No. 16 (Stockholm, Stockholm School of Economics, Center for Risk Research) (1994).
13. Slovic, P., Layman, M., Kraus, N. N., Flynn, J. H., Chalmers, J. and Gesell, B. *Perceived Risk, Stigma, and Potential Economic Impacts of a High-level Nuclear Waste Repository in Nevada*. Risk Anal. **11**, 683–696 (1991).
14. Slovic, P., Layman, M. and Flynn, J. H. *Images of a Place and Vacation Preferences: Report of the 1989 Surveys* (Nevada Nuclear Waste Project Office, Carson City, NV) Report No. NWPO-SE-030-90 (1990).
15. Slovic, P., Lichtenstein, S. and Fischhoff, B. *Images of Disaster: Perception and Acceptance of Risks from Nuclear Power*. In: Energy Risk Assessment. Eds G. Goodman and W. Rowe. pp. 223–245 (London: Academic) (1979).
16. Weart, S. *Nuclear Fear: A History of Images* (Cambridge, MA: Harvard) (1988).
17. Smith, K. *Perception of Risks Associated with Nuclear Power*. Energ. Environ. Monitor **4**(1), 61–70 (1988).
18. Erikson, K. *Toxic Reckoning: Business Faces a New Kind of Fear*. Harvard Bus. Rev. 118–126 (January–February 1990).
19. Erikson, K. *Radiation's Lingering Dread*. Bull. At. Sci. 34–39 (March 1991).
20. Kraus, N. N., Malmfors, T. and Slovic, P. *Intuitive Toxicology: Expert and Lay Judgments of Chemical Risks*. Risk Anal. **12**, 215–232 (1992).
21. Slovic, P., Flynn, J. H., Mertz, C. K. and Mullican, L. *Health Risk Perception in Canada* (Department of National Health and Welfare, Ottawa) Report No. 93-EHD-170 (1993).
22. Tengs, T. D., Adams, M. E., Pliskin, J. S., Safran, D. G., Siegel, J. E., Weinstein, M. C. and Graham, J. D. *Five-hundred Life-saving Interventions and Their Cost Effectiveness* (Harvard School of Public Health, Center for Risk Analysis) (1993).
23. Sandman, P. M., Weinstein, N. D. and Klotz, M. L. *Public Response to the Risk from Geological Radon*. J. Commun. **37**, 93–108 (1987).
24. Carlson, E. *Suburban Radium Lode Gives New Jersey a Headache*. Wall Street J. 23 (23 December 1986).

25. Bord, R. J. and O'Connor, R. E. *Risk Communication, Knowledge, and Attitudes: Explaining Reactions to a Technology Perceived as Risky*. Risk Anal. **20**, 499–506 (1990).

26. Morgan, M. G., Slovic, P., Nair, I., Geisler, D., MacGregor, D., Fischhoff, B., Lincoln, D. and Florig, K. *Powerline Frequency Electric and Magnetic Fields: A Pilot Study of Risk Perception*. Risk Anal. **5**, 139–149 (1985).

27. MacGregor, D., Slovic, P. and Morgan, M. G. *Perception of Risks from Electromagnetic Fields: A Psychometric Evaluation of a Risk-communication Approach*. Risk Anal. **14**(5), 815–828 (1994).

28. Florig, H. K. *Containing the Costs of the EMF Program*. Science **257**, 468–492 (1992).

29. Drottz-Sjoberg, B. and Persson, L. *Public Reaction to Radiation: Fear, Anxiety or Phobia?* Health Phys. **64**, 223–231 (1993).

30. United States Environmental Protection Agency. *Unfinished Business: A Comparative Assessment of Environmental Problems*. (Washington, DC: EPA) (1987).

31. Evans, N. and Hope, C. *Nuclear Power: Futures, Costs, and Benefits* (Cambridge University Press) (1984).

32. Heising, C. D. and George, V. P. *Nuclear Financial Risk: Economy-wide Costs of Reactor Accidents*. Energy Polic. **14**, 45–52 (1986).

33. Kasperson, R., Renn, O., Slovic, P., Brown, H., Emel, J., Goble, R., Kasperson, J. and Ratick, S. *The Social Amplification of Risk: A Conceptual Framework*. Risk Anal. **8**, 177–187 (1988).

34. Petterson, J. S. *Perception Vs. Reality of Radiological Impact: The Goiania Model*. Nucl. News **31**(14), 84–90 (1988).

35. Covello, V. T., Sandman, P. M. and Slovic, P. *Risk Communication, Risk Statistics, and Risk Comparisons: A Manual for Plant Managers*. (Chemical Manufacturers Association, Washington, DC) (1988).

36. Covello, V. T., von Winterfeldt, D. and Slovic, P. *Risk Communication: Research and Practice*. Unpublished manuscript (Columbia University, School of Public Health, New York) (1988).

37. Covello, V. T., von Winterfeldt, D. and Slovic, P. *Risk Communication: A Review of the Literature*. Risk Abs. **3**, 171–182 (1986).

38. Hance, B. J., Chess, C. and Sandman, P. M. *Improving Dialogue with Communities: A Risk Communication Manual for Government* (New Jersey Department of Environmental Protection, Trenton, NJ) (1988).

39. Krimsky, S. and Plough, A. *Environmental Hazards: Communicating Risks as a Social Process* (Dover, MA: Auburn House) (1988).

40. Sandman, P. M. *Explaining Environmental Risk*. (Environmental Protection Agency, Office of Toxic Substances, Washington, DC) Report No. TS-799 (1986).

41. Slovic, P. *Informing the Public About the Risks from Ionizing Radiation*. Health Phys. **41**, 589–598 (1981).

42. Slovic, P. *Informing and Education the Public About Risk*. Risk Anal. **4**, 403–415 (1986).

43. Slovic, P., Fischhoff, B. and Lichtenstein, S. *Informing People About Risk*. In: Product Labeling and Health Risks. Report 6, Eds L. Morris, M. Mazis and I. Barofsky. pp. 165–181 (The Banbury Center, Cold Spring Harbor, NJ) (1980).

44. Sharlin, H. I. *EDB: A Case Study in the Communication of Health Risk*. Risk Anal. **6**, 61–68 (1986).

45. Sowby, F. D. *Radiation and Other Risks*. Health Phys. **11**, 879–887 (1965).

46. Rothschild, N. *Coming to Grips with Risk*. Address Presented on BBC Television; Reprinted in the Wall Street Journal (November 1978).

47. Wilson, R. *Analyzing the Daily Risks of Life*. Tech. Rev. **81**, 40–46 (1979).

48. Cohen, B. and Lee, I. *A Catalog of Risks*. Health Phys. **36**, 707–722 (1979).

49. Reissland, J. and Harries, V. *A Scale for Measuring Risks*. New Sci. **83**, 809–811 (1979).

50. Huyskens, C. *Problems in Risk Comparisons*. In: Radiation and Society: Comprehending Radiation Risk. Swedish Risk Academy Vol. 1, pp. 131–146 (Vienna: International Atomic Energy Agency) (1994).

51. Slovic, P., Kraus, N. N. and Covello, V. *What Should We Know About Making Risk Comparisons?* Risk Anal. **10**(3), 389–392 (1990).

52. Wilson, R. *Testimony Before the Subcommittee on Nuclear Regulation, Committee on the Environment and Public Works* (U.S. Senate, Washington, DC) (7 May 1987).

53. Drottz, B. and Sjöberg, L. *Risk Perception and Worries After the Chernobyl Accident*. J. Environ. Psychol. **10**, 135–149 (1990).

54. Gadomska, M. *Risk Communication*. In: Radiation and Society: Comprehending Radiation Risk. Swedish Risk Academy Vol. 1, pp. 147–166 (Vienna: IAEA) (1994).

55. Hohenemser, C. and Renn, O. *Chernobyl's Other Legacy: Shifting Public Perceptions of Nuclear Risk*. Environment **30**, 3 (1988).

56. Otway, H., Haastrup, P., Connell, W., Gianitsopoulas, G. and Paruccini, M. *Risk Communication in Europe After Chernobyl: A Media Analysis of Seven Countries*. Ind. Crisis Q. **2**, 31–35 (1988).

57. Wynne, B. *Sheepfarming After Chernobyl: A Case Study in Communicating Scientific Information*. Environment **31**(2), 10–15; 33–39 (March 1989).

58. Johnson, F. R., Fisher, A., Smith, V. K. and Desvousges, W. H. *Informed Choice or Regulated Risk? Lessons from a Study in Radon Communication*. Environment **30**(4), 12–15; 30–35 (1988).

59. Adelstein, S. J. *Uncertainty and Relative Risks of Radiation Exposure*, J. Am. Med. Assoc. **258**, 655–657 (1987).

60. Atman, C. J., Bostrom, A., Fischhoff, B. and Morgan, M. G. *Designing Risk Communications: Completing and Correcting Mental Models of Hazards Processes, Part I*. Risk Anal. **14**(5), 779–788 (1994).

61. Bostrom, A., Atman, C. J., Fischhoff, B. and Morgan, M. G. *Evaluating Risk Communications: Completing and Correcting Mental Models of Hazards Processes, Part II*. Risk Anal. **14**(5), 789–798 (1994).

62. Nisbett, R. and Ross, L. *Human Inference: Strategies and Shortcomings of Social Judgment* (Englewood Cliffs, NJ: Prentice-Hall) (1980).

63. McNeil, B. J., Pauker, S. G., Sox, H. C. Jr and Tversky, A. *On the Elicitation of Preferences for Alternative Therapies*. New Eng. J. Med. **306**, 1259–1262 (1982).

64. Tversky, A. and Kahneman, D. *The Framing of Decisions and the Psychology of Choice*. Science **211**, 453–458 (1981).

65. Slovic, P. *Perceived Risk, Trust, and Democracy: A Systems Perspective*. Risk Anal. **13**, 675–682 (1993).

66. Slovic, P., Flynn, J. H. and Layman, M. *Perceived Risk, Trust, and the Politics of Nuclear Waste*. Science **254**, 1603–1607 (1991).

67. Fessendon-Raden, J., Fitchen, J. M. and Heath, J. S. *Providing Risk Information in Communities: Factors Influencing What is Heard and Accepted*. Sci. Technol. Hum. Values **12**, 94–101 (1987).

68. Efron, E. *The Apocalyptics* (New York: Simon & Schuster) (1984).

69. Lichtenberg, J. and MacLean, D. *Is Good News No News?* The Geneva Papers on Risk and Insurance **17**, 362–365 (1992).

70. Koren, G. and Klein, N. *Bias Against Negative Studies in Newspaper Reports of Medical Research*. J. Am. Med. Assoc. **266**, 1824–1826 (1991).

71. Wall Street Journal *How a PR Firm Executed the Alar Scare*. pp. A1–A3 (3 October 1989).

72. Levi, J. *Unproven AIDS Therapies: The Food and Drug Administration and DdI*. In: Bio-medical Politics. Ed. K. E. Hanna. pp. 9–37 (Washington, DC: Natl Acad. (1991).

73. Burns, W. J., Slovic, P., Kasperson, R. E., Kasperson, J. X., Renn, O. and Emani, S. *Incorporating Structural Models Into Research on the Social Amplification of Risk: Implications for Theory Construction and Decision Making*. Risk Anal. **13**, 611–623 (1993).

Radiation Protection Dosimetry
Vol. 68, No. 3, pp. 181–184 (1996)
Nuclear Technology Publishing

RISKS — IN TECHNOLOGY, SOCIETY AND THE MIND*

T. Hviid Nielsen
Centre for Technology and Culture
University of Oslo
Gaudstadalléen 21, N-0371 Oslo, Norway

Abstract — Risks have become reflexive. Modern risks are created by technologies, through the organisation of society, as well as in our mind's perception and communication. Modern risks are neither determined by scientific-technological factors alone, nor mere social construction, nor arbitrary subjective perception. The three sources of risk have been described and emphasised recently by the three sociologists Ulrich Beck, Anthony Giddens and Niklas Luhmann respectively. A comprehensive concept of risk capable of explaining the public perception and avoiding misunderstandings between safety experts and lay people must, however, consider and combine elements from all three.

THE HUMAN FACTOR AS A SAFETY RISK

In the autumn of 1994, immediately after the sinking of the passenger ferry 'Estonia', the general 'truth' that about 80% of all serious accidents are caused by human error was circulating in the media. The unspoken, but in the context plain, message was that the 'Estonia' accident was one of the 80% which had to be accounted for by human error.

Politicians and safety experts have long since moved on from the narrow and technocratic understanding of safety often ascribed to the early engineering profession. The human factor is now taken into consideration in a way and to an extent where it can explain almost anything, and therefore at times also explain away quite straightforward technical matters. Safety experts often consider lay people a considerable — if not the most important — safety risk. Lay people do not perceive risks as calculated by the statistics of probability. Nor do they act rationally as prescribed by the theory of rational choice. Safety experts' anecdotes about lay people make up an entire catalogue of deviation from rationality and traditional virtues. Double standards, discrepancy and inconsistency between 'real' and perceived risks, words and actions, demands to oneself and to others, and between good intentions and weakness of will etc., are the common characteristics of stereotypes or caricatures such as:

(i)   *The moralist* or the hypocrite, who is willing to suspend normal moral and legal relations, from justice to human rights, in order to find the responsible or guilty parties and 'save the earth'.

(ii) *The selfish* person or the free rider of progress, who is content to have nuclear power plants, as long as they are not in his own backyard.

(iii) *The destructive* or even self-destructive person, who seeks out hazards, out of indifference or ignorance, and embraces them without a parachute or insurance.

(iv) *The fearful* person or the timorous worrier, who never cycles without a helmet, always wears both braces and a belt and prays each evening that the threat of nuclear war will not come true.

(v)   *The weak-willed* person, who refuses to accept progress' old symbol, the black smoke from the chimney stacks, but reconciles himself with the clouds from his own tobacco.

(vi) *The populist* or wiseacre, who is always right simply due to his point of view, which is that of 'the people', and for whom civil disobedience is the next step.

The subject of this essay is modern society's production, distribution and perception of risk, not technical or technological safety. The essay deals with the normal state and daily routines, not the large and exceptional catastrophes. It utilises the expert knowledge of sociology, not that of safety engineers. It also attempts to understand, to explain and partly to defend lay people's understanding of safety and perception of risk.

The essay acknowledges the fact that safety experts now allott the human factor so much weight as correct and needed. It is, however, questioned whether safety experts have expanded their range of vision without shifting their optic and focus correspondingly? Do safety experts still too often transfer the instrumental engineering point of view to misconceived expectations about the human factor? Do they still too often expect the human factor to behave with the same automatic and quasi-mechanical rationality that they attribute to technology?

*This essay is a summary of Torben Hviid Nielsen. *Risici-i teknologien, i samfundet og i hovederne. Apropos risiko-begreberne hos Ulrich Beck, Anthony Giddens og Niklas Luhmann.* Retfærd. Nordisk juridisk tidsskrift. Nr. 73. 19. årg. 1996/II. 61-77 (in Danish).

THREE SOCIOLOGICAL CONCEPTS OR 'IDEAL TYPES' OF RISK

According to the pioneering work and a modern classic in the recent and extensive sociological literature on risk, Ulrich Beck's *Risikogesellschaft* from 1986[1-4], we are now facing a historical change of epoch. Modernisation is now dissolving the industrial society, just as it dissolved the feudal society in the nineteenth century and produced the industrial society. The industrial society's 'logic' of wealth production dominated its 'logic' of risk production, but the risk society has reversed this relationship.

The risk society's new technologies have lost their innocence. The gains of technical and economic progress are now overshadowed by the production of artificially manufactured, i.e. nuclear, chemical, ecological and biotechnological, risks. The risks of the old industrial society were limited, could be traced back to a concrete and responsible 'other' and compensated for or insured against. Risk society's new technologies and highly specialised division of labour has, however, created a general lack of responsibility. Chance and probability have taken the place of necessity and causality. 'Everyone is both cause and effect, and thus noncause ... You can do something and continue to do it without being held personally responsible. You can act in your own absence, as it were'. *Risikogesellschaft* is, thus, an excellent examination and demonstration of the new unresponsibility, which the Norwegian 'Internal Control Regulation' (Internkontrol) is meant to counteract.

Risks are also a central feature of the modern world in two books by Anthony Giddens from 1990 and 1991[5-7]. However, unlike Beck, Giddens neither identifies risk as the characteristic of a new epoch, nor as chiefly created by technology. Modernity has been a risk culture ever since the Renaissance, and institutional and social risks are as important as nuclear power, chemistry and biotechnology. The specific target of Giddens' criticism is 'the new institutional systems which are constituted by risks'. His 'risk profile' is, thus, not as prejudicially negative as Beck's. Modernity has also removed and reduced many of the old risks, and the new risks are not only or primarily negative side effects of technology. Chance and possibility are the other and positive aspect of risk, and the new opportunities of modernity cannot be separated from its risks. The new risks are the inseparable other side of modern people's freedom to choose different lifestyles and lifepolitics.

An increased awareness of risk as risk is as important as an increased production of new risks, and the general public has — with the more even distribution of this awareness — also become more aware of the limitations of the experts. Only a minority of people can, however, live with hazards so threatening and far removed from individual control constantly in 'the forefront of their minds'. 'People who worry all day, every day, about the possibility of nuclear war ... are liable to be thought disturbed. While it would be difficult to deem irrational someone who was constantly and consciously anxious in this way, this outlook would paralyse ordinary day-to-day life'.

Niklas Luhmann's *Soziologie des Risikos* from 1991 carries Giddens' 'awareness of the awareness of risk as risk' to its extreme[8]. Luhmann makes sense of the omnipresent awareness of risk by interpreting it as a symptom of an era obsessed with predictability and normality. Risks are situated as much in our minds as in technology and society, and Luhmann treats them as an internal phenomenon of awareness, more than as a reality in the external world.

Luhmann's focus of interest and explaining factor is changes in expectations — not the material transformation of Beck's industrial revolution or Giddens' Renaissance. We have become more aware of risks, because we are more dependent on predictability and safety. For Luhmann 'danger' is the linguistic opposite to 'risk' — as apposed to Beck's 'safety' and Giddens' 'fate'. Modern risks are reflexive, contingent on a 'second-order observation', and Luhmann's 'risk profile' is a 'mental map'. The era characterises every deviation from the predictable and normal as a risk, because it is obsessed with normality and predictability, and it is the tragicomedy of the era that understanding and communication reinforces or creates the phenomenon in a partially self-fulfilling prophecy.

THREE 'REGULARITIES' AND 'FILTERS' IN LAY PEOPLE'S PERCEPTION OF RISK

Lay people's or the public's awareness of risk as risk is illustrated by a few instructive data from an international survey on 'Attitudes towards the environment'[9,10] carried out in 1993.

The respondents were asked to indicate the danger of six new technologies for 'the environment' and for 'you and your family', and the responses demonstrate three regularities, also displayed by psychometrics and experimental psychology, in public perception (see Figure 1).

The public appear to perceive great dangers, their awareness of risk as risk is highly developed. The relative ranking of the dangers and the distance between the perceived risk for the environment and for oneself seems, however, to be a more reliable and significant measure, than the absolute level. The different dangers or risks are perceived in the same hierarchy for the 'environment in general' and for 'me and my family'. But all the types of danger are perceived as considerably more dangerous for 'the environment in general' than for 'me and my family'. Three regularities may underlie and explain this public perception.

(1) *Accidents* with low probability and high immediate consequences are perceived as more dangerous than the *normal state*, the daily dose.

(2) Risks against which one is *powerless* or has little influence are perceived as more dangerous than risks which one can *choose* or refrain from choosing.

(3) *Remote* risks — in both space and time — are perceived as more dangerous than *proximate* risks

The three regularities are often interpreted as a confirmation or proof that the stereotypes or caricatures previously outlined are widespread and ingrained in the public. The stereotype's double standards, discrepancies and inconsistencies are recognisable in the regularities, which in turn are all either falsified by safety experts' quantitative calculations or contradicted by more formal logic.

The three regularities represent sociologists' knowledge about how risks are perceived, not safety experts' knowledge about how risks arise. The public perception of risks is certainly not identical with (real) risks as measured and calculated by safety experts. The public perception is an expression of — as well as an impression on — the person who perceives. It depends as much on people's minds as on the outside world, as much on 'the eye of the beholder' as on what is seen. The three mental filters suggested and hinted at in Beck, Giddens and Luhmann's theories can thus be brought in to explain the three regularities in public perception.

(1) The indicated high level of risk awareness seems to show that the new risks are perceived and acknowledged, even though it has to happen through non-experience and second-hand. Abstract and remote risks are perceived — perhaps even at the expense of the concrete and near ones. Beck's warning and fear of 'non-perception' of new risks, because they require 'the sense organs of science' in order even to become visible, seems thus to be exaggerated or even superfluous.

(2) The hierarchy of types of danger and the difference between the perceived risk for oneself and others might be interpreted as an expression of Giddens' 'protective cocoon', i.e. a shield of confidence or trust which allows the environment to be perceived as inhabitable. ' "Filtering out' is the task of the protective cocoon'. The very same distances and separations in space and time, which made Beck fear that the new risks could be overlooked, makes it — according to Giddens — easier to push the risks behind the normalisation of the surroundings and live with them.

(3) The very fact that the survey was undertaken can finally, following Luhmann, be understood as much as a symptom of the era as a measure of its state. The constant surveying of the public opinion pro-creates a high awareness of risks as much as it depicts or describes real risks. The simple fact that the survey is required as well as the way it has been carried out is a sign of the era's obsession with risks, and the results are used to nourish its fascination with extremely improbable occurrences.

CONCEPTS OF RISK, COMMUNICATION AND (MIS)UNDERSTANDING

The sociologics of risk of Beck, Giddens and Luhmann respectively provided the basis for the three concepts of risk here cultivated and raised to the status of ideal types. The three concepts are all internally consistent as well as systematically different with respect to

(i) the cause and nature of modern risks,
(ii) the linguistic distinction or code and hence meaning of risks,
(iii) the function, effect and consequence of risks in modern society,
(iv) public perception and 'filtering out of risks', and, finally,
(v) strategies for reducing or living with risks (see Table 1).

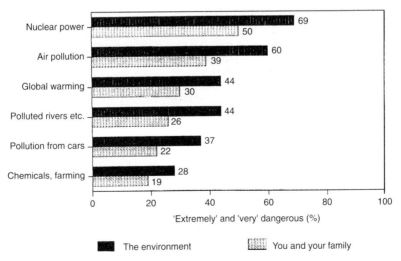

Figure 1. Public perception of risk, Norway 1993. Experienced danger. Categories were: extremely, very, fairly, not very, not at all.

Neither theoretical criteria, nor safety experts' analysis, nor the public perception of risk provides a good reason or foundation to prefer or dismiss one of the concepts at the expense of the others. The interpretation illustrates, however, a common and important (back) ground for the three concepts: modernity has become reflexive, and risks are an integral part of reflexive modernity, where they are created and can be found in technology, in society, and in the mind.

The three concepts seem to be three aspects or elements of risks, which experts and lay people often weigh and to which they attach different degrees of importance. Lay people's perception of risk tends to be as multi-faceted and open as the safety experts' concept of safety is instrumental and closed; And filters are in people's minds to prevent uncertainty seeping in, as much as in industrial chimneys to reduce emissions. Aspects or elements of all three concepts and their mental filters are often simultaneously present in lay persons' perception of risk. The silent and complex relationship between the three often appears to experts as inconsistency and double standards[11]. Especially in critical situations communication breakdown due to experts' and lay people's different understanding of safety and perceptions of risk, might well become a more serious safety risk, than lay people's presumed irrationalities and double standards.

Table 1. Three 'ideal' types of risk or three aspects of risk.

	Ulrich Beck	Anthony Giddens	Niklas Luhmann
Cause of development	Scientific and technical	Institutional	Administrative expectations
Linguistic code or antonym	Safety	Fate	Danger/disaster
'Function' in society	Latent side effects	Chance/ possibility	Superimposition of risks on decisions
Public perception	Second-hand, non-experience	Protective cocoon	Second-order observation
'Strategy'	Preventive technology politics	Life politics	Communication and rational decision making

REFERENCES

1. Beck, U. *Risikogesellschaft. Auf dem Weg in eine andere Moderne.* (Frankfurt am Main: Suhrkamp Verlag) (1986). English translation: *Risk Society. Towards a New Modernity* (London: Sage Publications) (1992).

2. Beck, U., Giddens, A. and Lash, S. *Reflexive Modernization. Politics, Tradition and Aesthetics in the Modern Social Order.* (Cambridge, UK: Polity Press) (1994).

3. Beck, U. *Ecological Enlightment. Essays on the Politics of the Risk Society.* (New Jersey: Humanities Press) (1995).

4. Beck, U. *Ecological Politics in an Age of Risk.* (Cambridge, UK: Polity Press) (1995).

5. Giddens, A. *The Consequences of Modernity.* (Cambridge, UK: Polity Press) (1990).

6. Giddens, A. *Modernity and Self-Identity. Self and Society in the Late Modern Age* (Cambridge, UK: Polity Press) (1991).

7. Giddens, A. *Beyond Left and Right. The Future of Radical Politics* (Cambridge, UK: Polity Press) (1994).

8. Luhmann, N. *Soziologie des Risikos* (Frankfurt am Main: Suhrkamp Verlag) (1991). English translation: *Risk: a Sociological Theory* (Berlin & New York: Walter de Gruyter) (1993).

9. Norsk Samfunnsvitenskapelig Datatjeneste. NSD Rapporter, Nr. 100. Knut Kalgraff Skjåk og Bjurg Bøyum. *Undersøking om verdier, natur og miljø 1993* (in Norwegian) (Bergen) (1994).

10. Seippel, Ø. *Fra natur til handling* (in Norwegian). Reports from Alternativ Fremtid 3/1995 (Oslo) (1995).

11. Slovic, P. *Perception of Risk.* Science **236**, 285 (1987).

Radiation Protection Dosimetry
Vol. 68, No. 3/4, pp. 185–190 (1996)
Nuclear Technology Publishing

ON PROBABILISTIC RISK ANALYSIS OF TECHNOLOGICAL SYSTEMS

B. Natvig and J. Gåsemyr
Department of Mathematics, University of Oslo
PO Box 1053, Blindern, 0316 Oslo, Norway

Abstract — The reliability of a system is defined as the probability of system functioning. In reliability theory one is studying how the reliability of a system can be assessed from the reliabilities of its components. In the first part of this paper the safety of a nuclear power plant is considered from a reliability theory point of view. In particular, we focus on the Chernobyl catastrophe in 1986 and the incidents at Le Bugey in 1984 and Barsebäck in 1992. Some main areas of modern reliability theory of interest for the safety of nuclear power plants are indicated. In the second part of the paper risk and risk aversion are considered by first showing how these concepts are applied in modern non-life insurance mathematics. At the end the link to the choice between different energy supplies is discussed.

RELIABILITY

The reliability of a system is defined as the probability of system functioning. In reliability theory one is studying how the reliability of a system can be assessed from the reliabilities of its components. At the 18th European Meeting of Statisticians in Berlin, GDR, on 22–26 August 1988, the first author organised a session on 'Reliability of large technological systems'. This topic was obviously a hot one at the time, due, for example, to the Chernobyl catastrophe on 26 April 1986. At the time of the accident, for many people a nuclear power catastrophe was considered very unlikely. However, even before the Three Mile Island accident on 28 March 1979, the American Reactor Safety Study[1] had been strongly criticized[2,3], indicating the dangers of nuclear power plants.

The following opinion on the Chernobyl accident expressed by Laaksonen[4], of the Finnish Center for Radiation and Nuclear Safety, is especially interesting:

"The Chernobyl accident provided a discouraging example of a phenomenon which would be extremely difficult, if not impossible, to foresee and take into account in a probabilistic risk analysis. Also, the events which are usually considered in the safety analyses have almost been standardised 15 years ago.

The accident took place when the operators were decreasing the reactor power, prior to taking the plant out of service for scheduled maintenance. A special test of electrical systems was to be made at the stage the reactor had reached the power of 700–1000 MW (20–30% of nominal power). At the beginning of the test the reactor was to be scrammed automatically and thus no interaction was expected between the reactor and the other plant systems.

In the course of test preparation a coincidence of unfavourable operational steps brought the reactor to a state where it could reach prompt criticality in a few seconds. The dangerous core characters were evoked by the operators who were lacking sufficient knowledge in reactor physics. During the 12 hours preceding the explosion the operators committed deliberately at least six severe violations of operating rules. Four of these were such that without any of them the accident would have been avoided:

(1) Continued reactor operation without the necessary differential reactivity worth in the control rods (operation below the permissible value was indicated clearly on a computer printout).
(2) Continued reactor operation below the minimum allowable power level.
(3) Blocking of the reactor scram signals associated with steam drum level and reactor coolant pressure.
(4) Blocking of the reactor scram signals associated with trip of both turbogenerator units.

The operator behaviour was of course unforgivable but I think it can be understood from the following viewpoints:

(i)   a common attitude on operational rules in the Russian plants has been obviously quite relaxed; the rules have been taken as guidelines and not as strict orders;
(ii) the safety record of RBMK reactors was good and no precursory events of this type had ever occurred;
(iii) Chernobyl unit 4 had an excellent reputation among the RBMK plants and the operators were evidently too selfconfident;
(iv) the operators were not able to raise the reactor power above 200 MW with the normal control systems (the power level followed changes in the coolant void content but the operators did not realise the situation clearly enough)."

What the Chernobyl accident really did was to call into question the existing risk and safety analyses of large technological systems. This issue will now be discussed more closely.

In applying reliability theory to such systems, the following problems arise:

(i) lack of knowledge on the functioning of the system and its components;
(ii) lack of relevant data;
(iii) lack of knowledge on the reliability of the human components;
(iv) lack of knowledge on the quality of computer software;
(v) lack of knowledge of dependences between the components.

The first and third problems are fundamental in the analysis of the Chernobyl catastrophe by Laaksonen (quoted above) and of the Le Bugey and Barsebäck incidents considered below. These problems make it almost impossible to assess the probability of failure of a large technological system. Hence, the use of risk analysis to back political decisions on controversial safety issues is dubious, to say the least. If, however, a political decision has already been made, risk analysis and reliability theory can contribute essentially to improving the safety of a system. This is just the case for Norwegian offshore activities and for the Swedish nuclear power industry. It should, however, be noted that the latter is in some trouble after the incident in the Barsebäck 2 reactor on 28 July 1992. The site is very close to Copenhagen and the Danish environmental movement OOA has, also on the basis of a report[5] from the first author, claimed the plant should be permanently closed. Since Denmark has decided not to have nuclear power plants, the risk imposed by the nearby Swedish nuclear reactors is especially questionable from an ethical point of view.

The incident showed that the emergency core cooling system could fail rapidly, in the case of a pipe rupture, due to a much faster than expected clogging of the strainer for emergency cooling water by washed down mineral wool insulation. The emergency core cooling system was modified and a so-called probabilistic safety analysis carried through during the autumn of 1992. The Swedish Nuclear Power Inspectorate determined on 4 January 1993 to restart the Barsebäck 2 reactor. The critique of this probabilistic safety analysis by the first author seems to be of general interest:

(1) Just a very minor part[6–8] of the documentation on the modified system was a proper probabilistic safety analysis and even this part was not very well founded. The rest was pure technical considerations. The Human Reliability Analysis is based on Swain's approach[9,10], THERP, which more or less treats the human components as technological ones. This approach is highly questionable.
(2) No probabilistic safety analysis was done for the complete safety system of the reactor. Therefore, there was no sufficient guarantee that the introduction of the modified emergency core cooling system had not led to a weakening of the remaining safety system.
(3) The sensitivity of wrong judgements in the safety analysis is tested by just varying one parameter at a time instead of a simultaneous sensitivity analysis of the parameters.

In a report[11] a series of interesting questions asked by the Swedish Nuclear Power Inspectorate are reviewed along with references to the answers given by SYDKRAFT — The Barsebäck nuclear power plant. Most of these answers are very brief, some covering just half a page, and they do not treat the matter in any depth.

Undoubtedly, the analysis contributed to improving the safety of the system. However, as presented, it seemed to promise more. Hence the critique also concerns the communication and the information on the contents of the analysis. Generally, openness and honesty are key points in all sorts of communication, and of utmost importance when dealing with radiation risks, due to public scepticism.

In the following some main areas of modern reliability theory of interest for the safety of nuclear power plants are indicated.

To improve the safety of a system we need measures of the relative importance of each component for system reliability. Barlow and Proschan[12] suggested that the most important component is that having the highest probability of finally causing system failure by its own failure. The first author has since developed a theory supporting another measure[13]. The component whose failure contributes most to reducing the expected remaining lifetime of the system is the most important one. The latter measure obviously is constructed to improve system life expectancy, whereas the first one is most relevant when considering accident scenarios.

It should be noted that both when carrying through a simultaneous sensitivity analysis of the parameters and when calculating measures of the importance of system components, interdependences should be accounted for. Actually, Norros[14] treats the measure of importance developed by the first author in the case of dependent components. Corresponding to a simultaneous sensitivity analysis one could suggest introducing measures of importance of groups of components. Anyway, our idea is that a simultaneous sensitivity analysis of the reliabilities of the most important components should be carried through in order to assess the uncertainty in system reliability.

The Chernobyl accident provided new data on nuclear power plants. What type of theory do we have to benefit from such data in future risk analyses in the nuclear industry? The characteristic feature of this type of theory is that one benefits both from data for the system's components and for the system itself. Furthermore, due to lack of sufficient data one is completely dependent on benefiting from the experience and judgement of engineers concerning the technological components and on those of psychologists and sociologists for the human components. This leads to subjectivistic probabilities.

The frequentistic interpretation of probability often makes little sense in dealing with risk analysis of rare events. However, both the subjectivistic and frequentistic probabilities are obeying the same natural rules of computation, based on the same axiomatic system, as opposed to the corresponding concepts in fuzzy set theory.

The methodology of statistical inference that can deal naturally with subjectivistic probabilities[15] is called Bayesian after the English clergyman and probabilist Thomas Bayes, who died in 1761. One starts by using expert opinion and experience as to the reliability of the components. This information is then updated by using data on the component level from experiments and accidents. Based on the information on the component level, the corresponding uncertainty in system reliability is derived. This uncertainty is modified by using expert opinion and experience on the system level. Finally, this uncertainty is updated by using data on the system level from experiments and accidents.

Theory in this area is under development at the University of Oslo[16,17]. It should be noted that the use of expert opinions is actually implemented in the regulatory work for nuclear power plants in the USA[18]. A general problem when using expert opinions is the selection of the experts. This problem is an important one needing further work. Asking experts technical questions on the component level[17], where the consequences for the overall reliability assessment on the system level are less clear, seems very advantageous. Too much experts' influence directly on system level assessments could then be prevented.

The journal *Nature*[19], published an article on an incident coming close to a catastrophe, which occurred during the night of 14 April 1984 in a French pressurised water reactor (PWR) at Le Bugey on the Rhône river, not far from Geneva. This motivates the socalled multistate reliability theory.

"The event began with the failure of the rectifier supplying electricity to one of the two separate 48 V direct-current control circuits of the 900 MW reactor which was on full power at the time. Instantly, a battery pack switched in to maintain the 48 V supply and a warning light began to flash at the operators in the control room. Unfortunately, the operators ignored the light (if they had not, they could simply have switched in an auxiliary rectifier).

What then happened was something which had been completely ignored in the engineering risk analysis for the PWR. The emergency battery now operating the control system began to run down. Instead of falling precipitously to zero, as assumed in the 'all or nothing' risk analysis, the voltage in the control circuit steadily slipped down from its nominal 48 V to 30 V over a period of three hours. In response, a number of circuit breakers began to trip out in an unpredictable fashion until finally the system, with the reactor still at full power, disconnected itself from the grid.

The reactor was now at full power with no external energy being drawn from the system to cool it. An automatic 'scram' system then correctly threw in the control rods, which absorbed neutrons and shut off the nuclear reaction. However a reactor in this condition is still producing a great deal of heat — 300 MW in this case. An emergency system is then supposed to switch in a diesel generator to provide emergency core cooling (otherwise the primary coolant would boil and vent within a few hours). But the first generator failed to switch on because of the loss of the first control circuit. Luckily the only back-up generator in the system then did switch in, averting a serious accident."

The article in *Nature* furthermore stated:

"But the Le Bugey incident shows that a whole new class of possible events had been ignored — those where electrical systems fail gradually. It shows that risk analysis must not only take into account a yes or no, working or not working, for each item in the reactor, but the possibility of working with a slightly degraded system."

In 1978 Barlow and Proschan initiated the development of multistate reliability theory where both the components and the system are described in a more refined way than just as functioning or failing. During the 1980s, the University of Oslo has been central in the development of this theory[20]. It has also been indicated how this theory can be applied to offshore electrical power supply systems and pipeline networks. Furthermore, efficient algorithms and computer software based on this theory have been developed.

RISK AND RISK AVERSION

The risk notion is often used in an imprecise way not only in daily language, but also among so-called experts. The Norwegian Nuclear Power Commission Report[21] gives the following incorrect definition:

'Risk is the probability of a certain undesirable consequence.'

This contributes to a very unclear discussion of risk aversion in their work. The usual mathematical definition is[22]:

'Risk is the expected loss of utility.'

Hence risk is a weighted average of economical losses due to different consequences, with the corresponding

probabilities as weights. The fruitfulness of this definition hopefully becomes evident from the following
discussion of risk aversion.

An important contribution to modern non-life
insurance mathematics is the application of utility
theory in the treatment of the client's and the insurance
company's risk assessments. Typical examples of problems that can be studied inside this theory are:

Why is the insurance company willing to accept the
risk which the client wishes to get rid of?

What prize (premium) is the client willing to pay for
insurance of a certain risk?

How is a less likely major loss assessed compared
to a more likely minor loss?

Consider a potential insurance client A, who will be
referred to as a person, but might as well be a company,
a society or another economic unit. A carries a risk that
can cause him an economic loss in the coming year,
such as a risk associated with fire and water damage
or liability.

Assume that it is possible to give a simple number
for the personal loss of utility A feels by losing x dollars. Call this loss of utility $l(x)$. It may at first glance be
considered reasonable to assume that the loss function is
the straight line $l(x) = x$ shown in Figure 1(a). In this
case A assesses a loss of 20,000 dollars to be twice as
serious as a loss of 10,000 dollars. This may, however,
not be true. It can be more reasonable to assume that
the loss of the first 10,000 dollars is easier to accept
than the additional second 10,000 dollars. If A in
advance has lost a considerable part of his fortune, an
additional loss of 10,000 dollars can cause serious personal consequences as executor's sale and loss of credit,
leading to a significantly reduced standard of living and
loss of social position and prestige.

These points of view indicate that the loss function

should increase faster, the larger the loss is, as shown
in Figure 1(b). A marginal loss of 10,000 dollars is then
assessed as more serious, the larger the loss A has suffered in advance.

It can be shown that if A seeks insurance in spite of
the fact that the premium is higher than the expected
loss, then his assessment of loss is represented by the
convex loss function of Figure 1(b) and not the straight
loss function of Figure 1(a). He is risk aversive, making
him prefer a fixed premium compared to a rather
unlikely major loss, although the premium is larger than
the average loss associated with the risk.

In insurance companies the premiums are considerably higher than the expected claims because the premiums, in addition to covering claims expenses, shall
cover administration costs. Even so, people insure cars,
houses and furniture and companies have fire, stock
damage and product liability insurance. The clients'
actual behaviour accordingly corresponds to the
assumption of a convex loss function and we can conclude that they are risk aversive.

Now assume that A can choose between two risks, R
and S, where R has the lowest damage probability
whereas S has correspondingly smaller claims expenses
if damage occurs, such that the expected annual claims
expenses are identical for the two risks. It can then in
a similar way be shown that A prefers the risk S compared to R. Due to risk aversion, frequent minor losses
are preferred compared to rare major losses.

There are obvious similarities between A's choice of
risk R or S and the society's choice of nuclear, hydro-
electrical or fossil power. If we, without restrictions,
transfer the results above to the choice of different
energy supplies, they can be formulated as:

Two energy supply alternatives giving the same
expected annual loss do not have to be assessed as
equally risky. An alternative giving more frequent

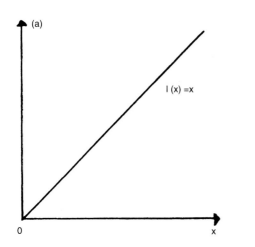

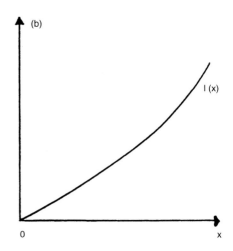

Figure 1. (a) A straight loss function. (b) A convex loss function.

incidents with moderate consequences is, under otherwise equal conditions, preferred compared to an alternative giving more rare incidents with catastrophic consequences.

Especially, it follows that the risk associated with nuclear power is underestimated if one is only considering expected annual loss. The risk aversion is linked to the possible catastrophic nuclear power accidents.

The probabilities of different types and degrees of damage associated with energy production are not known exactly. The probability of construction site accidents may be satisfactorily estimated from statistical data, whereas the probability of serious accidents with a new nuclear reactor type must be estimated from reliability studies including limited data from other not completely similar reactors. The possibility of incorrectly estimating the damage probabilities enters as an extraordinary contribution to the risk, which from a risk aversion point of view militates against the energy supply alternatives with the less certain estimated damage probabilities.

Generally, we hope that readers have the risk aversion point of view in mind when discussing different sorts of radiation risk. It is not irrational to be risk aversive when confronted with great uncertainties.

ACKNOWLEDGEMENT

The section on risk and risk aversion is a shortened version of a section in a book[23] by the first author. The latter section was originally written by Professor Ragnar Norberg in 1979. The authors are also grateful to a referee for a very careful reading of our manuscript and for some thought provoking comments which have been taken into account.

REFERENCES

1. Reactor Safety Study. *An Assessment of Accident Risks in US Commercial Nuclear Power Plants.* WASH-1400 (Washington DC: Nuclear Regulatory Commission) (1975).

2. Lewis, H. W. *et al. Risk Assessment Review Group Report to the US Nuclear Regulatory Commission* (Washington, DC: Nuclear Regulatory Commission) (1978).

3. Natvig, B. *Litt om Bruk og Manglende Bruk av Pålitelighetsteori i Kjernekraftutvalgets Innstilling (On the Use and Misuse of Reliability Theory in the Nuclear Power Commission Report)* (The Faculty of Science, University of Oslo) (1979).

4. Laaksonen, J. *The Accident at the Chernobyl Nuclear Power Plant.* In: Proc. Society of Reliability Engineers, Scandinavian Chapter-Symposium, Otaniemi, Finland, 14–16 October 1986 (Technical Research Centre of Finland, Electrical Engineering Laboratory, Otakaari 7B, SF-02150 Espoo, Finland) (1986).

5. Natvig, B. *Angående Probabilistisk Sikkerhetsanalyse (PSA) av Nødkjølningsfunksjonene ved Barsebäckreaktorene (On the Probabilistic Safety Analysis (PSA) of the Emergency Cooling Functions of the Barsebäck Reactors).* Letter of 6 May 1993 to the Director General of the Swedish Nuclear Power Inspectorate (1993).

6. Moritz, P. *Barsebäcksverket — Sammanfattning av säkerhetsanalyserna til följd av åtgärder/översyn i nödkylsystem (system 323 och 322). (The Barsebäck Nuclear Power Plant — A Review of the Safety Analyses of the Modified Emergency Core Cooling System (System 323 and 322)).* PBQ-9211-25 rev. 1 (Swedish Nuclear Power Inspectorate) (1992).

7. Moritz, P. *Barsebäcksverket — Analys av mänskligt felhandlande vid backspolning av 323- och 322-silar. (The Barsebäck Nuclear Power Plant — An Analysis of Human Failure on Backwashing of the 323 and 322 Strainers).* PBQ-9211-10 (Swedish Nuclear Power Inspectorate) (1992).

8. Jacobsson, P. and Jönsson, J. *Barsebäcksverket — Analys av system 322 och 323 med modifierade backspolningsalternativ samt beräkning av härdskadefrekvens. (The Barsebäck Nuclear Power Plant — An Analysis of Systems 322 and 323 with Modified Backwashing Alternatives and Calculation of Core Damage Frequency).* ES-9211 m 008 (Swedish Nuclear Power Inspectorate) (1992).

9. Swain, A. D. *Human Reliability Analysis: Need, Status, Trends and Limitations.* Reliab. Eng. Syst. Saf. **29**, 301–313 (1990).

10. Swain, A. D. and Guttmann, H. E. *Handbook of Human Reliability Data.* NUREC/CR-1278 (Sandia Laboratories) (1983).

11. Zander, K. *SKI — Frågor och svar* (Swedish Nuclear Power Inspectorate — Questions and answers) PBQ-9211-26 2. issue (1992).

12. Barlow, R. E. and Proschan, F. *Importance of System Components and Fault Tree Events.* Stochastic Process. Appl. **3**(2), 153–173 (1975).

13. Natvig, B. *New Light on Measures of Importance of System Components.* Scand. J. Statist. **12**(1), 43–54 (1985).

14. Norros, I. *Notes on Natvig's Measure of Importance of System Components.* J. Appl. Probab. **23**(3), 736–747 (1986).

15. Berger, J. O. *Statistical Decision Theory and Bayesian Analysis* (New York: Springer Verlag) (1985).

16. Natvig, B. and Eide, H. *Bayesian Estimation of System Reliability.* Scand. J. Stat. **14**(4), 319–327 (1987).

17. Gåsemyr, J. and Natvig, B. *Using Expert Opinions in Bayesian Prediction of Component Lifetimes in a Shock Model.* Math. Oper. Res. **20**(1), 227–242 (1995).

18. Chhibber, S., Apostolakis, G. E. and Okrent, D. *On the Use of Expert Judgements to Estimate the Pressure Increment in the Sequoyah Containment at Vessel Breach.* Nucl. Technol. **105**(1), 87–103 (1994).

19. *Near-Catastrophe at Le Bugey.* Nature **321**, 462 (29 May, 1986).

20. Natvig, B. *Multistate Coherent Systems.* In: Johnson, N. L. and Kotz, S. (Eds) Encyclopedia Statist. Sci. **5**, 732–735 (New York: Wiley) (1985).

21. Norwegian Nuclear Power Commission Report (NOU 35A). *Kjernekraft og Sikkerhet (Nuclear Energy and Safety)* (The Oil and Energy Department, Oslo) (1978).

22. DeGroot, M. *Optimal Statistical Decisions* (New York: McGraw-Hill) (1970).

23. Natvig, B. *Sannsynlighetsvurderinger i Atomalderen (Probability Assessments in the Nuclear Age)* (Universitetsforlaget, Oslo) (1987).

Radiation Protection Dosimetry
Vol. 68, No. 3/4, pp. 191–196 (1996)
Nuclear Technology Publishing

LAYPEOPLE'S UNDERSTANDING OF RADIOACTIVITY AND RADIATION

E. K. Henriksen
Department of Physics, University of Oslo
PO Box 1048 Blindern, N-0316 Oslo, Norway

Abstract — It may be argued that the population should have sufficient understanding of radiation phenomena to secure individual safety as well as democratic decisions. To attain this, it is necessary for the communicators of radiation information to be familiar with the lay person's perceptions of these phenomena. A questionnaire survey was conducted to examine non-experts' conceptions of radiation phenomena. The survey revealed incomplete understanding of concepts such as radioactive decay, half-life and absorption of radiation and a lack of differentiation between radiation and radioactive material. Many respondents did not distinguish between sources of ionising radiation and other environmental hazards. Nuclear power plants and submarines were the most feared sources of radiation. There are indications that the lay understanding of radiation phenomena and risk is to a large extent formed by mass media and that 'school knowledge' of these phenomena is not applied in situations belonging to the 'real world'. To resolve this problem, new teaching and information procedures are needed. These should take into account the learners' preconceptions and should integrate 'school knowledge' with considerations belonging to the 'real world'.

INTRODUCTION

Since the discovery of X rays in 1895, ionising radiation has been a part of our life and consciousness. From the very beginning, radiation has been shrouded in myths — of exaggerated expectations as well as excessive fear[1]. Radiation has been characterised partly as a life-force, partly as a doomsday power destined to cause the ultimate destruction of mankind. In our own time, fear seems to be the prevalent characteristic of the public perception of radiation phenomena, and the treatment in the media of incidents like the Chernobyl accident has greatly contributed to the spreading of uneasiness and fear.

Why should we expect the public to know something about radioactivity and radiation? There may be many answers to this question; three of the most evident are the following:

(1) *The pragmatic reason*
    People should be capable of protecting themselves from the harmful effects of radiation as well as avoiding excessive fear.
(2) *The democratic reason*
    People should be capable of informed judgements in political matters involving radiation phenomena: nuclear energy, waste disposal, exposure limits etc.
(3) *The educational reason*
    The individual derives pleasure and fulfilment from knowing something about the world around him/her.

How can knowledge about radiation phenomena be effectively communicated to laypeople? In the constructivist approach to learning, the learner is viewed as actively creating his/her own understanding in an interaction between the notions he/she already holds and the input provided by external sources such as the teacher, peers or the mass media. Within this understanding of learning, the learner's ideas and conceptions prior to instruction are seen as important factors in the learning process, and it thus becomes paramount for a communicator to be familiar with the conceptions already present in those with whom he/she wishes to communicate. This principle also holds true in the field of radiation, and a number of publications have dealt with pupils' and laypeople's conceptions of radiation phenomena. For instance, Lijnse *et al*[2] described concepts of radioactivity and radiation held by 15 and 16 year old pupils in the Netherlands, and Eijkelhof and Millar[3] analysed British newspaper reports of the Chernobyl accident to identify features of the lay understanding of radiation phenomena.

The present survey was conducted to investigate the understanding of radiation phenomena and risk among Norwegians with a reasonable level of general education, but lacking specialisation in physical science.

METHODS

Respondents

The survey was administered in the form of a questionnaire given to 270 students in an elementary physics course at the University of Oslo. This group was chosen for two main reasons: (1) the group was fairly large and easily accessible, and (2) the group mainly consisted of first-year students who had completed secondary education, but had not received formal instruction on radiation since leaving school. This student group can in no way be said to represent the general public; nonetheless it can be assumed that the results are indicative of conceptions and attitudes found among 'the enlightened public' — people with a general, secondary education in the direction of natural sciences, but no specialisation.

Of the 270 students 191 (71%) completed the questionnaire. Of the respondents 53% were women, 45% were men and 2% did not state sex. It can not be excluded that the 29% who did not respond, differed from the respondents in relevant respects. Since this survey does not aim to establish percentages of persons holding this or that conception, but rather aims to identify a few commonly held conceptions of radiation phenomena among non-specialists, the possible bias from non-respondents should not render the results irrelevant.

The questionnaire

The questionnaire consisted of 13 questions. Two of these gave background information about gender and background in secondary school, 7 measured knowledge and understanding of radioactivity and radiation, and 4 were designed to give information about radiation fear and attitudes. Most questions were open-ended. As far as possible, the questions were connected to real-life examples that the students might know from media coverage of current issues related to radiation. The questions which are referred to in the paper are presented in Table 1.

Coding and analysis

The answers to the open-ended questions in most cases fell into one of 5–10 categories, defined after reading the answers from about 20% of the respondents. All answers were then assigned to the appropriate categories and coded.

To obtain a measure of each respondent's level of understanding, a point system was developed. Each of the questions concerning knowledge and understanding was appointed a maximum number of points, adjusted to the presumed difficulty of the question. For each question, points ranging from zero to maximum were awarded to respondents according to their degree of understanding as judged by the investigator. The sum of the points from all knowledge questions was taken as a measure of each respondent's level of understanding. The maximum number of points obtainable for each question is presented in Table 1. To find out whether the level of understanding influenced respondents' attitudes and level of radiation fear, the respondents were divided into two groups: those who scored lower than median on the knowledge questions (the low-score group), and those who scored higher than median (the high-score group).

The data were analysed using SPSS version 6.1 for Windows. A significance level of 95% was applied.

RESULTS AND DISCUSSION

Knowledge of the radiation process

A major aim in this survey was to get an overview of the respondents' understanding of central concepts concerning radioactivity and radiation phenomena.

Table 1. Questions and point assignments.

The table shows the questions treated in the analysis and, for the questions measuring knowledge, the number of points assigned for a 100% correct answer. For partially correct answers, the number of points was reduced as judged appropriate by the investigator. The questions concerning gender and school background have been omitted, as has one question not relevant to this analysis.

Questions	Max no of points
1. (a) Are you afraid of being exposed to radiation in your daily life? *If yes:*	
(b) Where do you think this radiation comes from?	
2. (a) Do you think there are radiation sources (radioactive substances) in the house where you live? *If yes:*	
(b) Which ones?	
3. Radiation from radioactive substances may be divided into 3 main types.	
(a) What are they called?	2 points
(b) What constitutes the radiation in each case?	4 points
4. After the reactor accident in Chernobyl in 1986, radiation could be detected from a range of Norwegian foodstuffs, particularly mutton and reindeer meat. How had the food become radioactive?	2 points
5. After the Chernobyl accident, restrictions were imposed on the sale of mutton meat with radioactivity exceeding 600 Bq/kg. Radioactivity is measured in becquerel (Bq). What is the definition of 1 Bq?	3 points
6. The radioactive substance caesium-137, which was found in mutton after the Chernobyl accident, has a half-life of 30 years. What is meant by this?	3 points
7. Many types of spice are irradiated in order to kill bacteria. We say that the radiation is absorbed in the spice. What do you think happens in the spice when radiation is absorbed?	3 points
8. What sorts of injuries can be found in people who have been exposed to radiation from radioactive substances?	See below*
9. In Sweden, more than half the electric energy is supplied by nuclear power. Do you think this should continue? Give a reason for your answer.	
10. The Russian submarine 'Komsomolets' sank near the island of Bjørnøya in 1989. Many people think that the sub should be raised.	
(a) Do you think that the 'Komsolets' is a threat to the environment in the Northern seas? *If yes:*	
(b) In what way?	

*Points were awarded according to the number of radiation injuries mentioned; 1 point for each type of injury listed (when correct). Exception: 2 points were awarded for mentioning mutations when these were explicitly connected with the initiation of cancer.

From the answers to question 3, it appeared that 89% of the respondents knew of the three radiation types alpha, beta and gamma, whereas only 34% could correctly state what the radiation consisted of in each case. The definition of a becquerel (question 5) was known to 25%. It should not be regarded as very alarming that most respondents were unable to define particular concepts such as the becquerel or α, β and γ radiation. These concise definitions are for expert use. More important, in view of the reasons for knowing stated in the introduction (the pragmatic, the democratic and the educational reason), is the lack of understanding of central features and processes related to radioactive decay and absorption of radiation.

A prevalent tendency among the respondents was the lack of differentiation between the concept of radioactive material and that of radiation, most apparent in the answers to question 4:

'Radiation from the ruined reactor in Chernobyl had gone into the lichen on which the sheep and reindeer grazed.'
'The radioactivity/radiation/becquerel (?) was transported with the wind . . .'

It has previously been observed that laypeople have difficulties distinguishing the concept of radiation from that of radioactive material[2,4]. Eijkelhof and Millar[3] found that laypeople did not distinguish between being irradiated and ingesting particles of radioactive material. The undifferentiated concept of radioactive material/radiation leads to problems with the concepts of activity and dose and is a serious obstacle to understanding the nature of radiation hazards and the appropriateness of countermeasures.

When asked about the concept of half-life (question 6), 74% of the respondents gave a definition which might be called correct. An often encountered wording was: 'The amount of radioactive material is halved after 30 years'. However, the wording in some of the clearly wrong answers indicated that some of the acceptable answers might conceal a misunderstanding:

'It [half-life] means that it takes 30 years for 1 kg of ^{137}Cs to be reduced to 1/2 kg. The mass decreases because the substance gives away alpha irradiation, which is particles'.

The answer betrays a lack of understanding that disintegration of a radioactive atom involves the creation of a new nucleus. It is quite right that a substance containing 1 kg of caesium after 30 years would contain only half a kilogram of caesium — but it is also a part of the story that the substance would during this same period have gained almost half a kilo of ^{137}Ba! The total mass of the substance is only marginally decreased as a result of the emitted particles. Many answers of the type: 'The amount of radioactive material is halved' might conceal a similar misunderstanding. It is tempting to speculate that the concept that the emitted particles constitute a

mass loss leading to a halving of the radioactive sample's mass during one half-life, might have arisen because the word 'half-life' invites the invention of explanations: whereas it is impossible to guess what a becquerel might be for one who has not been given the definition, the very word 'half-life' suggests that something is halved. For someone lacking a formal level of knowledge in the area of radiation, it might seem reasonable to suppose that it is the mass that is halved — mass being a very tangible concept with which most people are familiar.

Another answer sometimes given to question 6 was: 'It takes 30 years before the substance is unharmful'. Many used a wording which would be more appropriate for chemical substances: 'Half of the radioactive matter is degraded in 30 years'. It has previously been observed by Lijnse *et al*[2] that half-life is often perceived by laypeople as 'the active period of the substance' or 'the time that the substance is dangerous'. The latter notion is potentially hazardous in given situations and deserves some consideration.

To find out if the respondents knew what was meant by "absorption of radiation", an example was used concerning the absorption of radiation in spice which is irradiated to kill bacteria (question 7). The question appeared to be difficult — only 55% attempted an answer. One of the best answers was given by a respondent who understood more than she knew:

'Don't know. There is energy in the radiation, perhaps the temperature rises or spontaneous reactions can happen if there are some [reactions] which lack the energy to go by themselves (?)'.

The concept of absorption of radiation is problematic for at least two reasons: firstly because it takes a good deal of physical insight to understand what is actually happening, and secondly because the word 'absorption' has a slightly different meaning in everyday language than in scientific use[4]: we say that a sponge absorbs water, and know that the water will come out again if we squeeze the sponge. Thus, it may seem plausible that radiation which is absorbed in a substance, remains in the substance and may be re-emitted later in its original form. This concept was found among the respondents in this survey in statements such as:

'Some of the radiation remains in the spice'.

10% of the respondents answered that 'the radiation is taken up by the spice', and some of these added that the radiation was 'stored' in the spice, which gave reason to suspect that they really meant that the spice became radioactive. Twelve per cent said explicitly that the radiation made the spice radioactive. This concept is probably a consequence of the lack of differentiation between radiation and radioactive material.

The survey also dealt with the radiation sources to which we are exposed in our daily lives and the health consequences of exposure to ionising radiation. When asked whether they believed that there were radiation sources in their home (question 2), 62% answered in the affirmative. It appeared from the answers that there was considerable confusion concerning what a source of radiation is. Many seemed to regard this as an expression for almost any undesirable agent in buildings: electric and magnetic fields, asbestos, toxic chemicals in building materials etc. Confusion between sources of radiation and other environmental hazards has also been described in the literature. For instance, Durant et al[5] found that almost 50% of the respondents in a survey of public understanding of science believed that nuclear power stations could cause acid rain.

The respondents had clear perceptions of the kinds of damage that ionising radiation can cause to the human body, and a wide variety of answers were given to the question concerning this (question 8). The most frequent answer was cancer (mentioned by 75%), whereas mutations were mentioned by 49% and genetic damage by 36%. Other effects mentioned included birth defects, damage to cells and organs, death, sterility or decreased reproductive capacity, skin damage, hair loss and burns. The results gave no information about the extent to which the respondents imagined these effects to appear (or after what kind of doses). It is worth mentioning that the most important effect, from an expert point of view, is cancer, presumed to be initiated by mutations. Genetic effects (alterations in the offspring of irradiated individuals) have so far only been detectable in animal experiments, not in humans.

No significant difference was found between women's and men's level of understanding as measured by the total score on the knowledge questions. This is in contrast to Lucas'[6] finding that significantly more men than women were able to give acceptable answers to radiation questions in a survey of the British public. The contrast may be due to differences in the populations examined: whereas all respondents in the present survey had completed secondary school and begun university studies in natural science, Lucas' respondents were a sample of the general population where it may be assumed that women on the average had a lower level of education than men.

To sum up, the investigation revealed an incomplete understanding of some central concepts concerning radiation phenomena. Somewhat faltering formulations of answers (for instance 'becquerel is radiation density') indicate that some of the respondents may have a feeling of what it is about without being able to give their answer an exact formulation. Knowledge of the biological effects of radiation was reasonably good.

Radiation fear and attitudes

Central aims in this survey were to detect whether respondents feared radiation and to investigate their attitudes to the applications of radiation. It appeared that whereas 62% believed that there were sources of radiation in their home (question 2), only 16% were afraid of being exposed to radiation in their daily life (question 1). Significantly more women than men were afraid (χ^2 = 5.37; p = 0.02), whereas no significant difference was found between the high- and low-score group (the groups with the greater or lesser knowledge of radiation phenomena, respectively) in the proportion of respondents who were afraid of radiation. Those who were afraid, regarded nuclear power and nuclear submarines as the greatest hazards. UV radiation was also brought in and connected to an assumed depletion of the ozone layer. No one mentioned radon as a threat, although it was mentioned by many as a radiation source they knew to be in the house.

In the present study, Sweden was used as an example to examine the respondents' attitudes towards nuclear power (question 9). This resulted in the question yielding slightly different information from what was intended: whereas the objective was to measure attitudes to nuclear power in general, the answers clearly concerned Sweden's use of such energy in particular. There was a small majority of antagonists to Swedish nuclear power among the respondents: when asked whether Sweden should continue its production of nuclear power, 36% answered yes and 43% no, whereas 14% were uncertain and 7% failed to answer. A significantly higher proportion of women than men were negative to nuclear power (χ^2 = 17.08; p = 0.00004). A small, but significant difference was found between the high-score group and the low-score group in their attitude to Swedish nuclear power, the high-scorers being the more positive (χ^2 = 4.76; p = 0.03). Half of the protagonists (50%) gave as a reason that the control of plants in Sweden was so good that the risk of accidents was minimal, whereas 26% claimed that nuclear power was an environment friendly alternative. Of the antagonists, 69% gave the risk for accidents as a reason for their standpoint, whereas 21% mentioned problems concerning storage of nuclear wastes. The risk of leakages was also mentioned. It was evident that whereas Swedish nuclear power was regarded as relatively safe, the attitude to nuclear energy in general was sceptical, and it was often presented as a necessary evil.

Atomic energy resistance in the Scandinavian population has been reported by Löfstedt and Ringius[7] and by Skjåk and Bøyum[8], who showed that 50% of the Norwegian population regarded nuclear power as 'extremely or very dangerous to themselves and their families'. Radiation and radioactivity are, for many people, associated with danger and fear, and surveys have shown that atomic energy and radioactive contamination rank high among people's conceptions of risks[8,9]. This is probably closely connected to earlier observations that it is the aspects of uncontrollability, catastrophic potential and involuntary exposure which give radiation its aura of dread. These characteristics of radiation are especially prevalent in connection with nuclear power[9].

Another matter of interest was the respondents' attitudes to radioactive waste, exemplified by the Russian submarine 'Komsomolets' which sank in the Barents sea in 1989 (question 10). The respondents were asked whether they personally believed the sub to be a threat to the environment in the northern seas: 51% answered 'yes' and 17% 'no', whereas 13% were uncertain and 13% failed to answer. There were significantly more women then men who believed that the Komsomolets was a threat ($\chi^2 = 8.64$; $p = 0.034$), whereas no difference was found between the high- and the low-score groups. Of those who answered 'no', some stated that the amount of radioactive material was too small to be a real threat; others thought that the contamination around the sub would be very localised, making a very small contribution to the overall state of the area. Of those who did judge the sub to be a threat, 34% stated that it was a danger to the marine flora and fauna in the area. 'Contamination/irradiation of the environment' was given by 27% as a reason for fearing Komsomolets, whereas 15% thought the radioactivity would contaminate fish and thereby constitute a health hazard to people and 8% said simply that the fish would become radioactive.

In the present investigation of attitudes to radiation and its applications, women tended to be more worried about radiation and more sceptical about nuclear power than were men. This tendency has also been demonstrated in similar studies[7,8,10], and seems to represent a general difference in women's and men's cautiousness towards a range of perceived risks such as electromagnetic fields[11], car exhaust and chemicals used in food production[8].

IMPLICATIONS FOR IMPROVING PUBLIC UNDERSTANDING OF RADIOACTIVITY AND RADIATION

It is evident from the above discussion that the lay model of radiation phenomena differs significantly from the experts' model. How has the lay model of radioactivity and radiation arisen? Lucas[12] has reviewed literature indicating that informal mass media are important sources of scientific knowledge for the public. A comparison between the mass media's treatment of radiation phenomena after the Chernobyl accident and pupils' conceptions about such phenomena, seemed to indicate that the press played a considerable role in forming non-experts' understanding of such phenomena[2]. Indications of the role of the media were found also in the present study, for instance in statements such as 'becquerel is radioactivity per kg of meat' (clearly related to the press treatment of the sales limits for contaminated meat after the Chernobyl accident). Also, typical wordings from newspaper headlines, such as 'the threat from the east' (referring to nuclear reactors in Russia), appeared in the respondents' answers.

In the constructivist approach to learning, the learner's ideas and conceptions prior to instruction are seen as important prerequisites for learning. In recent research in science education, laypeople's conceptions are called 'alternative conceptions', 'children's science', 'commonsense beliefs' or 'everyday conceptions'. Typical properties of such conceptions are that they serve as consistent explanatory models for the persons nurturing them, and that they tend to 'survive' formal education. A typical example from mechanics is the notion that an object will come to rest unless it is kept in motion by a force. This is contrary to Newton's first law and the scientific view of motion — but it works in daily life! With reference to this theory of 'everyday conceptions', Lijnse et al[2], after studying lay conceptions of radiation, claimed that in areas where satisfactory 'everyday conceptions' exist (often conveyed through the mass media), people do not feel the need to apply 'school knowledge' to phenomena they encounter in real life. Thus, formal knowledge about radiation phenomena, acquired in a classroom context, will not be applied in order to understand the situations arising in the 'real world', as for example after the Chernobyl accident.

This tendency could also be observed in the answers given in the present survey. For instance, one of the respondents was able to give excellent 'classroom' definitions of becquerel, alpha, beta and gamma radiation, but nevertheless stated in a subsequent question that meat became radioactive after the Chernobyl disaster 'because the animals ate food which had been irradiated', thereby betraying that the confusion between radiation sources and radiation was still present. Thus, the answers to the questions concerning real-life situations which had been treated in the media, might not measure what the school education had taught the students, but rather what the media had taught them. The gap between the 'real world' and the realm of school knowledge could also be identified in answers to the questions regarding the sources of radiation exposure in everyday life. When asked which sources of radiation the respondents feared, they mostly mentioned sources that are frequently mentioned in mass media and by environmentalists and that have a threatening ring in most people's ears: nuclear power plants, nuclear submarines, radiation through a depleted ozone layer and so forth. In the question concerning the radiation sources the respondents thought they had in the home, the 'school knowledge' seemed to appear: many had heard about radon (which is the single most important of the everyday exposures), and they also knew that for instance smoke detectors may contain radioactive matter. This knowledge, however, was not connected to the more emotional sphere; apparently it was not perceived to concern 'the everyday world', even though the radiation sources mentioned (for example, smoke detectors) are very much part of everyday life.

How can the constructivist approach to learning and the insight available into the lay perceptions of radioactivity and ionising radiation best be applied to bridge the gap between the lay and the expert models of radio-activity, radiation and risk? How can the desired level of knowledge in the population (refer to the reasons for knowing stated in the Introduction) be attained?

As already mentioned, lay ideas are amazingly persistent, even after formal instruction. Thus, Eijkelhof[13] reported that a number of lay ideas concerning radiation were maintained by secondary school pupils in the Netherlands after a course unit on radioactivity. The lack of success of school courses and information campaigns in the past may have been partly due to lack of consideration for the preconceptions of the learners. Millar et al[4] developed a teaching unit on radioactivity and ionising radiation that explicitly took into account the pupils' preconceptions in the field. Hopefully, this and similar programmes may in the future contribute to improving the public understanding of such phenomena.

According to the reasons stated in the Introduction to educate the public on radiation issues, a sufficient level of knowledge should ensure democratic decisions and personal safety. Is there any evidence that an individual's level of knowledge actually has an effect on his or her political considerations and judgements? The findings from the present survey do not lend much support to such a hypothesis: there was no significant difference between the high-score group and the low-score group with respect to the degree of radiation fear or the attitude to the submarine Komsomolets; however, a small, but significant difference was found between the two groups in the proportion who were positive to Swedish nuclear power. Lucas[6] found that there was little relationship between knowledge about the nature of radioactivity and attitudes to nuclear power policy. In a study of perceived risk of electric and magnetic fields, MacGregor et al[14] found that after a briefing about health effects of such fields (in which it was stated that no adverse health effects had yet been reliably demonstrated), the respondents ended up being more worried than before the briefing.

In view of these findings, the prospects for attaining the objectives presented in the Introduction seem gloomy indeed. If information and knowledge don't have the power to influence attitudes, how can rational decisions and personal well-being then be secured? The way out of this impasse may lie in taking the lay conceptions into account and increasing the integration between factual information and practical/political considerations when designing teaching and information materials for use in schools, official fora and mass media, so that the connection between factual knowledge and the 'real world' is made clear. Within school curriculum development, this is called the STS (Science, Technology and Society) approach. The unit developed by Millar et al[4] and similar approaches in the teaching of radiation topics show some promise. However, further research is needed to establish the best ways of presenting information on radiation topics in various fora and to various parts of the population.

REFERENCES

1. Weart, S. R. *Nuclear Fear. A History of Images* (Cambridge, MA: Harvard University Press) (1988).

2. Lijnse, P. L., Eijkelhof, H. M. C., Klaassen, C. W. J. M. and Scholte, R. L. J. *Pupils' and Mass-media Ideas about Radio-activity*. Int. J. Sci. Educ. **12**, 67–78 (1990).

3. Eijkelhof, H. M. C. and Millar, R. *Reading about Chernobyl: the Public Understanding of Radiation and Radioactivity.* School Sci. Rev. **70**, 35–41 (1988).

4. Millar, R., Klaassen, K. and Eijkelhof, H. *Teaching about Radioactivity and Ionising Radiation: an Alternative Approach.* Phys. Educ. **25**, 338–342 (1990).

5. Durant, J. R., Evans, G. A. and Thomas, G. P. *The Public Understanding of Science.* Nature **340**, 11–14 (1989).

6. Lucas, A. M. *Public Knowledge of Radiation.* Biologist **34**, 125–129 (1987).

7. Löfstedt, R. E. and Ringius, L. *Danish Perspectives on Transboundary Environmental Risks: An Example from Copenhagen.* Working Paper 1994: 10 from Center for International Climate and Environmental Research, Oslo (CICERO) (1994).

8. Skjåk, K. K. and Bøyum, B. *Undersøking om verdier, natur og miljø 1993.* Report no 100 from "Norsk samfunnsvitenskapelig datatjeneste" (1994).

9. Slovic, P. *Perception of Risk.* Science **236**, 280–285 (1987).

10. Larsen, A. K. *Atominformasjon i Finnmark.* StrålevernRapport 1994: 8 Norwegian Radiation Protection Authority (1994).

11. Mærli, M. B. *Opplevelse av risiko i forbindelse med elektromagnetiske felt.* IMK-rapport no 15, University of Oslo (1995).

12. Lucas, A. M. *Scientific Literacy and Informing Learning.* Stud. Sci. Educ. **10**, 1–36 (1983).

13. Eijkelhof, H. M. C. *Radiation and Risk in Physics Education.* Doctoral dissertation at the University of Utrecht (1990).

14. MacGregor, D., Slovic, P. and Morgan, M. G. *Perception of Risks from Electromagnetic Fields: A Psychometric Evaluation of a Risk-communication Approach.* Risk Anal. **14**, 815–828 (1994).

Radiation Protection Dosimetry
Vol. 68, No. 3/4, pp. 197–201 (1996)
Nuclear Technology Publishing

CHERNOBYL — SYSTEM ACCIDENT OR HUMAN ERROR?

E. Stang
Centre for Technology and Culture
University of Oslo, Norway

Abstract — Did human error cause the Chernobyl disaster? The standard point of view is that operator error was the root cause of the disaster. This was also the view of the Soviet Accident Commission. The paper analyses the operator errors at Chernobyl in a system context. The reactor operators committed errors that depended upon a lot of other failures that made up a complex accident scenario. The analysis is based on Charles Perrow's analysis of technological disasters. Failure possibility is an inherent property of high-risk industrial installations. The Chernobyl accident consisted of a chain of events that were both extremely improbable and difficult to predict. It is not reasonable to put the blame for the disaster on the operators.

HUMAN ERROR AS A DISASTER CAUSE?

Did human error cause the Chernobyl disaster?

The standard point of view is that the reactor operators, the reactor designers and the administrators of Soviet nuclear power committed serious errors that in turn led to a terrible disaster. Professor Bent Natvig cites a reliable Finnish expert saying that the Chernobyl operators 'were lacking sufficient knowledge in reactor physics'[1]. The original source of this point of view is the Soviet accident commission and its report to the IAEA[2]. It put all the blame on the two operators in charge when the reactor exploded.

Later Soviet reports have disagreed on whom to blame the most. Since 1989 Soviet — then Russian — reports on the Chernobyl accident have stressed latent institutional failures. The lack of a legal regulation for the use of nuclear energy, vague responsibilities for nuclear safety and a strong tendency to cover up accidents have been subjected to harsh criticism. If we take an institutional perspective the Chernobyl accident was a symptom of agony of an ill-designed 'socio-technical' system. Given the deepening crisis in Soviet society, Chernobyl seems to be an 'inevitable' disaster.

But the failure of the Soviet socio-technical system cannot be a sufficient explanation of the disaster. There may have been serious shortcomings in Soviet nuclear administrative bodies. But this does not explain why disaster struck there and then and not elsewhere at another time.

The search for the 'causes' of the disaster must be more specific. That is probably why there has been a tacit agreement that some 'human factor' must be the root cause of the disaster. Human beings and human behaviour may in turn be 'symptoms' of a malfunctional social system. Most analytical work done on the Chernobyl accident has attempted to establish a causal link between human decisions and actions and the horrifying events that destroyed an atomic reactor and released huge amounts of radionuclides to the biosphere.

The standard point of view seems to be that we must find the 'cause' of the disaster in order to explain why it happened. It can be argued that this standard point of view does not give a truthful picture of the Chernobyl disaster. The important thing is not to single out 'causes' but to grasp the complexity and unpredictability of a tragic technological disaster. The first part of the paper discusses some of the theoretical issues involved while the second part applies a system analysis to the Chernobyl accident scenario.

HUMAN ERROR IN A HIGH-RISK SYSTEM

Human errors no doubt contributed to the complex accident scenario at the Chernobyl reactor number 4. A nuclear reactor is a tightly coupled human–machine system with an enormous energy potential. It is a high-risk system. To get a truthful picture of the accident, we have to analyse the human errors in a high-risk system context. During the Chernobyl disaster human errors depended on a lot of other failures that made up the whole accident scenario. The question is whether the operators could reasonably have been expected to anticipate and prevent the danger.

Anotolij Aleksandrov, a former chairman of the Soviet Academy of Science and one of the founders of the Soviet nuclear industry, accused the Chernobyl operators of acting like bad car drivers. When a driver turns the wheel to the wrong side and crashes into a wall, no safety device can save the car. The comparison is false. There was a hidden flaw in the steering mechanism of the RBMK reactor, and it had been unknown even to Aleksandrov himself before the accident.

Human errors in technological accidents have been studied by a number of specialists in organisation theory and cognitive psychology. The analysis here is inspired by the studies of Charles Perrow, Jens Rasmussen and James Reason.

For the sake of simplicity, we limit our analysis of the human factor to the errors of the two chief operators on duty when the reactor exploded. The errors interacted with a sequence of unexpected events that involved the main technical sub-systems of the reactor: operation procedures, control room instrumentation, fuel assemblies, cooling water and emergency control rods.

The general idea behind this is that 'the human being

is part of the machine'; viz. the human operator is a part of the reactor system. If we accept this point of view, it becomes obvious that the human operator acts like a component of the reactor system. The erroneous operator actions during the Chernobyl disaster must then be interpreted within a multiple failure sequence that involved many components and sub-systems of the reactor system. A multiple failure sequence led to a disastrous explosion destroying the reactor.

It is important to insist on the idea of an integrated human–machine system. In everyday life we tend to think of 'human being' and 'machine' as so different that they cannot be parts of the same whole system. Common sense tells us that the human being operates the machine from 'outside'. The Chernobyl scenario makes it sensible to take the opposite view: the human operator operates the reactor system from 'inside'.

Some might object that the human being can never be treated like a system component. The human being has a conscious mind making him able to choose what to do. This is true — even under the constraints of a reactor control room. The system viewpoint is problematic — but it is a useful analytical tool. It prevents us from picking out individual errors as the 'root cause' and makes us look at the accident context as a whole.

It is worth keeping in mind the relation between the concepts of 'cause' and 'accusation'. The word 'accusation' comes from the latin *ad causam*, that is 'to the cause'. When human error is found to be the cause of bad consequences, the human being will be 'the accused'.

In the system context, it is not relevant to say that 'this action caused this event'. The concepts of 'cause' and 'effect' are linear and mechanical notions, presupposing at least a regular, and predictable chain of events. (cf: 'a cause always produces the same effect'). In a system there is a network of interdependent actions and events. During the Chernobyl disaster, events did not follow a regular predictable sequence. Thus the concept of cause does not apply in the context of a system.

The scientific accounts of Chernobyl generally give a functional and system description of the material and physical events in the reactor 'hardware' that brought about the disaster. Curiously, the human operator, the most important 'system software', has been artificially excluded from the system description. These accounts construct a biased and incomplete view of the system–accident scenario.

In the Chernobyl case the search for 'responsible' persons certainly led to accusing and judging the wrong people. The main culprits in the Soviet accident report were the two young reactor operators in charge of the control room night shift. They both later died of radiation injuries.

The Soviet accident commission accused them of violating a series of operation rules, and of not realising that they were bringing the reactor to an unstable state forbidden by the operating regulations. According to the accident report they committed errors because they were 'incompetent'. This can hardly be called an explanation.

The report tell us little about why the operators commited errors. Human errors in a complex human–machine system do not explain the disaster. Human errors need explanation.

The Chernobyl plant manager and some plant officials were convicted and given long prison sentences. Higher ministry officials were criticised but not punished. There was a need to keep responsibility on the ground level after the disaster.

CHERNOBYL — A SYSTEM ACCIDENT

The concept of 'system accident' needs a more accurate definition. The American organisation sociologist Charles Perrow calls system accidents normal accidents, to underline that failure is an integrated system property. His underlying assumption is simple: No technology is perfect. The more complex the technology, the higher the probability of system failure. This system approach to accidents provides a good tool for analysing the Chernobyl accident sequence.

(1) A human–machine system consists of many interactive and tightly coupled parts; the proper functioning of the whole depends on the proper functioning of the parts, the proper functioning of the parts depends on the functioning of the whole.

(2) Complex technology is prone to multiple failure sequences (cf. daily life use of computer programs), and reactor systems are no exception. The failure of a part may interact with other parts and lead to failure of the system as a whole. Multiple failure possibility is not a 'flaw', but an inherent and 'normal' system characteristic.

(3) There are possible multiple failure sequences that cannot be predicted either on the design level, or on the operating level. Some of them result from unplanned, unexpected interactions between parts of the system, so-called 'complex interactions'.

(4) The human operator is a system component, no *deus ex machina* that intervenes at the critical moment. Human failures are component failures. Human component failure may enter into complex interaction with other components. Thus, human failure is part of a multiple failure sequence.

(5) There are some — rare — complex interaction sequences that will bring the system to a halt and eventually destroy it. High energy concentrations mean risk of system destruction and catastrophe for the system's environment. This is what happened at Chernobyl.

The notions of system and of complex interaction of tightly coupled parts cast new light on the operator errors during the Chernobyl disaster.

THE CHERNOBYL ACCIDENT SEQUENCE

The Chernobyl accident sequence started during a safety experiment simulating a design base accident. The purpose was to improve the capacity of turbine generators to supply electricity to essential sub-systems during a plant blackout.

The operators started reducing the power level about 24 h before the explosion. It is significant that the disaster occurred when the reactor was not working under the ordinary production regime, and when non-standard procedures were used in the system.

Most accident accounts agree that the operators committed an exceptionally grave error when the so-called operational reactivity margin, the ORM, had reached an unauthorised low level. If they had followed operating regulations and shut down the reactor at that critical moment, the disaster would not have happened. Let us look at the ORM error from the point of view of the system as a whole.

In the RBMK boiling water design it is important to maintain a minimum number of neutron absorbing control rods in the core in order to control the global fission process. The minimum permitted operational reactivity margin (ORM) was equivalent to 30 fully inserted control rods at full power before the disaster.

Prior to power reduction the ORM was 31. The reactor operators lowered several control rods into the core to reduce power. Printouts from the computer system show that seven hours into the shutdown procedure (and 17 h before the explosion), the ORM had fallen to 13 control rods. This is well below the minimum authorised level.

The low ORM at this stage was due to many factors. The reactor contained many old fuel elements with a substantial amount of fission products. Fission products facilitated formation of neutron-absorbing gases — 'reactor poisons' — in the core. The poisoning of the reactor was enhanced by the reduced power level. The automatic power control compensated for this by withdrawing more control rods.

The processes that lowered the ORM are an example of a complex interaction between the power control sub-systems, the state of the fuel elements and the reactor power level. The test planners obviously did not foresee this kind of complex failure, and the operators thought that they could handle it.

There were several reasons for the operators not to shut down the reactor at this moment. The system context explains why they committed this 'error'.

(i) The low ORM occurred during reduced power level, where the operating procedures were not explicit enough. They required, for example, 'special permission' to continue reactor operation down to an ORM.

(ii) The reactor operators were not aware of the safety significance of the ORM. They did not know about the possibility of an uncontrollable power excursion at low ORM. There had been no scientific study of this before the disaster, hence not even reactor specialists had realised the danger.

(iii) The reactor operators had to perform the estimation of ORM themselves, since there was no direct monitoring of this parameter. This provides evidence of the fact that the safety significance of ORM was not realised by the reactor designers.

(iv) Operators worked under production pressure, and were determined to complete tests despite difficulties. 'Production pressure' stresses the human component.

(v) The operators were probably used to operating the RBMK reactors at low ORM in order to get more energy out of the fuel elements, though this has never been officially admitted.

The most important single factor seems to be that neither the operators nor the designers had realised how ORM might interact with a possible, though very improbable, physical state of the reactor. In hindsight, and in hindsight only, this was a very grave human error. In any case the operators cannot be blamed for ignoring this. Their ignorance of the danger explains why they did not keep strictly to the operating regulations and permitted a very low ORM.

Running RBMK reactors at a low ORM was probably a common and accepted practice. The reason is obvious: this permits a more economical use of expensive nuclear fuel. This fact has never been officially recognised, but enough oral testimonies have been received from experienced RBMK operators to indicate that it is true. We may call the ignorance of the danger of low ORM a latent error. A latent error normally does not lead to an accident, but may do so under exceptional conditions.

And exceptional conditions did occur during the Chernobyl accident sequence. Post-accident research has revealed that the RBMK design was vulnerable to a power excursion when running at low power, with low ORM, xenon poisoning of the central parts of the core, a distorted neutron field, and an increased coolant flow rate. Under such circumstances, the reactor had a high positive void coefficient, meaning that boiling in the coolant might dramatically increase energy production. A local power increase in the reactor could trigger a positive feedback process leading to a power excursion.

Before the disaster actually happened, there had been no research about a possible power excursion under these particular conditions. This is an extremely important fact. Ignorance of a fundamental property of the reactor constituted a big but unmeasurable disaster risk.

The test was planned to start at 2 pm at 30% of full power. At this point the local power grid dispatcher ordered reactor number four to stay connected to the grid. The test had to be postponed until late at night.

Strictly speaking, this was not a system event. But no real human–machine system is closed: it is connected to an environment that may act upon it. In this case the postponement of the safety test was one of the factors contributing to the accident.

At 11 pm the deputy chief engineer decided to proceed with the test. But he had to wait for the turn of the night shift at midnight.

During this phase of the accident sequence the staff had an overriding priority: to maintain the reactor power at a sufficient level to complete the test. The reactor power was lower than planned, but the low ORM made it difficult to increase power to the planned level.

A decisive event occurred at 28 min past midnight, one hour before the explosion. The operators had to switch from local to global automatic power control mode, due to low reactor effect. A component failure during the transfer lowered more absorbing rods into the core. The reactor effect dropped to near zero.

The operators knew from experience that the RBMK is difficult to control at low power levels. The drop in power should normally make them shut down the reactor, and wait several hours for the natural decay of reactor poisons. They hesitated, then decided to go on with the test. They were clearly unaware of the real danger. Again, the error resulted from ignorance of system properties and a strong motivation to accomplish a difficult task.

During the following sequence of events the reactor operators had to withdraw still more control rods from the core in order to increase power. The water level in the steam drums fluctuated, and made it difficult to feed the steam turbines. The operators increased the coolant flow to regulate the water level in the steam drums.

These actions contributed to increasing the temperature of the cooling water at the core inlet, and to bringing down the ORM to a very low level, probably as low as 10. There seems to have been a considerable error margin in the devices that measured the ORM, due to bugs in the reactor diagnosis computer program. The operators may have been misled by the instrumentation.

The human errors that eventually were committed at this stage reflect a lack of knowledge about the real danger. Errors also originated in a stressed situation, when several reactor parameters did not function normally, and when operator attention was directed at stabilising reactor power before completing the safety test.

We must bear in mind that the reactor operators had no direct access to the physical processes in the core. They may very well have been misled by the instrumentation in the control room.

The final seconds of the accident sequence show a multiple failure sequence that resulted from an unpredictable complex interaction between the emergency shutdown system, the coolant flow rate and temperature, and the fuel assemblies.

A few seconds before the explosion, at about 1.25 am, the reactor operators pressed the emergency shutdown button. We do not know why they did it, since the reactor parameters were relatively stable at that time. It was shut down manually because the automatic scram had

been disconnected to prevent an interruption of the test. The disconnection of this safety device was an operator error that did not influence the accident.

The emergency shutdown signal made a large number of emergency control rods move into the core from above. Instead of reducing the power, the control rods increased the power in the lower part of the core.

Post-accident research has shown that the emergency control rods will increase power in the lower part of the core when they interact with an unstable reactor. While the power level is reduced in the upper part, it increases in the lower part during the first phase of emergency shutdown. In other words, the brakes of the reactor function like the gas pedal. This is due to a design feature of the control rods. It was a property that remained hidden during normal operating conditions. The catastrophic potential of this design feature became evident after the system accident.

The control rod problem would not have led to an uncontrollable power rise if it had not been for another reactor property: the positive void coefficient. It means that voids (boiling) in the coolant increases reactor power. A slight power increase led to intense boiling because water temperature was already near boiling point at the coolant inlet at the bottom of the core. The positive void coefficient was known before the accident, but it is possible that complex interactions had not been studied.

The combined effects of positive void, low ORM, etc led to an explosive power increase. It was a self-amplifying process, which destroyed the fuel elements and stopped the control rods in seconds.

Some experts still hold that the decisive void effect was created by cavitation in the circulation pumps in the cooling circuit. It is also unclear why the power surge was so violent. The exact course of the catastrophic nuclear events will, however, never be reconstructed because the physical state of the reactor at the moment of the explosion is unknown.

An extremely unlikely series of events produced the Chernobyl disaster. It is a revealing illustration of how multiple failures may interact with each other when components are very tightly coupled and when the processes involved are fast and violent. Human errors were parts of this system–accident scenario.

The human system component did fail, but that does not mean that humans caused the accident.

The Chernobyl accident reminds us that we humans are capable of building technological devices and of making them function, but without understanding them in depth. If we stop accusing the wrong people of the bad actions, we may learn more about why things go wrong.

The system accident perspective is also important if we want to improve safety policy for complex technical systems with a catastrophic potential.

After the Chernobyl disaster the social status of reactor operators fell radically in the Soviet Union. The prestige of reactor specialists also suffered a heavy blow. Accusations and blame spread to all levels of the institutions governing Soviet atomic power. Probably, the best specialists suffered the heaviest moral blow, since they felt morally responsible anyway. Two years after the accident, the chairman of the Soviet accident commission committed suicide. Thus the search for the 'human cause' of Chernobyl hardly contributed to improving nuclear safety.

All technological disasters are in a deeper sense 'human-made', even when human error does not trigger the accident sequence. When operators trigger an accident sequence like they did in the Chernobyl accident, all the blame should not be put on them. The source of the risk is not the operator himself, but the dangerous industrial installation of which he or she is an integrated part.

REFERENCES

1. Laaksonen, J. *The Accident at the Chernobyl power plant*, In: Proc. Society of Reliability Engineers Conf., Otaniemi (1986). Also in B. Natvig and X. Gåsemyr: On Probability Risk Analysis of Technological Systems. Proc. Conf. Oslo (1995).
2. *Avarija na Chernobyl'skoj AES i eë posledstivija* (Moscow) (1986). (The Accident at the Chernobyl Nuclear Power Plant and its Consequences.)

Radiation Protection Dosimetry
Vol. 68, No. 3/4, pp. 203–208 (1996)
Nuclear Technology Publishing

ETHICAL VALUES IN RADIOLOGICAL PROTECTION

D. H. Oughton
Laboratory for Analytical Chemistry
PO Box 5026
Agricultural University of Norway
1432 Ås, Norway.

Abstract — Issues like consent, equity, control and responsibility are important for an ethical evaluation of radiation risks. This paper discusses the incorporation of ethical values in radiological protection policy and compares how ICRP recommendations promote their use in practice and intervention cases. The paper contends that in cases of intervention, where the overall aim is dose reduction, social and ethical factors are often alluded to when evaluating costs of an action. However, possible ethical or social benefits of intervention measures are seldom raised. On the other hand, when assessing a practice, wherein the net effect is an increase in radiation dose, one is more likely to find an appeal to ethical factors on the benefits side of the equation than with the costs. The paper concludes that all decisions concerning radiological protection should consider both positive and negative ethical aspects. Some intervention actions have social and ethical benefits besides dose reduction; some practices have social and ethical costs besides an increase in radiation dose.

INTRODUCTION

It is well established that economic and social factors are of importance in radiological protection, even if there is still discussion on how exactly they should be incorporated. The most familiar appeal to social values occurs in the ICRP's second principle of radiological protection, namely the ALARA principle. This dose optimisation principle states that exposure to radiation should be kept 'as low as reasonably achievable' (ALARA), economic and social factors being taken into account'[1,2]. In other words, ICRP recommends that, even below permitted dose limits, radiation doses should be reduced if the benefits of doing so outweigh the economical and social costs of lowering exposure.

In 1993, ICRP stressed the need to be aware of the ethical implications of value judgements and decision-making methods in radiological protection[3], but what these ethical values might represent and how they might apply to the management of radiation risks in practice was not discussed. Of course, when selecting relevant factors for radiological protection it is often difficult to draw a clear line of demarcation between ethical and social values. Studies of risk perception have unearthed a plethora of psychological factors that can account for different degrees of risk aversion[4,5]. However the role of ethical values in shaping these perceptions is less evident — although a Swedish study did indicate that the moral value of an activity was the dominant factor in accounting for risk acceptability[6]. Whereas some social and psychological 'biases' in risk perception have a clear moral relevance (e.g. voluntariness, control, equity), others do not lend themselves to defence by ethical argument (e.g. familiarity, dogmatism). This distinction is particularly important for policy and decision-making because ethical values are generally deemed to be prima facie. This means that ethical principles can be overridden but not by simple appeal to non-ethical, social or psychological arguments.

With this in mind, the aim of this paper is to highlight the types of principles that are important for an ethical evaluation of radiation risks, to show why these principles can be defended using ethical analysis, and to discuss their incorporation in radiological protection policy. In particular, I will focus on the way ICRP recommendations either promote or overlook the use of ethical values in assessments of interventions (i.e. actions that aim to reduce exposure to radiation) and practices (i.e. actions that increase exposure to radiation).

PRACTICE AND INTERVENTION

ICRP makes a clear and very important distinction between practice and intervention[2]. Practices include authorised releases from nuclear power stations, exposure to workers in nuclear research or industries (including miners), the disposal of radioactive waste and medical exposures. Interventions include countermeasures to limit radiation exposure after an accident, attempts to reduce radon exposure, and can also include measures taken to optimise doses from existing practices. Both intervention and practices are subject to the first principle of radiation protection, the principle of justification, whereby an action can only be justified if the benefits exceed the costs. However, dose constraints (the third principle of radiological protection) differ for practice and intervention. Legal dose limits are, as a rule, simply not applicable to accidental situations[1,7,8], although dose optimisation helps determine how best to use resources to reduce radiation exposure levels.

JUSTIFICATION AND OPTIMISATION: COST–BENEFIT ANALYSIS

With respect to ethics, the most common critique of cost–benefit analysis is that it is based on a utilitarian moral doctrine[9]. Utilitarians (e.g. John Stuart Mill, Jeremy Bentham) judge an action in terms of its consequences — the best action being that which brings the 'greatest good to the greatest number'. On the other hand, deontologists (e.g. Immanuel Kant) or contractarians (e.g. John Rawls) examine whether or not the action or policy violates any particular moral right or duty. Moral philosophers argue that decision-making processes which only consider the utility of actions are ethically and/or rationally inadequate because they fail to recognise concepts such as rights, duties, fairness and justice[10–12]. Of course, even the strictest utilitarian recognises that factors like choice, control and consent have utility values[13], but they attribute importance to rights only because of their ability to increase utility, not because of any intrinsic or inalienable value[14].

Although ICRP's principle of justification has been singled out as being flawed because it appears to be based on utilitarian ethics[15], it should be pointed out that the philosophy of radiological protection would not satisfy a strict utilitarian: a utilitarian would not agree to be constrained by dose limitations[16]. Furthermore, if social (and ethical) factors should be taken into consideration when comparing the relative costs and benefits of various methods of dose optimisation[3,17,18], it seems logical that social factors also have some role to play in the justification of radiation risks.

A major problem with the ALARA principle is that no guidance is given for how to deal with potential conflicts between economic and social factors. Furthermore, no guidance is given as to whether social costs of an action should be defined in terms of the consequences of an action or in terms of the social and ethical costs of the action itself. Without getting into a detailed analysis of whether a consequentialist or a deontological doctrine is the correct point of departure, it should suffice at this stage to note that practical ethical analysis is going to have to address both the consequences and the attributes of a particular course of action[19]. Both moral philosophers and economists have stressed that ethical weighting can and should be included in risk-cost-benefit analysis[20–22]. A stable society requires agreement in recognition of broadly based ethical norms such as respect for life, equality of opportunity, and the right not to be subjected to harm against one's consent[23]. A radiation protection policy that fails to comply with these basic beliefs is going to be difficult to defend.

The general hypothesis behind this paper is that much of the disagreement and confusion over the practical application of risk management procedures can be derived from insensitivity of radiological protection recommendations to social and ethical factors.

ETHICAL VALUES AND RADIATION RISK

A useful point of departure is to consider examples of questions that might be asked about the ethics of any radiation risk, practice or intervention action, and then to show why the underlying principles can be defended using ethical argument.

Has the person given free informed consent (real or implied) to the risk in question?

Respecting the norm of free informed consent is one of the pillars of medical and research ethics. This principle states that an agent (e.g. doctor or research scientist) may not knowingly expose a person to harm or a risk of harm without first obtaining the consent of that person. On these premises, it has been argued that the imposition of any risk is legitimate only after consent has been given by the affected individual or group of people[19,24]. The consent requirement holds because of the value given by society to autonomy, personal dignity and the right to life and bodily security. Consent is also important because it is conducive to minimising risks and maximising benefits for all parties.

Free informed consent must satisfy four conditions: disclosure, understanding, voluntariness and competence. In terms of medical ethics, the conditions mean that the subject should be given full information about possible risks and benefits, that the subject should understand and agree to the treatment or research, and that the subject be mentally and physically competent to give consent[25]. Of course, in many cases involving risks to the general public, obtaining unanimous consent from affected individuals is neither practical nor possible. It has been a matter of some contention among philosophers whether or not a risky industry could under the conditions stated previously, obtain the consent of the people exposed to risks[22,26–28]. Possible solutions to the problem include lay representatives, or implied rather than actual consent. For our purposes it should suffice to note that any industry or practice bringing about an increase in radiation dose has a prima facie duty to obtain (either directly or implicitly) some form of free, informed consent. It follows therefore that, wherever possible, practices leading to imposition of radiation risk on the public or workers should aim to satisfy the conditions of informed consent, even when direct consent cannot be obtained.

The practice and intervention cases differ with respect to the principle of free informed consent. For example, after an accidental release of radiation there is no agent to which the victim can offer consent for the increased harm: consent to the imposition of radiation risk is simply not an issue. Of course, consent to an increase in dose can become important if intervention practices cause high radiation exposure to certain individuals (e.g. clean-up workers) in order to reduce levels in the rest of the population.

Is the distribution of risks and benefits equitable?

Like the principle of consent, the relative distribution of risks and benefits is deemed important both psychologically and ethically. Equality in the moral status of people is one of the necessary conditions to obtain universality of ethical principles. However radiation risks often pose difficult questions with respect to temporal and spatial differences in distribution, because inequities often arise between region, countries, age groups and even generations. Even when risks are small and judged acceptable, it is both unfair and unreasonable to expect one group of people to accept a risk of harm when another group reaps the benefits.

Although it might be argued that ICRP promotes equity by setting dose limits for the average population, it should be noted that those with the highest dose are not necessarily those at the highest risk. For a similar radiation dose, the probability of contracting cancer or other malformations, i.e. the risk, is higher in children and the unborn[2,29]. Average dose limits do not entail equal risks across the population. In general, permitted dose limits are lower for children than for adults, hence assessment of practice and intervention should give preference to the most sensitive group. Preferential treatment of the worst off group is justified on grounds of equity, and on grounds of fairness[10]. Moral philosophers favour equal protection of individuals over equal treatment[22,30].

Finally, practices and interventions differ with respect to the distribution of risks and benefits. Releases from a nuclear power plant tend to result in variable distribution of radiation risks among the public — people living close to the plant receive the highest doses, as well as inequitable division of risks and benefits between the public and the industry. On the other hand, in an intervention situation (for example after an accident) one is usually aiming towards a more egalitarian distribution of risk. Authorities try to identify those people most affected, either because of high levels of contamination or enhanced sensitivity (i.e. children and pregnant women): special effort is taken to identify and reduce radiation exposure in the groups most at risk[7,8].

Does the person have informed individual control over the risk in question?

Individual control over the risk in question is important for both voluntary and involuntary risks, hence this question differs from the consent principle. However, as in consent, availability of information is a major factor in determining the degree of control a person can attain over either imposed or voluntary risks. Many studies have shown that psychological stress following exposure to radiation risks is very real[30,31], and was even emphasised by the IAEA as representing the major physical health risk in the former Soviet Union[32]. However, inadequate information seriously reduces people's chance of attaining any degree of personal control over the risks in question. Medical literature shows that lack of individual control and failure to provide full information to patients can be in itself psychologically and physically damaging to health[34,35]. Government reassurances that everything is under control will relieve psychological stress to some extent, but only if authorities are trusted[36]. Most important is that information on risk levels should reflect the level of uncertainty in knowledge[37].

Apart from the material harm caused by lack of personal control, philosophers have argued that withholding information on risk is ethically objectionable. Gewirth argues that each person has a right to informed control over conditions relevant to the possible infliction of injury, because informed control is a component of freedom[26].

After the Chernobyl accident, many authorities in Europe were accused of not providing full information regarding the risks from Chernobyl and ways of reducing them[38]. In doing this, authorities were insensitive both to psychological harms and to social and ethical considerations such as autonomy and rights to information[39]. Withholding information also reduces the ability of an individual to give consent to any negative effects of an action or policy because it prevents disclosure, voluntariness and understanding, as well as restricting the choice of alternatives. People cannot give free informed consent if they have no alternative.

Is the person being compensated for exposure to the risk?

Most philosophers agree that some form of compensation is necessary to counteract the increase of risk in particular groups of the population. Higher wages for nuclear workers is the most obvious example. Compensation tends to promote equity and is often necessary to obtain consent, as people are unlikely to consent to risks for which they have not been compensated. David Gauthier argues that since it is irrational for people to agree to a state of affairs wherein they are worse off, morality must incorporate some form of compensation and bargaining factors[40].

The compensation principle raises major practical difficulties: how to compensate, who to compensate and when to compensate. For example, should the person have to prove that he/she has been harmed, will be harmed or might be harmed by a particular practice? Who bears the burden of proof and what level of confirmation is required? Compensation is usually thought of as being more important for practices than for interventions — although some countermeasures do require compensation for social and economic harms. In many cases, a claim for compensation implies that some agent takes responsibility for the harm caused.

Can a third party be held responsible for bringing about the risk?

The notions of responsibility and blame are particularly relevant for radiation risks. A practice causes harm by imposing a radiation risk on an individual or group of people; an intervention prevents harm. Both moral philosophers and the law tend to honour distinctions between acts of commission, i.e. bringing about some harm, and acts of omission, i.e. failing to prevent some harm[41].

The distinction between causing deaths and not saving lives is common in medical ethics. When resources are limited, most people would condone letting one patient die in order to save a greater number lives, but would not accept killing a patient so that his organs could be used to save the lives of other people. In the famous 'trolley problem' presented by Philippa Foot, the act of diverting a runaway railway trolley away from a track where five persons are working, but onto a track where one person is working, seems easier to defend than the act of pushing a fat man on to the track in order to stop the trolley[41,42]. In both cases one dies so that five are saved; but it appears that factors other than consequences influence the moral reprehensibility of the actions.

Whether or not these distinctions can be defended ethically has been the subject of much philosophical debate[41-44]. However, it seems this debate might give important insight into the public's different attitudes to natural and technological sources of radiation risk[45]. For example one might argue that cancers brought about by the practice of the nuclear industry (acts of commission) are more morally reprehensible than cancers allowed by non-intervention in the accidental or natural radiation situation (acts of omission). Hence, on these premises, the distinctions might be used to support the stringent dose limits on the nuclear industry. However, it does not necessarily follow that one can justify a higher level of spending to reduce doses from existing practices than from natural or accidental sources.

In conclusion, the main problem brought into focus by all these questions is that ICRP has not discussed the normative ethical difference between intervention and practice. In the following section, evaluation of ICRP recommendations shows how this can lead to inconsistencies in the practical management of radiation risks.

Costs and benefits of intervention measures

In cases of intervention, where the overall aim is dose reduction, social and, more rarely, ethical factors are often alluded to when evaluating costs of an action. For example, the considerable social disruption and anxiety caused by evacuation and relocation of whole villages tends to raise the dose level at which authorities would implement a resettlement countermeasure. Likewise, cultural and ethical considerations (i.e. the interests of

the minority group of reindeer herders) played a significant role in the decision by the Norwegians to raise the allowed level of radiocaesium in reindeer meat[46]. ICRP recommendations also suggest that the way authorities act to reduce radiation hazards could be subject to ethical constraints, e.g. the criterion that all emergency workers must be informed volunteers[8].

What is surprising is that one seldom finds reference to ethical or social factors when assessing the benefits of certain actions, for example the positive psychological and ethical value of giving full information or enhancing a person's control over a risk (Table 1). Radiological protection authorities need to be aware that, for some countermeasures, reduction in dose is not the only benefit. If given together with good, clear information on the possible risks involved, some measures will tend to increase personal control, whilst others (i.e. state-controlled interventions) might provoke feelings of helplessness. For example, under present day recommendations, if the overall dose reduction would be rather low, many authorities would tend to refrain from giving advice that children be kept indoors after an accidental release, usually on grounds of not alarming the public. Such a risk communication policy is flawed as it is insensitive to the psychological and ethical benefits of a citizen's informed personal control.

As mentioned previously, full information is also one of the conditions of consent. However, in worldwide recommendations for actions after a nuclear accident, there does not seem to be any general guarantee that the local public is properly informed about risks[26].

Costs and benefits of a practice

When assessing a practice, wherein the net effect is an increase in radiation dose, one is more likely to find an appeal to ethical factors on the benefits side of the equation than with the costs. ICRP defines radiation risks (or 'detriments') only in terms of probabilities of physical harm — specifically, fatal and non-fatal cancers, or hereditary effects[3]. Earlier publications mentioned that other harms might be included in the radiation detriment, including psychological effects, but did not specify ethical and social costs of the practice[17,18]. The only justification needed for implementation of a practice leading to an increase in radiation dose is that 'it produces sufficient benefit to the exposed individuals or to society to offset the radiation detriment it causes'[3]. In summary, according to ICRP, the costs of intervention can include social and ethical consequences; the cost of a practice is measured only in terms of the degree of physical harm (Table 1).

Appeal to ethical factors in intervention and practice

ICRP is, superficially, sensitive to both consent and equal protection in intervention and accidental situations but not in normal practices. For example, informed consent is deemed of importance in many intervention actions (i.e. clean-up workers need to be informed volunteers); public consent is rarely an issue for evaluation of a practice. In an emergency situation, the special interests of the radiologically sensitive are taken into account[3]. In contradiction to the intervention situation, what ICRP does not recommend in the case of a practice, is identification and reduction of the risk to the most sensitive member of a population, namely children and pregnant women (i.e. the fetus). Finally, it seems that authorities are more willing to provide compensation to parties affected by intervention countermeasures (e.g. farmers, evacuees) than to provide compensation to parties affected by releases from a practice.

CONCLUSIONS

Radiological protection based on multidimensional risk assessment should include ethical analysis. Risk management is, fundamentally, a question of values. In a democratic society, there is no acceptable way to make these types of choices without involving the citizens affected by them. Management of both intervention actions to reduce radiation exposures, and instigation of practices that will increase radiation doses, could be made more publicly acceptable by ensuring that procedures reflect the values used by most members of the public in risk assessment. In both accidental and normal situations people have a right to participate in decisions that affect their lives, their property and the things they value. A radiological protection policy that abides by the principle of full and open information, and which recognises the benefits of informed consent and individual control over radiation risk, will help to protect this right.

Many inconsistencies in ICRP recommendations might be attributed to insensitivity to social psychological and ethical factors. Authorities should recognise that some intervention actions have social and ethical benefits besides dose reduction; some practices have social and ethical costs besides an increase in radiation dose. The issues discussed in this short paper probably raise more questions than they answer, but if this is the case, it goes to show that there is a need to address the role of ethics in radiological protection. It would be naïve to think that clarification of ethical issues would solve all problems or disputes within radiological protection, but ethical analysis might at least help to identify what it is that people disagree on.

ACKNOWLEDGEMENT

The author would like to thank the Ethics Programme of The Norwegian Research Council for a research grant to carry out this work.

Table 1. Typical appeal to social and ethical factors in radiological protection.

	Costs	Benefits
Intervention	Economic, social and ethical factors	Dose reduction
Practice	Dose increase	Economic, social and ethical factors

REFERENCES

1. International Commission on Radiological Protection, ICRP. *Recommendations of the ICRP*. Publication 26 (Oxford: Pergamon Press) (1977).

2. ICRP. *1990 Recommendations of the International Commission on Radiological Protection*. ICRP Publication 60 (Oxford: Pergamon Press) (1991).

3. ICRP. *Protection from Potential Exposure: A Conceptual Framework*. ICRP Publication 64 (Oxford: Pergamon Press) (1993).

4. Kahneman, D., Slovic, P. and Tversky, A. *Judgement under Uncertainty: Heuristics and Biases* (Cambridge University Press) (1982).

5. Slovic, P. *Perception of Risk*. Science **236**, 280–285 (1987).

6. Sjöberg, L. and Winroth, E. *Risk, Moral Value of Actions, and Mood*. Scand. J. Psychol. **27**, 191–208 (1986).

7. ICRP. *Protection of the Public in the Event of Major Radiation Accidents: Principles for Planning*. Publication 40 (Oxford: Pergamon Press) (1984).

8. ICRP. *Principles for Intervention for Protection of the Public in a Radiological Emergency*. ICRP Publication 63 (Oxford: Pergamon Press) (1993).

9. MacIntyre, A. *Utilitarianism and Cost Benefit Analysis*. In: Ethics and the Environment. Eds D. Sherer and T. Attig (Engelwood Clifts, NJ: Prentice-Hall) pp. 139–151 (1983).

10. Rawls, J. *A Theory of Justice* (Oxford University Press) (1971).

11. Føllesdal, D. *Rationality and Irrationality*. Epistemologia **IX**, 5–14 (1983).

12. Nozick, R. *The Nature of Rationality* (Princeton University Press) (1992).

13. Harsanyi, J. *Morality and the Theory of Rational Behaviour.* In: Utilitarianism and Beyond. Eds A. Sen and B. Williams (Cambridge University Press) pp. 39–62 (1982).

14. Scheffler, S. *Consequentialism and its Critics* (Oxford University Press) (1988).

15. Sumner, D. and Gilmour, P. *Radiation Protection and Moral Theory.* Environ. Values **4**, 241–255 (1995).

16. Lindell, B. *The Risk Philosophy of Radiation Protection.* Radiat. Prot. Dosim. **68**(3/4), 157–163 (1996) (This issue).

17. ICRP. *Cost-benefit Analysis in the Optimization of Radiation Protection.* ICRP Publication 37 (Oxford: Pergamon Press) (1983).

18. ICRP. *Optimization and Decision Making in Radiological Protection.* ICRP Publication 55 (Oxford: Pergamon Press) (1989).

19. Shrader-Frechette, K. S. *Ethics of Scientific Research* (Maryland: Rowman and Littlefield) (1994).

20. Kneese, A. V., Ben-David, S. and Schulze, W. D. *The Ethical Foundations of Benefit-cost Analysis* In: Energy and the Future. Eds D. Maclean and P. G. Brown (Totowa, NJ: Rowman and Littlefield) pp. 59–74 (1982).

21. Barde, J.-P. and Pearce, D. W. *Valuing the Environment* (Paris: OCDE) (1990).

22. Shrader-Frechette, K. S. *Risk and Rationality* (University of California Press, Berkeley) (1991).

23. Rawls, J. *Political Liberalism* (New York: Columbia Press) (1993).

24. Shrader-Frechette, K. S. *Risk and Ethics* In: Radiation and Society: Comprehending Radiation Risks. (Vienna: IAEA) Vol. 1, pp. 167–182 (1994).

25. Beauchamp, T. and Childress, J. *Principles of Biomedical Ethics* (Oxford University Press) (1983).

26. Gewirth, A. *Human Rights and the Prevention of Cancer.* In: Human Rights: Essays on Justification and Applications (University of Chicago Press) pp. 181–196 (1982).

27. Leonard, H. B. and Zeckhauser, R. J. *Cost-Benefit Analysis Applied to Risks: its Philosophy and Legitimacy.* In: Values at Risk. Ed. D. Maclean (Maryland: Rowan and Littlefield) pp. 31–48 (1986).

28. MacLean, D. *Risk and Consent.* In: Values at Risk. Ed. D. Maclean (Maryland: Rowan and Littlefield) pp. 17–30 (1986).

29. Otake, M. and Schull, W. J. *In utero Exposure to A-bomb Radiation and Mental Retardation: A Reassessment.* Br. J. Radiol. **57**, 409 (1984).

30. Dworkin, R. *Taking Rights Seriously* (Harvard University Press) (1977).

31. Weisæth, L. *Reactions in Norway to Fallout from the Chernobyl Disaster.* In: Cancer and Radiation Risk. Eds T. Brustad, F. Landmark and J. B. Reitan (New York: Hemisphere) pp. 149–155 (1990).

32. WHO. *Working Group on the Psychological Effects of Nuclear Accidents.* Summary Report EUR/ICP (Geneva: WHO) (1990).

33. IAEA. *The International Chernobyl Project.* (Vienna: IAEA) (1991).

34. Egbert, L., Battit, G., Welch, C. and Bartlett, M. *Reduction of Postoperative Pain by Encouragement and Instruction of Patients.* New Engl. J. Med. **270**, 825–827 (1964).

35. Morris, T., Greer, S. and White, P. *Psychological and Social Adjustment to Mastectomy: a Two Year Follow-up. Cancer I* **40**, 2381–2387 (1977).

36. Drottz-Sjöberg, B.-M. *Medical and Psychological Aspects of Crisis Management During a Nuclear Accident.* In: Nuclear Accidents and Crisis Management. Eds B. Stefenson, P. A. Landahl and T. Ritchey (Stokholm: Royal Academy of War Science) pp. 33–48 (1993).

37. Covello, V. T., Sandman, P. M. and Slovic, P. *Guidelines for Communicating Information about Chemical Risks Effectively and Responsibly.* In: Acceptable Evidence: Science and Values in Risk Management. Eds D. G. Mayo and R. D. Hollander (Oxford University Press) pp. 66–90 (1991).

38. Gould, R. *Fire in the Rain: The Democratic Consequences of Chernobyl* (Baltimore: The John Hopkins University Press) (1990).

39. Oughton, D. H. *Ethical Issues in Communication and Management of Radiation Risks.* Environmental Risk and Ethics: Proceedings from the Ethics-Program, SUM (Oslo) pp. 1–11 (1995).

40. Gauthier, D. *Morals by Agreement* (Oxford University Press) (1986).

41. Foot, P. *Virtues and Vices and Other Essays in Moral Philosophy* (Oxford: Basil Blackwell) (1978).

42. Thompson, J. J. *Killing, Letting Die and the Trolley Problem.* In: Rights, Restitution and Risk (Harvard University Press) pp. 78–116 (1986).

43. Glover, J. *Causing Deaths and Saving Lives* (London: Penguin) (1982).

44. Kagan, S. *The Limits of Morality* (Cambridge University Press) (1991).

45. Oughton, D. H. *Natural, Technological and Scientific Casualties,* In: Proc. Int. Cong. on Logic, Methodology and Philosophy of Science (Florence: LMPS) pp. 389–390 (1995).

46. Strand, P., Brynildsen, L. I., Harbitz, O. and Tveten, U. *Measures Introduced in Norway after the Chernobyl Accident.* In: Environmental Contamination following a Major Nuclear Accident (Vienna: IAEA) pp. 191–201 (1990).

Radiation Protection Dosimetry
Vol. 68, No. 3/4, pp. 209–212 (1996)
Nuclear Technology Publishing

RISK MANAGEMENT STRATEGIES FOR THE RADON PARADOX IN RADIATION PROTECTION

A. Poffijn†, G. X. Eggermont‡ and A. Van Deynse§
†Ministry of Public Health, Service for Protection against Ionising Radiation
RAC-Vesalius 2/3, B-1010 Brussels, Belgium
‡Radiation Protection, University Brussels
AZ-Cyclotron, Laarbeeklaan 103 B-1090, Brussels, Belgium
§Laboratory for Nuclear Physics, University Gent
Proeftuinstraat 86 B-9000 Gent, Belgium

Abstract — Indoor radon is recognised as being the most important radiation burden for the general public. In Belgium, as in many other countries, exposure levels giving rise to yearly risks of more than 10^{-2} have been found. This latter value is normally considered unacceptable for the public. Moreover, an important fraction of the population lives in houses with radon levels of more than 400 Bq.m^{-3}, representing a risk level of 10^{-3} per year or more. A level of this order is the limit for authorised and regulated activities at work. Prevention and intervention opportunities exist for these situations. The dose reduction opportunities are limited, but higher than the total collective dose in all nuclear activities. The analysis of radiation protection approaches, communication and decision-making for radon, compared to nuclear industrial activities shows incoherence at different levels. As a first attempt to develop a rational and coherent approach, cost-benefit analysis was applied to radon. Four optimisation scenarios were developed: three about remediation and one about prevention. Referring to the α values applied by radiation protection authorities in France, Sweden and the Netherlands, the different scenarios are found to be highly justified. They all represent well-spent money for public health. Furthermore, in order to select priorities for the governmental approach about radon, multi-attribute analysis was applied. Cost, detriment and perception were used as criteria. As potential government strategy the following alternatives were put forward: pay no attention at all; provide information; organise measuring and information campaigns, offer technical and financial sustenance for remediation; draw up specific regulations.

INTRODUCTION

Indoor radon is considered as the most important radiation detriment for the general public[1]. In Belgium, as in many other countries, exposure levels occur, with a risk of more than 10^{-2} per year[2]. This value is normally considered as unacceptable for the public. Moreover, an important fraction of the population lives in houses with radon levels of more than 400 Bq.m^{-3}[3], representing a risk level of 10^{-3} per year. A level of this order is the limit for authorised and regulated activities at work. Prevention and intervention opportunities exist for such situations[4]. The global dose reduction capacity is rather limited. However the reduction opportunities are still higher than the total collective dose received by workers in all nuclear activities[3].

The Belgian IRPA affiliated Radiation Protection Association, the National Science Policy Council and the Health Policy Council were consulted by the federal government and made clear policy recommendations for radon. As they were based on scientific evidence, numerous measurements and international comparisons, finally a national radon action programme was defined having five priorities:

(i)   information of, and communication with, the general public,
(ii) mapping on a national, regional and local level (including geological correlation studies),
(iii) information to and training of architects and building contractors,
(iv) regulation about remedial actions and prevention,
(v)   quality control.

This programme is far from complete. It is criticised by nuclear experts and social scientists and lacks substantial financial support for practical remedial activities.

In order to solve the radon paradox and its apparent contradictions the radiation protection approach and risk communication policy for radon were compared with practices in nuclear industrial activities and medicine.

Optimisation techniques were applied combining rationality and equity with insight in risk perception.

COMPARATIVE OPTIMISATION REFERENCES

First, a cost–benefit analysis was made for various radon policy proposals. The results have been presented earlier[2,3]. All radon actions proposed were found to be justified. Important dose savings could be obtained at relatively low cost.

These findings have been re-evaluated according to the recent recommendations of ICRP 65[5]. The proposed dose convention (1.7 mSv.y^{-1} per 100 Bq.m^{-3}) was applied instead of the 'old' conversion factor of 5 mSv.y^{-1} per 100 Bq.m^{-3}. Radon experts still continue to debate[6] on ICRP's most recent approach and guidance, illustrating the extent of the paradox.

Considering the increased importance of risk communication in risk management, our radon policy scenarios[3] were differentiated for different categories of risk level in order to adjust the approach to the specific target group. Moreover it allowed a comparison of radon policy options with industrial and medical radiation protection practices.

In optimisation there is a general trend to express the cost per man.Sv, α, as a function proportional to dose or dose rate.

The range of radon exposures was divided in different categories according to the reference values proposed by international and national authorities. The effective doses corresponding to these values were then compared with elements from the dose limiting system for occupational exposure. The considered boundaries for the different exposure (and related dose) categories are:

- 4000 Bq.m^{-3} corresponds with 68 mSv.y^{-1}, needing intervention.
- 1000 Bq.m^{-3}, the limit for existing dwellings in Switzerland. The related dose coincides with the ICRP 60[7] limit for workers.
- 400 Bq.m^{-3}, the action level proposed by the European Union (EU). This value corresponds with a dose by which the EU makes a distinction between controlled and supervised areas, and is slightly higher than the ICRP 26[8] limit for the public.
- 150 Bq.m^{-3}, the US-EPA action level.
- 50 Bq.m^{-3}, the overall mean indoor radon concentration in Europe. The corresponding dose is slightly lower than the ICRP 60 limit for the public.

Comparisons were made with radiation protection efforts in other fields of exposure to ionising radiation. A recent CEPN study[9] presents amounts spent in France to save a man.Sv at different dose and risk levels in hospitals as well as in nuclear plants. It seems that in France an α value of 30 k\$ per man.Sv is applied at 1 mSv.y^{-1} and of 100 k\$ per man.Sv at 5 mSv.y^{-1} up to 400 k\$ per man.Sv at 15 mSv.y^{-1}. In Sweden, the marginal costs considered reasonable for radiation protection measures[10] are based on the average national gross annual product per person. Society seems willing to spend 1–10 times this average for a year's postponement of death. This yields α values of the order of 80 to 400 k\$ per man.Sv. Moreover the range of Swedish and French α values is in accordance with values proposed[11] in the Netherlands (50–200 k\$ per man.Sv).

In our cost–benefit study, dose reductions due to each proposed radon scenario were calculated over 50 y. The estimated costs of different options include a large scale measurement campaign, control measurements, remedial action investment costs, maintenance costs including present value corrections, cost of building guides, related research and the costs of eventual information campaigns.

Out of this two factor analysis, α values were derived for the different exposure categories, corresponding with dose levels very similar to those studied by CEPN. Again all proposed scenarios were found to be justified. Only the option to prevent exposures in new buildings

of more than 50 Bq.m^{-3} could be discussed on its economic value.

The difference between protection for radon and nuclear energy essentially concerns the actors who have to pay for the protection and the perception of the exposed and general population. Specific radon actions have advantages for public health and have to be paid essentially with personal or public budgets. Radon is a natural risk, usually not perceived as a threat. The industrial radiation protection culture, on the contrary, has industrial objectives and a communication challenge due to the outrage, translated in communication strategies.

To take this into account a two factor cost–benefit analysis has to be completed with additional qualitative attributes in a multi-attribute analysis.

MULTI-ATTRIBUTE ANALYSIS OF RADON POLICY SCENARIOS

A multi-attribute analysis (MAA) was performed only for the scenarios related to radon exposure levels of respectively more than 1000 and 400 Bq.m^{-3}. For the other scenarios it was considered to be much less relevant to perform such an analysis. Indeed, for the scenario concerning the very high radon concentrations (>4000 Bq.m^{-3}), dose levels compare to emergency levels around nuclear power plants and intervention through immediate action is evident. Cost–benefit α values range from 360 and 2500 \$ per man.Sv. The total cost depends largely on the extent of the measuring campaign necessary to detect the cases. The upper limit of 2500 \$ per man.Sv includes the whole cost of a huge nationwide measuring campaign. Enormous dose savings are possible and protective measures are highly urgent. A case by case approach is needed once diagnosed.

As long as ICRP 65 recommendations remain valid, no multi-attribute analysis is considered useful for the scenario referring to the EPA action level. The EPA scenario remains valid on a cost–benefit basis, as maximum α values of the order of 9000 \$ per man.Sv remain much lower than the reference values applied in other nuclear activities.

For the scenario studying the prevention of radon levels of more than 50 Bq.m^{-3} in new constructions only a cost–benefit analysis was done. It is a long term action realised by the renewal of the building stock, with a slow renewing rate of about 100 y. It is worthwhile to start this scenario with a cost of about 68,000 \$ per man.Sv saved, as its α value still lies in the range of α values considered by Dutch, French and Swedish institutes as corresponding to justified actions.

For the multi-attribute analysis (MAA), VISA (Visual Interactive Sensitivity Analysis), from Strathclyde University, Scotland[12] was used. VISA is a personal computer tool to support decision making confronted with multiple criteria of quantitative and qualitative nature.

In the scenarios studied, cost, detriment, individual and collective perception have been used as criteria. Decision involves a choice between a number of alternatives which can be well defined and described according to criteria which are judged to be relevant to the decision. As potential government strategies, the following alternatives were put forward:

(i)   pay no attention at all (doing nothing),
(ii) offering risk quantifying opportunities and practical references (info.),
(iii) organise measuring and information campaigns (measure),
(iv) offer technical and financial sustenance for remedial actions (action),
(v)   draw up specific building regulations and action levels for existing dwellings (law).

VISA is based upon a simple weighted multi-attribute value function, providing a shell for the input of a model of this type and extensive facilities for analysis, including visual interactive sensitivity analysis. It is ideally suited to problems concerned with the evaluation of a few alternatives in the light of information about performance on many criteria. The input parameters arc the weights and the scores of the different criteria used. The aim of scoring is to assign values to each alternative reflecting their performance on each criterion at the bottom level of the hierarchy. The weight assigned to each criterion is essentially a inter-relational scaling factor which relates the scores of criteria.

To calculate the weight for the cost, the maximum cost of the alternatives with the money spent in France[9] have been compared for similar dose levels in other domains. If this maximum is less than or equal to 1/10 of the reference value mentioned by CEPN, the weight has been put equal to zero.

For the weighting of the criterion detriment, the incidence of lung cancer due to radon was compared with that due to smoking. An incidence due to radon 10 times higher than that due to smoking is considered as completely unacceptable and is given an extremely high weight on the detriment. A distinction was made between smokers and non-smokers, as there is a difference of about a factor 10 between the mortality risk due to radon for both groups. As put forward by ICRP 65, 7.3×10^{-5} mSv^{-1} has been used as detriment per unit effective dose for the general population.

The perception criterion was split into an individual and collective component. The individual component is composed of two major parts: the strictly personal attitude to the radon health problem on one side, and the attitude related to the change in the value of the house for the different alternatives on the other side. The collective reaction, representing the collective component to the different strategies, is believed to be the preponderant factor affecting decisions taken by authorities at all levels.

The weighting factors used for the different criteria

and the results of the analysis for the scenarios studied are represented in Figures 1 and 2.

DISCUSSION

The result for the scenario '>1000 Bq.m^{-3}' (Figure 1) shows that remedial actions remain justified. It had already been found in cost–benefit analysis that α values are lower than 3000 $ per man.Sv. The MAA preference for remedial action is due to the fact that a lot of lung cancers are prohibited in a small group of highly exposed persons. The strategy of imposing specific regulatory measures (law) also scores high in the risk management preferences. It has a low cost for the

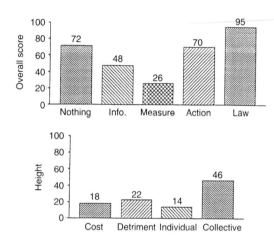

Figure 1. The result of MAA for the scenario '>1000 Bq.m^{-3}'. The upper figure gives the overall score of the different alternatives. The lower figure shows the weight of the different criteria.

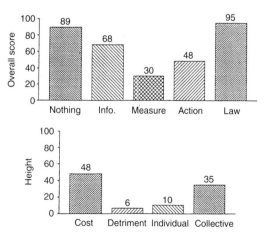

Figure 2. The result of MAA for the scenario '>400 Bq.m^{-3}'. The upper figure gives the overall score of the different alternatives. The lower figure represents the weight of the different criteria.

government and is combined with the feeling of equity for the public.

The result for the scenario '>400 Bq.m^{-3}' (Figure 2) shows that, in contradiction with the cost–benefit analysis, remedial actions are less justified. The optimised action in this case is rather to draw up a regulation or to start a good information campaign.

Applying CEPN logic for spending money for radiation protection purposes, it would be worthwhile to spend some 2×10^9 \$ for avoiding radon exposures of more than 400 Bq.m^{-3}.

It is surprising that 'paying no attention at all' also has a high score, even for the '>1000 Bq.m^{-3}' scenario. This is due to the 'low' cost of this alternative. Moreover, as there is almost no concern about radon among the public (in Belgium), the government can afford to 'pay no attention at all'.

Finally it should be stressed that because of the small number of criteria, the results could seem to be manipulated. This is typical for a MAA and is a characteristic limitation of the VISA program. The input is determining the output. More criteria and more levels in the hierarchy with a more complex decision tree could still yield what decision makers are really asking for.

REFERENCES

1. CEC. *Radiation Atlas. Natural sources of ionizing radiation in Europe.* p. 8.

2. Eggermont, G. and Poffijn, A. *Radon Exposure Standards: A Paradox in Radiation Protection.* In: Proc. Radon in our Euregion, Liège, 1993. Ann. Belg. Assoc. Radiat. Prot. **19**(1–2), 409–425 (1994).

3. Eggermont, G. and Poffijn, A. *The Optimization of Communication and of Decision Making in Radon Policies.* In: Proc. IAEA Conf. on Radiation and Society, Paris, October 1994 (in press).

4. Poffijn, A., Eggermont, G., Hallez, S. and Cohilis, P. *Mapping and Mitigation in the Affected Area of Visé.* Radiat. Prot. Dosim. **56**(1–4), 77–80 (1994).

5. ICRP. *Protection against Radon-222 at Home and at Work.* Publication 65. Ann. ICRP **23**(2) (Oxford: Pergamon) (1994).

6. Vanmarcke, H. *Lack of consistency in the ICRP Approach on Protection Against ^{222}Rn at Home and at Work.* Health Phys. **67**(6), 668 (1994).

7. ICRP. *1990 Recommendations of the International Commission on Radiological Protection.* Publication 60. Ann. ICRP **21**(1–3) (Oxford: Pergamon) (1991).

8. ICRP. *Recommendations of the International Commission of Radiological Protection.* Publication 26. Ann. ICRP **1**(3) (Oxford: Pergamon) (1977).

9. Lefaure, C., Abadia, G. and Aubert, B. *Peut-on parler d'Optimisation de la Radioprotection dans les Domaines Médical et Industriel non Électronucléaire en France?* Radioprotection **30**(1), 25–46 (1995).

10. Bengtsson, G. and Moberg, L. *What is a Reasonable Cost for Protection against Radiation and other Risks?* Health Phys. **64**(6), 661–665 (1993).

11. Nederlandse Gezondheidsraad. *Radon, Assessment of an Integrated Criteria Document,* Pub. 1993/03, Den Haag (1993).

12. Belton, V. *Visual Interactive Sensitivity Analysis for Multiple Criteria Decision Aid* (SPV Software Products, Edinburgh) (1993).

Radiation Protection Dosimetry
Vol. 68, No. 3/4, pp. 213–217 (1996)
Nuclear Technology Publishing

SOCIAL INTERVENTION AND RISK REDUCTION — INDIRECT COUNTERMEASURES

N. A. Higgins and M. Morrey
National Radiological Protection Board
Chilton, Didcot, Oxfordshire OX11 0RQ, UK

Abstract — An indirect countermeasure (IC) is an action which is intended to mitigate detrimental effects experienced by individuals or the community after an accident. Indirect countermeasures (ICs) achieve this, not by averting radiation risks arising from the accident, but by removing or reducing other risks and sources of stress or harm to which the community may be subject. ICs naturally fall into two categories: social action ICs, which range from introducing compensation payments to providing information centres; and risk reducing ICs which mitigate risks to which the population might be exposed, such as radon. By including a consideration of ICs in an assessment of the optimal response, it is likely that a decision maker will become aware of a greater range of harms and benefits that might result from the application of a countermeasure. The decision maker will then be in a better position to judge the appropriateness of any action.

INTRODUCTION

Considerable guidance exists within the radiation protection community on the application of countermeasures aimed at reducing radiation exposures which are the direct result of an accident (direct countermeasures). However, there is little guidance provided on the application of countermeasures aimed at improving the overall situation for people in contaminated regions by addressing factors other than the radiation risk arising directly from the accident (indirect countermeasures). Examples of indirect countermeasures (ICs) include compensation payments, improved general health care, information programmes, and countermeasures to reduce other risks, such as that from radon. An IC can be implemented either as a stand alone action, or in conjunction with other direct and indirect countermeasures, in order to make these more effective.

The authors have adopted the following definition of ICs: 'actions which aim to improve the state of the affected population without directly reducing the radiation dose received as a result of the accident'. This definition includes both measurs that act to improve the dose- (or cost-) effectiveness of direct countermeasures and measures that would not normally be considered in the context of radiation protection after an accident. In the case of the former, the difficulty is in quantifying the interaction; for example, assessing the change in the level of compliance with countermeasure advice that might follow from an information campaign. In the case of the latter, it is the relevance of such countermeasures to radiation protection that requires exploration. The research summarised in this paper was initiated to develop an understanding of the role these countermeasures currently occupy and the implications they could have for radiation protection after accidents[1]. A debate on their further application within or external to the radiation protection environment can then take place. The purpose of this paper, therefore, is to initiate discussion on the principles and philosophy of ICs and the role they may play in future accident management.

The International Commission on Radiological Protection (ICRP) recommends that an intervention must be justified, in that it should result in more benefit than harm when implemented, and that its manner of implementation should be optimised, taking account of both monetary costs and social factors[2]. These principles are intended to apply to countermeasures aimed at directly averting doses resulting from the accident. If ICs are contemplated, then the application of these principles needs to be extended to cover the justification and optimisation of countermeasures with respect to all the risks and harms to which the affected population is exposed; in other words the harm of radiation exposure resulting from the accident would need to be compared with the other harms to which the population is exposed. The optimum countermeasures strategy would then be the one which minimised the overall harm.

Before developing the general ideas more fully, some examples will be discussed and a classification introduced which will illustrate the potential role of ICs. ICs may be characterised or classified in several ways[1]. However, for this discussion they will be viewed in terms of two distinct types of action: direct physical actions that mitigate a real risk to individuals or groups (but not the direct radiation risk from the accident), and social and psychological measures that act either to help the population understand and implement countermeasure advice or to create an improved social and physical environment which is more sympathetic to the needs of the community. The first category of countermeasures will be termed risk reducing indirect countermeasures and the second will be termed social action indirect countermeasures. These two classes of actions and their relationship with direct countermeasures will be discussed below, both practically and in terms of the philosophy of their application.

RISK REDUCING INDIRECT COUNTERMEASURES

The optimisation of countermeasures with respect to a wider set of harms and benefits appears at first sight to be a completely new step. However, ICRP imply that all the anticipated consequences of a countermeasure should be considered when carrying out an optimisation study[3]. It therefore seems compatible with ICRP's recommendations and intentions to include all the physical health risks in the range of factors explicitly considered when determining the consequences of a direct countermeasure. For example, if the relocation of a population is considered, it is not unreasonable to check that the proposed destination for the population is not an area of high radon exposure; otherwise, the total radiation exposure of the population may be higher after the countermeasure than before[4]. If it is accepted that evaluation of the wider health risks should form part of the justification and optimisation process for direct countermeasures, it becomes pertinent to consider whether this process for direct countermeasures should itself be carried out within a broader context. This view suggests that the conventional approach of restricting the health risks considered to those from radiation exposure caused by the accident is actually incomplete in that an optimisation is being carried out which is implicitly constrained. Any answer produced can clearly only provide an optimal solution within the implicit constraints, with the result that any proposed action may be suboptimal when viewed in the wider context.

Set against the above argument are a number of factors that may mediate against the inclusion of risk reducing ICs within the radiation protection intervention framework. Chief among these are social acceptance and equity. For risk reducing ICs to be fully effective in the context of accident response, the exposed population must, in most cases, be prepared to accept a risk trade-off (risk arising from the accident relative to other risks to which they are exposed). Whether, and to what extent they will accept such a trade-off is not known, but plausible arguments can be constructed that exposed populations may wish to discount (and possibly disregard) risks, or attempts to reduce risks, not arising directly from the accident. Again, any proposed application of a risk reducing IC must address the problem of equity. Improved regulation and inspection might, for example, reduce the death rate from industrial accidents but the trade-off in this case would be between a general risk to the whole community of long term health effects from radiation, albeit not equally shared, against the sudden death and injury of a sub-group of the population.

Possible actions for consideration as risk reducing ICs are listed in Table 1. For clarity these are grouped under the headings 'radiological health risks', 'environmental health risks', 'accident health risks' and 'other health risks'. The examples given within each category illus-

trate the types of risks intended; it should be noted that the 'accident health risks' category specifically excludes those risks arising from the radiation accident itself. The list in Table 1 is clearly not exhaustive, but provides insights on the nature and potential application of risk reducing ICs.

Examples of risk reducing ICs which have been implemented in the CIS after the Chernobyl accident range from the setting of low radon levels[5] (100 Bq.m^{-3} for existing houses and 50 Bq.m^{-3} for new houses), to a reduction in the use of prophylactic photofluorography examinations as a screening procedure to detect tuberculosis[6], to restrictions on the use of pesticides and herbicides[7,8]. Without the development of an appropriate formalism it is difficult to assess the efficacy of such a broad range of countermeasures.

SOCIAL ACTION INDIRECT COUNTERMEASURES

This class of ICs may also be viewed as an extension to the existing processes of optimising the radiation protection response to an accident. In this case, however, there is a further subdivision of actions into (i) those that can be considered countermeasures in their own right and (ii) those that act as modifiers to existing or proposed countermeasures of either the direct or risk reducing IC kind. Where social action ICs are carried out in order to improve the benefits obtained from direct countermeasures, they are clearly within the existing scope of the radiation protection framework. However, when considered in their own right, like risk reducing ICs, they are not currently within this scope. To include them requires the extension of the justification and optimisation process to consider countermeasures which address all the harms to which an affected population might be exposed.

The type and nature of the actions that can be described as social action ICs vary widely. This is illus-

Table 1. Examples of risk reducing indirect countermeasures.

Category of risk	Examples
Radiological health risks	Radon. Medical diagnostic irradiation.
Environmental health risks	Chemical pollution. Natural disasters, e.g. fire and flood.
Accident health risks	Industrial accidents. Road accidents.
Other health risks	Endemic conditions, e.g. goitre. Conditions promoted by custom or general economic level.

trated in Table 2, where some examples of the countermeasures are listed, under the two headings 'compensation countermeasures' and 'social psychological' countermeasures. Although many social and psychological countermeasures will be encompassed by the existing radiological protection framework they are a new category of action, in the sense that radiation protection philosophy has not yet been developed fully to include their application after an accident. In particular, their interaction with direct countermeasures has not yet been worked out in detail[9].

Many of the countermeasures in Table 2 were applied after the Chernobyl accident such as the improvement of medical facilities[10], the mounting of information campaigns[6,11], the introduction of compensation payments, and the provision of amenities such as gas supplies[12]. Research carried out within the CEC/CIS collaborative programme into the psychological effects of the accident and subsequent countermeasures indicates that a direct countermeasure, such as relocation, will have associated with it a number of social and psychological factors which strongly influence its effectiveness[13,14]. These are related to such things as the time taken to implement the countermeasure, whether it is voluntary, the provision of alternative houses, jobs etc. (i.e. material provision), and the extent to which communities are broken up (i.e. preservation/destruction of the social structure). The social and psychological factors associated with the implementation of a countermeasure will have a potential impact of the health of the affected population, both clinically, in terms of morbidity and psychosomatic conditions, and sub-clinically, in terms of greater strain and anxiety in the community. These effects will in turn have measurable costs in terms of health care, demands for

Table 2. Social action indirect countermeasures.

Category	Example
Compensation:	
Financial	Money for: damage to health or livelihood, enforced changes to lifestyle, the purchase of alternative food.
Material	Provision of: new or improved amenities, general infrastructure, transport, jobs, medical facilities (including new hospitals and local clinics), shops, sport and recreation facilities, schools and child care facilities, social services.
Social psychological	Provision of: information and counselling services, reassurance screening for medical conditions and ensuring that local people have a say in the actions that affect them.

more action justifiable only on social-psychological grounds, and political instability. Clearly a social action IC which could be used in parallel with a direct countermeasure could radically modify its effectiveness.

DISCUSSION

A community might be subject to many risks prior to an accident which, for a complex set of reasons are judged not to warrant intervention. If an accident happens, then, in addition to the radiological risks incurred, the accident may also create new non-radiological risks and stresses with which the community has to cope. At the same time, social perceptions of risk may change, i.e. anxiety over risks in general may be heightened as a consequence of the accident. In the balance of the harms and benefits required for justification and optimisation, this could result in changes in both the weight associated with social factors (e.g. the perception of risk), and their magnitude. This, in turn, could alter the level at which countermeasures were considered justified and the net benefit they provided (e.g. society becomes more risk averse).

There are therefore two modes of operation for ICs. In the first mode of operation additional direct countermeasures are not justified, but ICs (or direct countermeasures supported by ICs) are. This is illustrated in Figure 1, which shows a hypothetical change between before and after an accident of the net benefit provided by an IC. Justified Level 1 represents the situation before the accident, and Justified Level 2 represents the situation after the accident, when the weights and magnitudes associated with some social factors are presumed to have changed. The distribution of net benefits (or net costs) achieved by implementing the IC in various ways (analogous to changing the intervention level for a direct countermeasure (DC)) is represented by the largest curved line. The apex of this distribution represents the optimal mode of implementation. The corresponding distribution for a DC taken after the accident is shown by the smaller curve. Before the accident

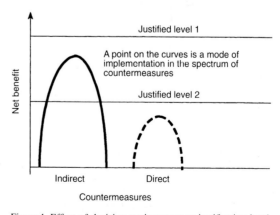

Figure 1. Effect of decision environment on justification level.

(comparison with Justified Level 1) the optimal mode for the IC is not justified and no action should be taken. After the accident (comparison with Justified Level 2), whilst direct countermeasures are not justified, ICs are.

In the second mode of operation action is justified to mitigate the direct radiological effects of the accident but an IC is taken because it achieves the same or greater benefit (reduction in health risk) for less harm. In Figure 2 the consequences of hypothetical DCs and ICs are illustrated in terms of two factors: benefit and (monetary) cost. The shaded area represents consequences which, in the circumstances following the accident, would render the countermeasures unjustified. The efficient frontier encompasses the set of countermeasure options which could be optimum, depending on the relative weight attached to each of the factors illustrated. The dotted lines indicate the continuation of the efficient frontier for each group of countermeasures considered in isolation. Countermeasures with consequences inside the area bounded by the efficient frontier cannot be optimum, because countermeasures exist within the efficient frontier which are either cheaper for the same benefit, or give more benefit for the same cost. It can be seen that it is possible for a DC to be justified, but not optimum, when considered with ICs.

The second mode of operation, when one or more direct countermeasures are justified, is more likely to contain the special case of the joint application of a direct countermeasure supported by one or more ICs to produce an optimum result which is more effective

and/or acceptable to the population. If an IC is considered which acts to modify the application of a DC, the combined result may lie beyond the efficient frontier defined for single countermeasures of either type shown in Figure 2.

CONCLUSIONS

Some indirect countermeasures have been and are likely to continue to be applied *ad hoc* to mitigate the consequences of accidental releases of radioactivity. However, the above discussion illustrates that further consideration should be given to indirect countermeasures as a new and distinct group of actions that can be taken after an accidental release of radioactivity to the environment. It is only by considering ICs within the same framework as direct countermeasures that the questions of efficacy and equity can be fully resolved and guidance provided on what actions it may be appropriate to consider in particular circumstances.

ACKNOWLEDGEMENTS

The authors would like to thank Dr M. Savkin and Dr A. Gordeev for many helpful discussions of ICs concepts and for the provision of references to ICs applied after Chernobyl. They would also like to thank Dr I. Los for information on radon regulation in Ukraine. This work was performed under the auspices of the Joint CEC/CIS collaborative research programme.

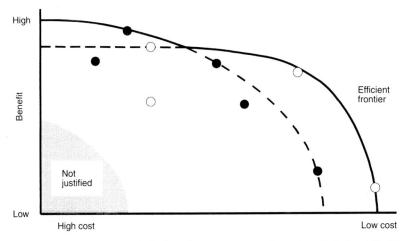

Figure 2. Partial and complete optimisation of countermeasures alternatives. ○, Indirect; ●, Direct.

REFERENCES

1. Higgins, N. A. and Savkin, M. N. *Indirect Countermeasures: A New Paradigm for the Assessment of Post Accident Intervention* (in preparation).

2. ICRP. *1990 Recommendations of the International Commission on Radiological Protection.* Publication 60 (Oxford: Pergamon Press) Ann. ICRP **21**(1–3) (1991).

3. International Commission on Radiological Protection. *Principles for Intervention for Protection of the Public in a Radiological Emergency.* Publication 63 (Oxford: Pergamon Press) Ann. ICRP **22**(4) (1991).

4. Pavlenko, T. A., Los, I. P. and Aksenov, N. V. *Efficiency Assessment of Relocation as a Countermeasure to Diminish Irradiation Doses of the 'Chernobyl' Population for Ukraine.* Radiat. Meas **25**(1–4), 415–416 (1995)

5. Los, I. P. Radiation Protection Institute, Kiev, Ukraine (private communication).

6. Report of the Institute of Radiation Hygiene. *Elaboration of Complex Measures Directed to Exposure Dose Lowering for the Population of Contaminated Districts* (St Petersburg, Russia) (1992).

7. Law of Russian Federation. *Social Defence of Citizens Subject to the Influence of Radiation as a Result of the Chernobyl Catastrophe.* No. 306–1 Adopted 18 June (1992).

8. Government decree of Russian Federation on the Regime in the Contaminated Territories No. 1008 25 December (1992).

9. Morrey, M. and Allen, P. *The Role of Social and Psychological Factors in Radiation Protection after Accidents.* Radiat. Prot. Dosim. **68**(3/4), 267–271 (1996) (This issue).

10. Law of Russian Soviet Federal Socialist Republic. *Social Defence of Citizens Subject to the Influence of Radiation as a Result of the Chernobyl Catastrophe.* Adopted 15 May (1991).

11. Decree of Council of Ministers of the Russian Soviet Federal Socialist Republic No. 151 15 May (1991).

12. Decree of the Council of Ministers of the USSR and the All Union Central Council of Trade Unions No. 886 20 October (1989).

13. Rumyantseva, G. M. *The History of Relocation caused by the Chernobyl Accident in Russia.* (Serbsky Institute) (1994).

14. Rumyantseva, G. M., Allen, P. T., Melnickuk, T. N., Margolin, S. A. and Plyplina, D. V. *Locus-of-Control in the Population Suffering from the Chernobyl Disaster and Living under Conditions of Chronic Ecological Stress.* Bekhterev Rev. Pychiat. Med. Psychol. **3**, 34–40 (1994).

Radiation Protection Dosimetry
Vol. 68, No. 3/4, pp. 219–225 (1996)
Nuclear Technology Publishing

A DISCUSSION OF THE LIMITATIONS OF THE PSYCHOMETRIC AND CULTURAL THEORY APPROACHES TO RISK PERCEPTION

L. Sjöberg
Centre for Risk Research
Stockholm School of Economics
Box 6501, 113 83 Stockholm, Sweden

Abstract — Risk perception has traditionally been conceived as a cognitive phenomenon, basically a question of information processing. The very term perception suggests that information processing is involved and of crucial importance. Kahneman and Tversky suggested that the use of 'heuristics' in the intuitive estimation of probabilities accounts for biased probability perception, hence claiming to explain risk perception as well. The psychometric approach of Slovic *et al*, a further step in the cognitive tradition, conceives of perceived risk as a function of general properties of a hazard. However, the psychometric approach is shown here to explain only about 20% of the variance of perceived risk, even less of risk acceptability. Its claim to explanatory power is based on a statistical illusion: mean values were investigated and accounted for, across hazards. A currently popular alternative to the psychometric tradition, Cultural Theory, is even less successful and explains only about 5% of the variance of perceived risk. The claims of this approach were also based on a statistical illusion: 'significant' results were reported and interpreted as being of substantial importance. The present paper presents a new approach: attitude to the risk generating technology, general sensitivity to risks and specific risk explained well over 60% of the variance of perceived risk of nuclear waste, in a study of extensive data from a representative sample of the Swedish population. The attitude component functioning as an explanatory factor of perceived risk, rather than as a consequence of perceived risk, suggests strongly that perceived risk is something other than cognition. Implications for risk communication are discussed.

INTRODUCTION

Risk perception is a topic of considerable interest both to researchers and policy makers. The public has, or is believed to have, strong demands on risk mitigation in certain areas of technology, in spite of reassurances from experts and administrators that risks are very small. The public may thus at times claim that a risk is very large while experts reject that notion. This state of affairs is an important factor behind much current and recent research on risk perception. Basically, the question is: what are the factors responsible for the public's perceived risk[1]?

Perceived risk, in turn, can be analysed in several perspectives. One is the level of perceived risk, another is risk acceptability, or risk tolerance. These two are not necessarily functions of one another. A further important dimension is for whom a risk is pertinent. Risk for a respondent personally is one thing, perceived risk to people in general quite another.

Note, however, the somewhat subtle and indirect persuasive power of the term risk *perception* in itself. 'Perception' is of course a form of information processing — more automatic and rigid than cognition. If risk conceptions are really perceptions it must be assumed that they are formed on the basis of information about the external world, ultimately based on sensory information, and that they can be seen as the result of more or less rigid information processing.

Note also that risks are usually described as hazards in a somewhat neutral manner, and they may or may not arise due to human activities. If hazards such as being struck by lightning or exposed to ionising radi-ation in a nuclear disaster are treated within a common framework, moral responsibility is disregarded. Perhaps this is the reason why morality has been largely lacking from risk perception studies[2,3].

The pioneer in this field of research was Starr, who suggested that two major factors behind the level of accepted risk are benefits and voluntariness[4]. More beneficial technologies are accepted in spite of some risks, and more voluntary activities as well. The number of exposed persons also played a role in acceptability. Disease risk was argued to be a yardstick for judging the acceptability of voluntary risks.

Starr's ideas were original and stimulating but his data were weak. He basically used archival data on accidents as a measure of perceived risk, and aggregated economics as measures of perceived benefits. Such data are hard to interpret in a straightforward manner[5]. Voluntariness was established on the basis of mere interpretation.

In the beginning of the 1970s two psychologists, Tversky and Kahneman, attracted much attention with the idea that information is processed on the basis of 'heuristics', i.e. rules of thumb, which are used to avoid the traps of cognitive overload[6]. The now famous heuristic rules of representativeness, anchoring and adjustment, and availability, were claimed to bias perceived probability, and hence risk perception (assuming that perceived risk is a function of subjective probability of an adverse event). In this paradigm, expert risk assessment was not seen to be a psychological problem. Whenever they held a view different from that of experts it was argued that the public should be 'educated'.

The work on heuristics has in the long run been less important for the study of risk perception than might have been believed initially. Most of this work consisted of demonstrations that people have misleading intuitions concerning probabilities as defined by probability theory, in judging well defined calculus problems. On the other hand, risk perception in applied settings is rarely if ever concerned with the well defined probabilities of statistical theory. Indeed, 'risk' is a fuzzy concept with a lot more to it than mere probability[7].

The heuristics paradigm established the field of risk perception as thoroughly *cognitive*; emotional and motivational factors were disregarded. Strong effects of framing and more or less subtle informational cues suggested to these psychologists that this topic, as so many others, could be conceived within an information processing framework.

Psychologists were the first social scientists on the stage of risk research, but they were soon followed by researchers in political science and anthropology. Some of the latter have developed an extensive theoretical framework called Cultural Theory which they claim can explain risk perception. Those claims will be dealt with below in some detail, but the present discussion turns first to a currently dominating cognitive psychological tradition.

THE PSYCHOMETRIC APPROACH

At the end of the 1970s Slovic and Fischhoff launched an original approach, now often called psychometric[8]. These psychologists have been highly successful among administrators and engineers/risk analysts in establishing the notion that perceived risk and its dimensions are psychological constructs which can be measured with psychometric methods. A psychological bias inherent in their work, and often criticised by sociologists, is an emphasis on individuals and their perceptions. Their work was to begin with, and still is in Slovic's case, decidedly quantitative. Others, including Fischhoff, have more recently turned to process analysis[9] and think aloud of protocols and the establishment of qualitative descriptions[10,11], but that development will not be further discussed in the present paper. It leads to interesting but somewhat awkward procedures; the more simple quantitative approach is still very much worthwhile pursuing.

Let us look in some detail at the classical 1978 paper in which the psychometric approach was launched. Subjects judged 30 activities and technologies in terms of:

(a) benefit to society (magnitude estimation, 10 assigned to lowest benefit);
(b) perceived risk (magnitude estimation, 10 assigned to lowest risk);
(c) acceptability of current level of risk (risk adjustment factor: how many times safer should it be, or how many times riskier could it be);

(d) nine risk dimensions:
   (i)   voluntary — involuntary
   (ii)   effects immediate — delayed
   (iii) known precisely by exposed persons — not known
   (iv)   known precisely to science — not known
   (v)   uncontrollable — controllable
   (vi)   new — old
   (vii) chronic — catastrophic
   (viii) common — dread
   (ix)   certain not to be fatal — certain to be fatal

These nine dimensions were all rated using seven category scales. Acceptable risk was estimated by multiplying current risk with the risk adjustment factor*.

The risk dimensions were not selected on the basis of a theory of risk perception. They represent a compilation of factors that had been mentioned as possibly important in the literature on risk acceptability that appeared largely in response to Starr's work, and was published in the first half of the 1970s[12]. There is still no theory behind the psychometric approach.

Participants in the initial study were 76 persons, 52 women and 24 men, members of Eugene, Oregon, League of Women's voters and their spouses**. Some subjects judged risk, others benefits. Risk was judged as general risk, not personal.

Analysing mean ratings

It was found that perceived risk correlated strongly with dread and severity of consequences, but not with the other seven dimensions. Adjusting risk to acceptable risk it was found that the nine dimensions correlated either with the adjustment factor or the estimated acceptable risk levels. Factor analysis yielded two factors called Technological Risk and Severity. These factors were used, together with perceived benefit, to predict acceptable risk, yielding a multiple R of 0.76. Level of risk was also subjected to a multiple regression analysis, resulting in a multiple R of 0.67.

The authors concluded that risk acceptability was highly predictable on the basis of these results. They stated (p. 149) that

'Conceivably, policy makers might use such relationships to predict public acceptance of the risk levels associated with proposed technologies.'

---

*The adjustment factor can be construed as demand for risk mitigation. It correlated 0.76 with level of perceived risk. This value is not given by Fischhoff *et al* and has been computed on the basis of mean adjustment ratings for two groups of subjects described in the paper.
**This group was of course not representative of the population, and the authors were careful to point that out. However, they also claimed that they were an example of people who were highly active politically and therefore of special interest in a risk perception study.

Another main conclusion from these results, often cited, is that perceived risk among the public is 'multidimensional'. Experts, on the other hand, are said to base their risk estimates only on fatality rates or some similar 'objective' and unidimensional measure[13].

These results were later followed up with larger groups of subjects (still convenience samples), a broader sampling of hazards and nine more risk dimensions[14,15]. The same statistical methods were used. Analyses were done on mean scores. The results were essentially similar. It was also claimed, on the basis of the psychometric work, that experts construe risk mainly in terms of expected fatalities while the public's risk perception is affected by a large number of psychometric dimensions[16].

A large number of studies have subsequently been carried out using these scales. The samples have been convenience samples or probability samples, often of doubtful representativeness due to low response rates. For example, an attempt was made to compare public risk perception in the USA and Japan, using 30 hazards rated on five of the psychometric dimensions[17]. With mailed questionnaires, the response rates were 52.6% in the USA and a mere 29% in Japan. The authors recommended caution in interpreting the Japanese data but claimed that the US response rate was 'acceptable'. A recently published study of some graduate students in France claimed that it was study of public opinion in that country[18]. It is not fair to blame such practices on the originators of the psychometric approach, but they undeniably set the stage for a paradigm.

A recent re-analysis of the original Slovic data again resulted in very high levels of explanatory power for mean ratings[19]. Perceived risk was related to the psychometric dimensions, and policy implications were again suggested. Policy implications assume that risk attributes such as expected mortality and effects on future generations are antecedent to perceived risk. They might as well be effects of perceived risk; more about this later.

Gardner and Gould published an important study in 1989[20]. This was, as far as I know, the first risk perception study to obtain data from probability samples from populations in some US states, and extensive home interviews were carried out, based on the psychometric approach. They covered the benefit side of technologies more extensively than had been done by the Oregon group, but limited their design to six technologies and three of the Slovic dimensions (catastrophic potential, dread, and known to science). Furthermore, they performed individual differences analyses rather than mean score analyses on relationships between perceived risk and risk acceptability on the one hand, risk and benefit dimensions on the other. The mean variance accounted for in risk perception was 0.288. For risk acceptability the value was much lower, viz. 0.140.

There is a subtle, but very important, difference in the models applied by Slovic *et al* and by Gardner and Gould. Slovic analysed mean ratings and estimated models of variation between technologies. Gardner and Gould, on the other hand, analysed each technology separately and estimated models of individual differences. These two approaches answer different questions and are bound to give different results. The Slovic approach analyses reasons why people, on the average, judge different technologies differently; the Gardner and Gould approach analyses why different people judge one and the same technology differently. The aggregated risk perception data used by Slovic is much easier to account for statistically, and he reported correlations in the 0.7–0.8 range. These data may seem impressive but the high level of explanatory power found is really mostly a function of aggregation.

When a risk policy maker wants to know why people react the way they do to a given technology, he must take individual differences into account. The psychometric approach will then, according to the results achieved by Gardner and Gould, only account for a minor share of the variance. Hence, the psychometric dimensions do not explain why people react the way they do to any given technology such as nuclear power. This fact seems not to be widely realised.

In much work using the psychometric approach, validity criteria employed have been less informative than one might have wished. First, as pointed out above, researchers have usually analysed mean ratings rather than raw data. It is well known that correlations among means are usually much higher than corresponding statistics for raw data at the level of single individuals; in this case the strategy of using means led to a faulty impression that the psychometric dimensions explain perceived risk almost completely. Second, the factorial structure of the dimensions has been extensively studied. While this structure may be of some interest, it is quite limited, the variables subjected to factor analysis being very few in most studies. The finding that only a few factors were needed to account for the data is therefore not at all surprising. In addition, an invariant factorial structure is not sufficient to establish the validity of these dimensions for explaining perceived risk, it is entirely irrelevant. The structure may well be more or less invariant and perceived risk still only very partially accounted for.

A more recent development is the introduction of trust in the study of risk perception[21–24]. Freudenburg introduced it within a sociological framework[25]. Several American studies have shown that trust is an important determinant of perceived risk and risk acceptance in that country[26]. Swedish work[27] has given less support to the notion, however. This may be a case of important cultural variation.

The present mainstream approach to risk perception and communication is undoubtedly the psychometric one, extended by including the trust variable. A well-known philosophy of risk communication, due to Sandman[28–30] defines a concept of 'outrage' with reference to the psychometric factors. The idea is that social dilemmas of risk communication can be explained, and perhaps resolved, by risk perception being determined by the psychometric set of dimensions. In a recent textbook on environment and human behaviour, Gardner and Stern[31] cited the psychometric dimensions as major factors behind lay risk perception; they seem to be, by now, an established 'truth' about risk perception and are seldom if every discussed critically.

There is, however, one contender: the so-called Cultural Theory of risk perception.

CULTURAL THEORY OF RISK PERCEPTION

The Cultural Theory of risk perception is another, and somewhat newer, approach to risk perception[32]. It is a deviation from mainstream psychological analysis, based on work in anthropology and political science. It is argued that perceived risk is 'selected' in order to sustain and strengthen social relations, and that there are three or four clusters of values and risk perceptions, termed the egalitarian, individualistic and hierarchy cultural biases. Less work has been reported on these notions, but some seemingly promising beginnings were reported by Dake and Wildavsky in a paper which has given rise to considerable interest[33]. This work has been reviewed elsewhere by the present author, and it was concluded that cultural biases account for only about 5% of the variance of perceived risk[34]*.

In the present paper, problems of the psychometric and Cultural Theory approaches to risk perception are considered at greater depth. In particular, the explanatory power of the approaches are investigated and compared. In a subsequent section, alternative approaches are described and finally some comments are made on risk communication, based on the findings reported in the paper.

EMPIRICAL TESTS

Validity of the psychometric approach

The results are here reported of a study of risk perception in the psychometric framework. A group of 94 teachers (mostly high school) rated 36 hazards on level of risk and the same nine scales that were used in the Fischhoff et al (1978) paper[8]. The dimensions were rated using a 0–100 scale for level of risk and bipolar 7-category scales for the other dimensions.

A multiple regression analysis was run for each of the 36 hazards. Risk level was the dependent variable, the 9 psychometric dimensions independent variables. Each of the 36 analyses was run using a stepwise procedure. The mean amount of explained variance

(adjusted) was 0.216. The maximum achieved was 0.429. These results agree well with the Gardner and Gould data; they give only a slightly lower level of explanatory power*.

A tally was kept of the number of times each psychometric dimension entered the model selected in the stepwise regressions. All dimensions entered about equally often, with the exception of 'common/dread' which entered in most models, 23 in all.

Cultural Theory dimensions in isolation from other variables

Four scales of cultural biases (British version) were used to predict risk ratings. The mean amount of variance explained was 0.051. This low value agrees very well with that obtained in other studies.

Comparison of the psychometric approach and Cultural Theory

A number of analyses were run on the 36 risk ratings, using stepwise regression. The three major cultural biases were included as explanatory variables. The mean adjusted R^2 rose from 0.216 to 0.238, implying that Cultural Theory adds virtually no explanatory value beyond that due to the psychometric dimensions. Again, this finding is in complete harmony with other findings on Cultural Theory.

A MODEL OF PERCEIVED RISK

We have seen, so far, that perceived risk is rather hard to account for. A much more thorough study is therefore warranted. One example of such an analysis is published elsewhere[27]. A large random sample of the Swedish population judged nuclear waste risk and many aspects of such risks, and other related variables such as trust in expertise and attitude to nuclear power. (Data were obtained from 1099 respondents, yielding a response rate of 64.6%).

Both personal and general risks were judged. Results were quite similar, so only results for general risk are presented here.

In a multiple regression analysis, 65% explained variance was achieved. The most important explanatory variables and their beta weights were:

attitude to nuclear power (−0.113);

risk to future generations (0.111);

trust in competence of experts who are against nuclear power (0.148);

---

* US data gave a somewhat more positive picture; about 9% of the variance was explained.

* Gardner and Gould used a straightforward multiple regression approach in the article referred to here, rather than a stepwise procedure. Their samples were much larger than the present one. They used only three of psychometric dimensions; nine were used here.

trust in competence of pertinent authorities (−0.175);
trust in risk assessment by experts who are against nuclear power (0.148);
trust in risk assessment by pertinent authorities (−0.123);
pooled psychometric dimensions* (0.180);
risk sensitivity** (0.248);
risk of background radiation (0.381).

What we see here is the following:

attitude enters as a determinant of risk;
several trust factors also enter, including trust in 'dissident' scientists;
psychometric dimensions carry a modest weight;
general risk sensitivity, which could also be a measure of scale use strategy, enters strongly;
a specific radiation factor is very important.

Hence, the psychometrics + trust approach which has so far dominated psychological analysis of risk perception is strongly enhanced by adding attitude to the risk generating agent, a specific risk factor and a scale use factor. The amount of explanatory variance reached in this way is probably close to the true variance and about three times the level achieved by the classic psychometric approach, 12 times that of Cultural Theory. It remains to be seen if such models can be constructed for other risks.

SPECIFIC FEAR: A FURTHER ANALYSIS

Judgments of risk were available from a data set from the general population (54% response rate, gross sample size = 1100). The study dealt with nuclear power and radiation risks[35]. The initial task involved rating 26 hazards on a 0–6 risk scale. These ratings were factor analysed. Four factors accounted for 55% of the total variance. They were subjected to maximum likelihood factor analysis and direct oblimin rotation. The rotated factor loadings and the factor intercorrelations are given in Tables 1 and 2.

The four factors are readily interpreted as follows:

(i)   radiation,
(ii) economy,
(iii) environment,
(iv) accidents and crime victimisation.

The first and third factor correlated rather strongly; all factors correlated to some extent. (There was, in other words, a general risk sensitivity tendency.) The nine radiation risks (in bold face in Table 1) all had their highest loading on the radiation factor, with the exception of radon (but the wording in the questionnaire was

'radon gas' and radiation was not mentioned). This was true for such widely different technologies as nuclear power and X ray diagnostics, supporting the notion of a specific radiation fear connected with technologies, and also related to environmental concern.

CONCLUSIONS

The psychometric approach was launched in papers where all analyses were performed on mean scores, not raw data. High explanatory power was therefore easily achieved, but for mean scores only. When raw data are

Table 1. Rotated loadings of risk estimates. Ionising radiation hazards in bold face.

	Factor number			
	1	2	3	4
High level nuclear waste	0.94	−0.04	−0.03	−0.03
Nuclear waste transport	0.90	−0.04	−0.07	0.04
Nuclear waste site	0.88	0.03	0.08	0.03
Swedish nuclear power plants	0.80	−0.02	0.05	0.00
Economic decline	0.01	0.80	−0.11	0.11
Unemployment	−0.09	0.72	−0.05	−0.01
Inadequate food	0.04	0.59	0.05	0.03
Industrial pollution	0.06	0.09	0.74	−0.06
Motor vehicle exhausts	−0.03	−0.03	0.70	0.02
Global warming	0.09	0.12	0.70	−0.14
EMF	0.21	0.09	0.63	−0.08
Radon gas	0.14	0.13	0.57	−0.06
Ozone layer depletion	0.18	0.16	0.51	−0.10
Inadequate dietary habits	0.06	−0.03	0.51	0.09
Burglary	−0.04	0.09	−0.07	0.75
Assault	−0.04	0.19	−0.06	0.66
Traffic accident	0.10	−0.06	0.12	0.48
Lightning	0.17	−0.02	0.06	0.34
Inadequate medical care	0.05	0.39	0.07	0.30
Alcohol	−0.07	−0.09	0.44	0.16
X ray diagnostics	0.24	0.15	0.14	0.16
Irradiated food	0.39	−0.01	0.39	0.08
Foreign nuclear power plants	0.48	0.04	0.22	0.08
Natural background radiation	0.44	0.08	0.26	0.06
Smoking	−0.09	−0.08	0.48	0.06
Sun's rays	0.05	0.37	0.28	0.03

Table 2. Intercorrelations among risk perception factors.

	Factor number			
	1	2	3	4
1	1.00			
2	0.31	1.00		
3	0.53	0.18	1.00	
4	0.25	0.30	0.31	1.00

---

*21 dimensions were used; they were found to be unifactorial and were pooled to one index.
**Measured as the average rating of a number of non-radiation risks.

analysed, as in the present paper, and individual difference models are estimated, a very different picture emerges. The explanatory power is, on the average, in the 0.2–0.3 range. This level is not very high, but still quite an achievement when compared to the main theoretical contender of Cultural Theory.

As for *Cultural Theory*, the results reported here agree very well with the picture provided in a review of other similar studies published elsewhere[34]. In isolation, the theory accounts for some 5% of the variance of perceived risk (or concern). When added to another model, in the present case the psychometric model, it accounts for a very minor additional share of the variance of perceived risk.

Defenders of Cultural Theory have suggested a number of objections to the present conclusions (see my discussion in Ref. 34). Space does not allow for a repetition of that discussion here; but just a few points are noted.

It is often argued that correlations are somehow misleading as measurements of strength of a relationship. Regression coefficients are held to be better. But regression coefficients are dependent on the unit of measurement. Therefore they cannot be used for comparing the strength of a relationship across different scales, and that is clearly needed. Extreme values have sometimes been compared, e.g. extreme groups on the egalitarian scale have been compared with regard to perceived risk of nuclear power. The result is often that differences are found, even large ones. However, here is another statistical illusion. Even a very weak correlation allows for large differences if the extreme groups are extreme enough. Finally, it is very common to refer to statistical significance as an argument in favour of the theory. This is a tedious argument indeed. Statistical significance is in no way related to substantial significance, as any elementary statistics text will tell. Also, weak correlations cannot usually be believed to be drastically boosted with more reliable measurements. Correction for attenuation due to random measurement errors raises the typical cultural theory validity of 0.05 to about 0.07.

Our research on nuclear waste risk suggests strongly that perceived risk can be almost exhaustively explained by adding attitude, risk sensitivity and a specific fear component to the models. Attitude appears to be driving perceived risk, not the other way round, according to structural equations modelling. The variable risk sensitivity can be a reflection of scale use habits, true risk sensitivity or both. More research needs to be done to decide on that issue. The specific fear component, in this case background radiation risk, must of course be customised to fit each risk being studied. *The idea of the psychometric approach that general risk dimensions can account for perceived risk must be abandoned if risk is to be explained.*

A few words about risk communication are finally called for. Both the heuristic and psychometric approaches imply that risk communication is basically a problem of education and information. However, risk communication is a difficult business[36]. People's risk perception is not easily changed, and there is no or little correlation between actual knowledge and perceived risk, and between perceived knowledge or competence in an area and perceived risk, among the public. Lack of trust in experts and the establishment is often cited as a reason for such difficulties, particularly in American work[25]. However, trust appears to be stronger in at least some European countries and we have found trust to be of relatively minor importance in our studies (e.g. Ref. 27). Implications of Cultural Theory for risk communication are even less clear.

The best known approach to risk communication is perhaps due to Sandman[28–30], who speaks of 'outrage' as a determining factor behind risk perception and demand for mitigation. Outrage, according to Sandman, is a collective term referring to the psychometric dimensions + trust. Since we have seen here that this approach explains only a minor part of risk perception (and even less of mitigation demands) there is surely room for improvement in risk communication. The general experience that success in risk communication remains elusive testifies to the lack of thorough understanding on the basis of current procedures.

Is risk perception a cognitive phenomenon? I believe that this question really is not much different from asking how cognitive are attitudes and preferences. Zajonc argued, some time ago, that 'preferences need no inferences'[37]. Such different types of data as similarities and preferences are only moderately strongly related, and spatial models based on similarities often fail to produce the spatial representation needed for preference data[38,39]. The cognitive psychological approach to risk perception is clearly insufficient; social (attitudes and moral dimensions) and perhaps clinical (specific fears) aspects need to be taken into account. Risk perception is much more than just information processing.

REFERENCES

1. Sjöberg, L. and Drottz-Sjöberg, B.-M. *Risk perception*. In: Comprehending Radiation Risks. A Report to the IAEA. Eds. B. Lindell *et al* (Vienna: International Atomic Energy Agency) pp. 29–59 (1994).

2. Sjöberg, L. *Risk and Society. Studies in Risk Taking and Risk Generation* (Hemel Hempstead, England: George Allen and Unwin) (1987).

3. Sjöberg, L. and Winroth, E. *Risk, Moral Value of Actions, and Mood*. Scand. J. Psychol. **27**, 191–208 (1986).

4. Starr, C. *Social Benefit versus Technological Risk*. Science **165**, 1232–1238 (1969).

5. Otway, H. J. and Cohen, J. J. *Revealed Preferences: Comments on the Starr Benefit–Risk Relationships* (Laxenburg, Austria: IIASA) (1975).

6. Tversky, A. and Kahneman, D. *Judgment under Uncertainty: Heuristics and Biases.* Science **185**, 1124–1131 (1974).

7. Drottz-Sjöberg, B.-M. *Perception of Risk. Studies of Risk Attitudes, Perceptions and Definitions.* RHIZIKON: Studies of Risk and Hazard, Vol. 1 (Stockholm: Stockholm School of Economics, Centre for Risk Research) (1991).

8. Fischhoff, B., Slovic, P., Lichtenstein, S., Read, S. and Combs, B. *How Safe is Safe Enough? A Psychometric Study of Attitudes towards Technological Risks and Benefits.* Policy Sci. **9**, 127–152 (1978).

9. Svenson, O. *Process Description of Decision Making.* Organ. Behav. Hum. Perform. **23**, 86–112 (1979).

10. Atman, C. J., Bostrom, A., Fischhoff, B. and Morgan, M. G. *Designing Risk Communications: Completing and Correcting Mental Models of Hazardous Processes, Part 1.* Risk Anal. **14**, 779–788 (1994).

11. Atman, C. J., Bostrom, A., Fischhoff, B. and Morgan, M. G. *Designing Risk Communications: Completing and Correcting Mental Models of Hazardous Processes, Part II.* Risk Anal. **14**, 789–798 (1994).

12. Sjöberg, L. *Strength of Belief and Risk.* Policy Sci. **11**, 39–57 (1979).

13. Fischhoff, B., Slovic, P. and Lichtenstein, S. *Lay Foibles and Expert Fables in Judgments about Risk.* Am. Stat. **36**, 240–255 (1982).

14. Slovic, P., Fischhoff, B. and Lichtenstein, S. *Facts and Fears: Understanding Perceived Risk.* In: Societal Risk Assessment: How Safe is Safe Enough? Eds R. Schwing and J. Albers (New York: Plenum) (1980).

15. Slovic, P., Fischhoff, B. and Lichtenstein, S. *Characterizing Perceived Risk.* In: Perilous Progress: Managing the Hazards of Technology Eds R. W. Kates, C. Hohenhemser and J. X. Kasperson (Boulder, CO., Westview) pp. 92–125 (1985).

16. Slovic, P., Fischhoff, B. and Lichtenstein, S. *Rating the Risks.* Environment **21**(3), 14–20, 36–39 (1979).

17. Hinman, G. W., Rosa, E. A., Kleinhesselink, R. R. and Lowinger, T. C. *Perception of Nuclear and other Risks in Japan and the United States.* Risk Anal. **13**, 449–456 (1993).

18. Karpowicz-Lazreg, C. and Mullet, E. *Societal Risks as seen by the French Public* Risk Anal. **13**, 253–258 (1993).

19. Gregory, R. and Mendelsohn, R. *Perceived Risk, Dread, and Benefits.* Risk Anal. **13**, 225–242 (1993).

20. Gardner, G. T. and Gould, L. C. *Public Perceptions of the Risk and Benefits of Technology.* Risk Anal. **9**, 225–242 (1989).

21. Flynn, J., Burns, W., Mertz, C. K. and Slovic, P. *Trust as a Determinant of Opposition to a High-level Radioactive Waste Repository: Analysis of a Structural Model.* Risk Anal. **12**, 417–429 (1992).

22. Frewer, J. J., Shepherd, R. and Howard, C. *What Factors Determine Trust in Information about Technological Hazards?* The Society for Risk Analysis: Annual Meeting, 1994.

23. Frewer, L. J., Shepherd, R. and Sparks, P. *Validation of Cultural Bias in the Context of Risk and Trust Perceptions Associated with Food-related Hazards.* Br. Psychol. Soc. Abstr. **2**, 42 (1993).

24. Slovic, P., Flynn, J. H. and Layman, M. *Perceived Risk, Trust, and the Politics of Nuclear Waste.* **254**, 1603–1607 (1991).

25. Freudenberg, W. R. *Risk and Reactancy: Weber, the Division of Labor, and the Rationality of Risk Perceptions.* Social Forces (1993).

26. Dunlap, R. E., Kraft, M. E. and Rosa, E. A. (Eds) *Public Reactions to Nuclear Waste.* (Durham: Duke University Press) (1993).

27. Sjöberg, L. and Drottz-Sjöberg, B.-M. *Risk Perception of Nuclear Waste: Experts and the Public* (Centre for Risk Research, Stockholm School of Economics) (1994).

28. Sandman, P. *Risk Communication: Facing Public Outrage.* US Environ. Prot. Agency J. **13**, 21–22 (1987).

29. Sandman, P. *Hazard versus Outrage in the Public Perception of Risk.* In: Effective Risk Communication, Ed. V. T. Covello (New York: Putnam Press) pp. 45–49 (1989).

30. Sandman, P. M. *Responding to Community Outrage: Strategies for Effective Risk Communication.* American Industrial Hygiene Association, Fairfax, VA (1993).

31. Gardner, G. T. and Stern, P. C. *Environmental Problems and Human Behavior* (Boston: Allyn and Bacon) (1996).

32. Douglas, M. and Wildavsky, A. *Risk and Culture* (University of California Press, Berkeley, CA) (1982).

33. Wildavsky, A. and Dake, K. *Theories of Risk Perception: Who Fears What and Why?* Daedalus **119**(4), 41–60 (1990).

34. Sjöberg, L. *Explaining Risk Perception: An Empirical and Quantitative Evaluation of Cultural Theory* (Centre for Risk Research: Stockholm) (1995).

35. Sjöberg, L. *Risk Perceptions by Politicians and the Public* (Centre for Risk Research: Stockholm) (1996).

36. Sjöberg, L. *The Risks of Risk Analysis* Acta Psychol. **45**, 301–321 (1980).

37. Zajonc, R. B. *Feeling and Thinking — Preferences need no Inferences.* Am. Psycol. **35**, 151–175 (1980).

38. Derbaix, C. and Sjöberg, L. *Movie Stars in Space: A Comparison of Preference and Similarity Judgments.* Int. J. Mark. Res. **11**, 261–274 (1994).

39. Sjöberg, L., Derbaix, C. and Jansson, B. *Preference and Similarity: Affective and Cognitive Judgment?* Scand. J. Psychol. **28**, 56–68 (1987).

Radiation Protection Dosimetry
Vol. 68, No. 3/4, pp. 227–230 (1996)
Nuclear Technology Publishing

FORMING HOMOGENEOUS CLUSTERS FOR DIFFERENTIAL RISK INFORMATION

B. Mårdberg
Swedish War College
PO Box 27 805
S-115 93 Stockholm, Sweden

Abstract — Latent risk situations are always present in society. General information on these risk situations is supposed to be received differently by different groups of people in the population. In the aftermath of specific accidents different groups presumably have need of specific information about how to act to survive, to avoid injuries, to find more information, to obtain facts about the accidents etc. As targets for information these different groups could be defined in different ways. The conventional way is to divide the population according to demographic variables, such as age, sex, occupation etc. Another way would be to structure the population according to dependent variables measured in different studies. They may concern risk perception, emotional reactions, specific technical knowledge of the accidents, and belief in the information sources. One procedure for forming such groupings of people into homogeneous clusters would be by statistical clustering methods on dependent variables. Examples of such clustering procedures are presented and discussed. Data are from a Norwegian study on the perception of radiation from nuclear accidents and other radiation sources. Speculations are made on different risk information strategies. Elements of a research programme are proposed.

INTRODUCTION

Latent (i.e. not manifest) risk situations are always present in society. Let us face some of them. Consider the risk situations in a community area shaped by chemical factories, dangerous goods transport, radiation at hospitals, locally active Chernobyl fallout etc. The radiation problems constitute some very specific risk situations perceived differently by different groups of a population. This is well known from psychological studies of the Chernobyl accident (see e.g. References 1 and 2). Our problem is to adapt information strategies to different risk perception patterns.

General information on these risk situations is supposed to be differently received by different groups of people in the population. In the aftermath of specific accidents people presumably have different needs of specific information about how to act to survive, to avoid injuries, to find more information, to obtain facts about the accidents etc. Identifying groups of people as targets for different risk information is therefore a prerequisite for effective risk communication.

A cluster analysis, defining patterns of reactions, is presented below as a basis for speculations on adaptive information strategies. The problem of relating patterns of cognitive and emotional responses to effective communication strategies is further identified as an important research area.

METHOD

As targets for information, different groups could be defined in different ways. The conventional way is to divide the population according to demographic variables, such as age, sex, occupation etc. Another way would be to structure the population according to dependent variables usually measured in different studies. They may concern risk perception, emotional reactions, specific technical knowledge connected with the accidents, and belief in the information sources. One procedure for forming such groupings of people into homogeneous clusters would be by statistical clustering methods on dependent variables.

Latent profile analysis[3] was used to generate clusters. A computer program[4–6] generates a number of 'best' solutions according to a criterion defined as discriminability (proportion of between-variance). The 'best' solution for eight indices is presented below. For the chosen solution five of eight clusters have statistically zero within-covariances (1%-level). Mean discriminability = 0.43, Wilks lambda = 0.020 and eta-square = 0.980. (Note that the clusters are forced not to overlap.)

AŃ EXAMPLE OF CLUSTERING BY LATENT PROFILE ANALYSIS

Data from the 1993 Norwegian study[7] of perception, motivation, coping, knowledge, and belief in information concerning radiation from nuclear accidents and other radiation sources illustrate the suggested methodology. In June 1993 a random sample was drawn from the Norwegian population stratified by counties and municipalities, i.e. of the Norwegian civilian adult population. The sample comprised a total of 1005 persons aged 15 to 90 years. There were 500 men and 505 women. The sampling procedure was designed by the Norsk Gallup Institutt. Personal interviews were carried out comprising a total of 145 specific questions. About 110 of these were of perceptual, attitudinal, and reaction types, i.e. dependent variables. For details on the sampling and the questionnaire setup see Tönnessen et al[7].

Indices were constructed by factor analysis and by the control for scale reliability (Cronbach's alpha). Twenty-one indices were identified.

Several analyses were performed on sets of indices to identify critical clusters as targets for differential risk information. The ten indices analysis included Locus of Control and Nature (Protection of) but these did not contribute well to the discrimination of the identified groups — probably due to low reliability coefficients, both alpha coefficients = 0.54. Finally, eight indices analysis was chosen for this presentation.

The indices used to define the clusters are presented below in terms of name and identifier, number of items (k) building up the index, reliability estimate, examples of items (those with better contribution to index reliability are chosen). Commonly the answering format is five categories, i.e. very low extent, rather low extent, rather great extent, very great extent, and don't know/no answer. Deviations from this format are indicated.

(1) *Understand*
Understanding factors connected to radiation fallout and accidents, e.g attention to reporting in media, information, knowledge etc.; k = 8, alpha = 0.73.

Examples of items:

How attentively do you follow reporting in the media on issues of radioactive contamination and nuclear power plant accidents?

How well do you know ways to find relevant information in case of a nuclear accident?

How good is your knowledge about how to protect yourself against radioactive fall out?

High values: understands, obtains (looks for) relevant information, has a good knowledge level.

(2) *Trust information*
Trust in information on radioactive contamination and nuclear accidents from politicians, media, and authorities; k = 8, alpha = 0.85.

Examples of items:

Please state to what extent you trust information on radioactive contamination and nuclear accidents from:

national politicians,
local media,
Radiation Protection Authorities,
Directorate of Health (now the Norwegian Board of Health).
experts/scientists.

Note: scale alternatives are 1 = very low extent; 2, 3, 4, 5, 6 = very great extent.

High values: High trust in information from politicians, media, and authorities.

(3) *Trust environmental (MILIEU) organisations*
Trust in antinuclear power and environmental organisations; k = 2, alpha = 0.86.

Example of items:

Please state to what extent you trust information on radioactive contamination and nuclear accidents from:

antinuclear power organisations,
environmental organisations.

'Note: scale alternatives are 1 = very low extent; 2, 3, 4, 5, 6 = very great extent.

High values: High trust in antinuclear power and environmental organisations.

(4) *Knowledge of radiation*
Sums items concerning knowledge about which radiation sources are stronger; k = 7, alpha = 0.77 (unweighted). This index is weighted according to the actual contribution of the sources, i.e. weight 7 for radon and 1 for fire alarm.

Example of items:

What sources do you think contribute the most in daily life to radiation?

radon,
radioactive fallout,
radiation at the place of work,
radiation in food.

High values: Good knowledge about which radiation sources are stronger.

(5) *Need for information*

and

(6) *Inform oneself*

are two indices comprising the same four (k = 4) questions applied to two different situations, i.e. the need for more information and whether you, during the last year, tried to keep yourself informed; alphas are 0.81 and 0.84, respectively.

Items:

Risk of injury to your health from radiation:
need for information,
keep informed.

Risk of nuclear accidents affecting Norway:
need for information,
keep informed.

What levels of preparation do authorities have regarding nuclear accidents:
need for information,
keep informed.

Things I have to do:
need for information,
keep informed.

Note: Evaluated as 1 = yes; 0 = anything else.

(7) *Motivation*

This index deals with concern about radiation issues being important and the risk of accidents in the future; k = 6, alpha = 0.64.

Examples of items:

What do you think is the risk of a new nuclear accident in the next ten years bringing radiation fallout to Norway?

What do you think is the risk of a new nuclear accident in the next ten years bringing radiation fallout to the district where you live?

How concerned are you with the issue of radioactive contamination and nuclear accidents in your daily life?

High values: Concern.

(8) *Coping*

Measures coping by items on preparedness; k = 3, alpha = 0.58.

Examples of items:

How well prepared are you for problems caused by nuclear accidents?

I am well prepared to tackle a nuclear crisis situation.

Note: Last item is evaluated as 1 agree completely, and 2, 3, 4, 5, 6 disagree completely.

High values: 'I am prepared', 'I am well equipped', authorities well equipped.

Table 1 summarises the output from the latent profile analyses. It shows the standardised observed profiles (generated from the latent ones by classification to the nearest profile). The scales are in z-scores.

The first profile relative to the total means is noted for negative responses in *Understand, Trust in environment organisations, Knowledge of radiation, Need for information, Inform oneself,* and *Coping.* The 82 people in this group have a low level of understanding (radiation) and do not search for information about radiation, do not trust environmental organisations, do not have good actual knowledge on radiation, do not keep themselves informed, do not think radiation is an actuality. Especially, they do not need more information (they say).

Profile 2 is noted especially for their good actual knowledge about radiation. They trust environmental organisations but not politicians, authorities, or media. They express a need for information, keep themselves informed, and think that radiation issues are important questions. N = 63.

The 113 people in Profile 3 judge that they are well prepared and that they and authorities are well equipped. They express high understanding, trust information, have a low need for information but keep themselves informed.

Profile 4 (N = 239) is an average group with some negative signs, i.e. do not trust environmental organisations, have low understanding, do not keep themselves informed and do not think radiation problems are important.

Profile 5 (N = 102) is especially noted for keeping themselves informed. They have a good understanding level (according to themselves), do not trust information, but have some need for information. Radiation is an important matter.

Table 1. Result of latent profile analysis. Categorised z-scores.

Variable	Profile								d(2)
	1	2	3	4	5	6	7	8	
1. Understand	−		++		+	+	− −	−	0.42
2. Trust information		−	+		−	+	− − −	+	0.38
3. Trust milieu	−	+		−		+		+	0.42
4. Knowledge of radiation	−	++++		(−)					0.46
5. Need for information	− − − −	+	−		(+)		+		0.55
6. Inform oneself	−	+ (+)	+	−	++		−	−	0.45
7. Motivation	−	+ (+)		−	+	+	++	−	0.37
8. Coping			+++				−	(−)	0.44
Number of individuals	82	63	113	239	102	224	50	132	$\bar{d}(2)$ = 0.43

d(2) is discriminability defined as the proportion of between-variance.
Plus and minus have the following meaning:

+ or −	> + or − 0.40
++ or − −	> + or − 1.00
+++ or − − −	> + or − 1.50
++++ or − − − −	> + or − 2.00
( ) means 'almost'	

The large Profile 6 (N = 224) is an average group with positive signs. Good understanding level, trust information and environmental organisations and think radiation is an important issue.

Profile 7 has a relatively low understanding level and people do not trust information. They express a need for information, but do not keep themselves informed. They think radiation issues are important but do not regard themselves to be well equipped. N = 50.

Profile 8 has a low understanding level, trust both information and environmental organisations. They do not keep themselves informed and judge the radiation problems as less important. They have a low coping level. N = 132.

DISCUSSION

Let us speculate on some information strategies in relation to the clusters defined for the 1993 data of the Norwegian survey.

Take Profile 2, with people who do not trust information but have a high knowledge level for radiation problems (according to themselves) and think that radiation is an important question. We would probably not let official people inform them on facts and risks in an accident — they would inform themselves.

What about Profile 3, they understand a lot, trust information, have a very good coping level themselves and look for information. How should they be informed? And Profile 5 with a similar profile concerning understanding and informing themselves but with low trust in official information, higher motivation and medium coping strategies. Could any one of them be used in information work for other people?

An interesting cluster is number 7. People in this group do not understand nor do they trust information nor inform themselves. They are not prepared for radiation accidents, all indicating a passive attitude, but they declare that they need information and judge the radiation sector an important one. The strategy should, maybe, be to activate them to study and search for information from experts, scientists, newspapers etc.

Differential risk information may concern both general and specific information. Examples of general information are facts about an accident — what really did happen? — and advice concerning protection for all people. Examples of specific information are locally developed risk patterns and radio alarms to threatened areas. A psychological assumption is that there are variations among people as to what information is perceived and received. One would expect that people with high arousal should first be informed on positive aspects of the situation to calm them in order to be able to receive information on facts. Low arousal people, on the other hand, are eager to catch facts directly about the situation and risk development in order to decide about how to act and presumably search for more information. Depending on the complexity of the result of the clustering procedure, i.e. the number of clusters and the dimensionality of the data set (number of latent dimensions of the manifest variables), and the possibilities for interpreting the clusters, different information strategies could be defined.

In fact, the needs for both general and specific information in threat situations indicate the need for the development of psychological models of information strategies. These would constitute the basis for information structures for authorities.

Information strategies should be anchored in psychological theory on perceiving, receiving, and assimilating/accommodating facts, advice/counselling and attitudes on emotionally loaded risk and catastrophe situations.

There is a great need for research in this area. The crucial steps of research advances in the area should be to:

(i) define critical sub-groups in terms of dependent variables, e.g. perception, reactions and knowledge;

(ii) define psychological models for perceiving and receiving facts in threatening situations and during accidents (please let me know if there are such models);

(iii) develop general and specific strategies for differential risk information (differential in relation to sub-groups defined by both independent and dependent variables).

REFERENCES

1. Drottz-Sjöberg, B.-M. and Sjöberg, L. *Risk Perception and Worries after the Chernobyl Accident.* J. Environ. Psychol. **10**, 135–149 (1990).

2. Renn, O. *Public Responses to the Chernobyl Accident.* J. Environ. Psychol. **10**, 151–167 (1990).

3. Gibson, A. W. *Three Multivariate Models: Factor Analysis, Latent Structure Analysis and Latent Profile Analysis.* Psychometrika **24**, 229–252 (1959).

4. Mårdberg, B. *LPA2 (A Clustering Program) Program Description. A Computer Program for Green's Solution of Latent Class Analysis Applied to Latent Profile Analysis.* Forskning fra Psykologisk Institutt i Bergen, Report No 2 (1974).

5. Mårdberg, B. *LPA2: A FORTRAN V Computer Program for Green's Solution of Latent Class Analysis Applied to Latent Profile Analysis.* Educ. Psychol. Meas. **35**, 163–166 (1975).

6. Mårdberg, B. *Monte Carlo Experiments for Evaluating Classification with Latent Profile Analysis.* Institute of Psychology, University of Bergen, Report No 4 (1975).

7. Tönnessen, A., Reitan, J. B., Strand, P., Waldahl, R. and Weiseath, L. *Interpretation of Radiation Risk by the Norwegian Population: A National Survey in 1993.* In: Biomedical and Psychosocial Consequences of Radiation from Man-made Radionucleides in the Biosphere. Ed. G. Sundnes (Trondheim: Tapir) pp. 251–278 (1993).

Radiation Protection Dosimetry
Vol. 68, No. 3/4, pp. 231–233 (1996)
Nuclear Technology Publishing

SOME REFLECTIONS ON ANTHROPOLOGY OF THE RISK OF RADIATION

D. Van Nuffelen
Radiation Protection Service
Cité Administrative de l'Etat, Quartier Vésale
B-1010 Brussels, Belgium

Abstract — Since any scientific result is, in the view of K. Popper, nothing else but a provisional truth, it is idle and unintelligent to claim that any given model is the best. This point correctly understood, it is true that some models are closer to reality than others, mainly because they are not sectarian, and as they are open to this reality which always partly escapes us, they reflect it better despite their implacable weaknesses. Man has to face the reality that involves radiological risk. The scientific study of man, anthropology, cannot confine it to a reductive and unilateral paradigm. Rather than taking the easy and wrong way by reducing man's part solely to the answers to an artificial questionnaire, social scientists have to question man's condition; and the human condition cannot be brought into scale. This paper examines these problems through the way various human groups define and treat the nuclear dangers.

INTRODUCTION

Anthropology of risk deals with the way human societies define and treat dangers. In the present state of knowledge, we know that each society, each culture and each sub-culture probably has its own system of thought and practice for recognising what are the dangers, for deciding which risks may be taken and which may not, for reducing or avoiding certain hazards, and so on. Such issues may be very different from one case to another. This difficulty leads scientists to pose two fundamental questions. What are the differences and why do they occur? In addition, what is common to all the observations, in other words, is it possible to build a general theory on the way *Homo sapiens* defines and treats risks he is faced with? This paper examines several empirical data resulting from many observations and field surveys. A short explanation is attempted, according to the cultural theory on risk selection and the social theory on risk construction. Note that, even if we deal with numerous ethnological and sociological data, any theory on anthropology of risk is nothing else but a given model of reality: as Karl Popper said, a provisional truth.

SOCIO-CULTURAL RISK CONSTRUCTION

It seems that a social and cultural construction of risks is used in each human society. The selection and definition of risks depend upon the socio-cultural system that gives them sense. To understand this point, let us have a look at the Hima. The Hima are nomadic cattle-herding people of Uganda. One of their fundamental beliefs is that women should be kept completely apart from cattle. They consider that contamination by contact with women causes cattle to sicken and die. This cultural rule frees women from work, which may seriously affect the survival chances of the community[1]. Accord-

ing to our scientific culture, the Hima curiously seem to prefer a symbolic definition of risk to an objective one. For them, however, this definition of risk is so deeply embedded in the way they conceive the world and existence that it appears as a quite normal, a quite natural, a quite rational representation. A deeper analysis shows here what we call a pollution belief. Such a belief justifies the social rules and the cultural habits of the community. In other words, it permits the Hima to preserve their social and cultural organisation and their segregationist relationships with a neighbouring ethnic group, the Iru.

This example shows how a risk may be a complex social construction of reality. If you know that a nomadic cattle-herding community is one of the simplest forms of society, you have an idea of the complexity of social construction of radiological risk in our civilisation. This example is also interesting in understanding the selection of risks. The Hima have selected a risk of contamination of the cattle by contact with women. Their neighbours, the Iru, have not. Consequently, in a similar territory, different societies may select different risks. In other countries, it must also be pointed out that different cultures promote a different selection from a similar range of dangers.

Now, what about us, moderns? In our modern post-industrial societies, many studies show that perceptions of risk vary with the institutional structures. According to several results from factor analysis, organisations in which group adherence is low and individual liberty high, promote venturing. Those in a group in which adherence is high and individual liberty high, condemn risks. When group adherence is low and individual liberty low, risks are regarded as fatalities. When group adherence is high and individual liberty low, risks are avoided[2]. Here, one must stress that, if this kind of study uses scientifically acceptable methods and techniques, the terms in comparison — high or low group adherence and individual liberty — do not seem always quite objective. The definition of such terms may vary with the research worker's own culture or experience. The organisations in which these elements are expected to be measured may be sociologically different from one situation to another. Just one example: in the United States of America, ecological associations — very often quite antinuclear — promote a high group adherence and a high individual liberty. In this country, antinuclear movements represent a very decentralised power. The main peculiarity of these organisations is sectarianism. For the members of such organisations, the struggle against radiological risk is a kind of religion. On the other hand, in the nuclear industry, you may find societies with high group adherence and also individual liberty. Nuclear energy is a symbol of modernity: it is sometimes a form of honour to work in such facilities: but it is hard to believe that nuclear industry condemns radiological risk as do antinuclear movements.

According to other studies, risks are very often perceived as everyday life disturbances. Thus social groups try to preserve their styles of living in refusing the implantation of nuclear facilities (the well known NIMBY effect), or else, when they live near the nuclear facility, in rendering its dangers commonplace or denying them[3]. In this sense, note that moderns are not very different from the Hima. When human beings try to give any signification to one given risk, they necessarily refer to the socio-cultural selection and construction their social group is making of it. Here two cultural biases appear. The first occurs while recognising the risk itself, which depends on the socialisation process. The second is generated by the necessity to preserve the socialised normal way of life, which implies a set of behaviours always related to social rules and values.

Consequently, it seems clear that perception of radiological risk is a social and cultural process. We may consider radiological risk itself as a societal fact. Not only because it is culturally selected and socially constructed, but also because it occurs in human society, it concerns human knowledge and human activity, it is related to our beliefs and practices: in other words, it represents what we call a problem of society. Furthermore, perceptions of risk depend on certain historical, political and economic conditions. The social idea of a danger related to ionising radiations appeared with Hiroshima/Nagasaki and has grown since the seventies with antinuclear movements and radiological accidents. In trade, however, some people still did not perceive the dangers of nuclear energy: the famous bikini was supposed to make women 'atomic bombs of sex appeal'[4]. All that shows how much the selections and the constructions of radiological risk form a very complex and dynamic sub-system included in our social system.

TECHNOLOGICAL RISKS

Nowadays, nuclear energy is more and more regarded as a major technological risk, representing a threat for great populations and territories, eliminating the boundaries of space and time[5]. Such a risk poses very interesting anthropological questions. One is the growing intervention of the techno-scientific actor in choices of society and the reducing control of the lay citizen over these choices. Is the ordinary man doomed to be more and more ignorant of nuclear knowledge and technology? Must he powerlessly undergo its positive and negative effects without giving his advice? Is he a primitive, a savage or a mental cripple when his thoughts and interrogations are not recognised nor understood by the nuclear establishment? From the anthropologist's point of view, the coexistence of different systems of thought and practice is a normal phenomenon in any complex society. For him, the question is not to separate out what is true and what is wrong in all these perceptions. Contrary to psychologists, the anthropologist may not speak about 'misperceptions' of radiological risk. His problem is to understand how society maintains enough cohesion to go on without too much trouble, and, possibly, to imagine what could be done to improve such a cohesion.

COSMOLOGIES AND COSMOGONIES

Another interesting question is the fact that radiological dangers touch human lineage. According to social and cultural representations, it means that mankind is threatened. This relationship between an important danger and mankind seems universal[6]. Such is the case in the relationship between radiological risk and human gestation. Indeed, it is not a rare occurrence that wives of nuclear workers and women living near a nuclear facility fear that they might give birth to monsters or become barren[3]. In fact, all human societies use systems of thought, belief, technique and practice to protect their descendants. Such systems most often organise relationships between sacred and profane things. This field of research leads to a study of what we call cosmologies and cosmogonies. In anthropology, cosmology is a set of theories, knowledge and beliefs used by a given culture to explain the universe, the world and existence. Cosmogony concerns more precisely the origins of these topics, in particular the birth of mankind. When they are shared by the members of a community, these semiological systems justify the social organisation. Because they provide a common signification to the social order, such systems must be preserved. It is probably the main function of the sacred, in this case, to protect social structure against risks. And it is probably the reason why, most often, sacred rituals and beliefs are used in human societies for giving a sense and a protection to the conception, the gestation and the parturition of human beings. For any given society, the survival of the descendants is a capital question. In this sense, human embryonic radioprotection may be explained as a particular modern form for protecting human descent[6]. In this sense too, we may have a better understanding of the social reactions against the storage of long-life nuclear wastes.

So, very deeply rooted anthropological constructions of reality — such as cosmologies and cosmogonies — may be related to radiological risk. Such constructions always deal with the most fundamental question posed by any human culture: the meaning of existence. They are based on what we call the 'thanatic fact' (from Greek thanatos, death), in other words the cognition of the finite duration of being. Consequently we may suppose that there are very deep relationships between the representations of radiological risk and these of death. Many observations may be explained by this approach. Social groups generally associate nuclear energy with the atomic bomb. Indeed, for many people, this form of energy is associated with a picture of mass destruction. It seems hard to delete the image of nuclear death. Problems may appear when it becomes too obviously incomprehensible for the members of a social group, in other words when their culture is no longer able to justify it. That was observed among the survivors of Hiroshima and Nagasaki, whose cosmological references were destroyed.

Another interesting question is the fact that radiological nuisances are sometimes described as punishments resulting from a too abnormal or amoral human activity. That is, all the problem of wickedness associated with the 'terrae incognitae'[2]. Even if many scientists and technicians commonly claim that the nuclear industry is very safe — which it probably is — some aspects of radiological risk are still unknown (for instance, biological risk effects of low doses on human beings, actual consequences of theoretically possible serious accidents). In such a context of uncertainty, many individuals willingly use myths and rites to conjure dangers. That is also observed in nuclear facilities. According to the cultural groups they belong to, nuclear workers may be divided into two sets: the 'rentiers' and the 'kamikazes'. The rentiers consider radioactivity as a contamination resulting from a contact with an impure thing. They try to 'preserve' themselves from ionising radiations. The kamikazes think that irradiation is a vital radiation capable of giving them strength and warmth. For them, 'receiving doses' is a kind of social value[3]. Here again, as you can see, the members of social groups always try to reduce the uncertainties they face by applying systems of thought and practice their culture or sub-culture considers as socially acceptable. What is acceptable in one group may be unacceptable in another. What is acceptable or not may be so deeply socialised that people do not have any awareness of the selection process. But that is not the question. What we have to do is, firstly, to recognise that radiological risk is selected and constructed, then, to study how this selection and this construction work. It is, it seems, the only way to maintain cohesion between the different social groups, particularly to maintain a semantic cohesion between us, scientists, and them, the so-called lay people.

CONCLUSION

The way human beings define and treat nuclear risks can be understood by an anthropological approach. That way is indeed related to deep sociocultural constructions of reality, as cosmologies and cosmogonies. Some so-called irrational attitudes and misperceptions can thus be seen as quite normal reactions when the context in which they occur is well grasped. Even 'strange' behaviours and beliefs observed[3] among certain workers in nuclear facilities are explained by this approach. Finally, the actor of radiological risk is nothing else but *Homo sapiens*, rooted in his social and cultural constructions of reality.

REFERENCES

1. Douglas, M and Wildavsky, A. *Risk and Culture. An Essay on the Selection of Technological and Environmental Dangers* (Berkeley Los Angeles: University of California Press) (1983).

2. Duclos, D. *La Peur et le Savior. La Société face à la Science, la Technique et leurs Dangers.* (Paris: La Découverte) (1989).

3. Zonabend, F. *La presqu'île au Nucléaire* (Paris: Odile Jacob) (1989).

4. Lecerf, Y. and Parker, E. *L'Affaire Tchernobyl. La Guerre des Rumeurs* (Paris, Presses Universitaires de France) (1987).

5. Lagadec, P. *La Civilisation du Risque. Catastrophes Technologiques et Responsabilité Sociale.* (Paris: Seuil) (1981).

6. Van Nuffelen, D. *Aspects Anthropologiques de la Radioprotection de l'Embryon* (Bruxelles: Service de Protection contre les Radiations Ionisantes) (1993).

Radiation Protection Dosimetry
Vol. 68, No. 3/4, pp. 235–238 (1996)
Nuclear Technology Publishing

THE NORWEGIAN PUBLIC'S PERCEPTION OF RISK FROM ELECTROMAGNETIC FIELDS

M. B. Maerli
Norwegian Radiation Protection Authority
PO Box 55, N-1345 Osteraas, Norway

Abstract — A survey with a representative sample of the adult Norwegian population reveals that the public is concerned about the health effects of electromagnetic fields; almost 2/3 of the population regard health effects as a likely consequence if exposed, the level of exposure is regarded as higher today than previously, and a clear majority now consider the fields to be more dangerous than they formerly believed. Despite this general concern, fewer consider personal effects to be probable; approximately one of six reports concern for personal injuries due to the fields. Further, the reported will to act in situations of known exposure from a (hypothetical) power line nearby is high, either by gathering information or putting up shielding against the fields. More concerned parts of the public also show a more committed engagement, including a higher willingness to make economic sacrifices for limiting the fields. There are special features of risk perception across the sample, and gender differences are particularly prominent. Women regard health effects more probable, and respond more strongly to situations of known exposure. People living near to power lines seem to be more aware of the fields, but at the same time cancer is regarded less probable by this group.

INTRODUCTION

Most of the recent research on the health effects of electromagnetic fields has been related to physiological and epidemiological aspects; the impact of electromagnetic fields on organisms, organs and cells has been the main issue in the search for possible health effects. Any emphasis on possible psychological aspects has, to a large extent, been related to different afflictions, e.g. depression or lack of ability to concentrate etc. Common reactions in the public due to known or presumed exposure to electromagnetic fields often seems omitted in scientific work. In March 1994 a survey was conducted to gain insight into these matters. A representative sample of 1014 Norwegians above 15 years of age were questioned on their opinion about electromagnetic fields and assumed health effects. The survey was carried out by personal interviews. This article presents the main findings from the survey. A complete review is presented elsewhere[1].

The framing of the survey inevitably influences some of the answers given. However, minimising such a bias was an important aim while preparing the questions, and the questionnaire in general. The generalisation from findings in a representative sample to presumed occurrences in the population poses additional uncertainties. The uncertainty of the numbers presented is dependent on the total number of people in the sample and the number of observations in each category of answers. At a 95% confidence level, the 'true' value in the population for a given percentage of observations and N = 1014 will be within approximately twice the range of the standard deviation given in Table 1.

FEAR OF HEALTH EFFECTS

The public is concerned about the health effects of electromagnetic fields. Approximately two thirds of the sample consider health effects to be probable due to exposure, and three quarters regard the fields as being more dangerous than they formerly believed. A clear majority also consider the levels of exposure to be higher than previously. Even though there is a high level of concern about possible health effects, fewer (approximately one out of six persons) find it probable personally to be affected by such health consequences (Table 2).

Despite a *general* concern, a majority still regard *personal* health effects as rather unlikely, and thus report a low level of 'daily concern' when it comes to these matters. Nevertheless as much as 10% of the sample regard it as highly probable or rather probable that they will be affected by the electromagnetic fields and report a 'daily concern'.

ASSUMED HEALTH EFFECTS

People regarding health effects as probable, were asked to quote the effect they assumed most likely to occur. The answers represented a broad range of proposed diseases, but with cancer clearly causing the highest concern. While 41% regard cancer as the most probable effect, other genotoxic injuries as, for instance, genetic malformation, were almost omitted in the answers. Approximately 17% assume more psychosomatically related illnesses, such as stress and insomnia, to be the result of the exposure, while somatic sufferings other than cancer, e.g. reduced immunity and rheumatism, are regarded the least probable types of illnesses arising from exposure from electromagnetic fields.

The findings also reveal a high level of insecurity, both when it comes to the probability for health effects, and the kind of effects likely to occur. Even among those regarding health effects as probable, as many as a third state that they do not know the kind of effects to be expected. A plausible explanation might be unknown mechanisms of possible impact on human health. The fields can thus easily be regarded as a possible cause for a wide variety of more or less 'obscure' suffering, without distinct origins.

REACTIONS

Electromagnetic fields are considered a lesser problem than ionising radiation or severe chemical pollution; but reported reactions due to known electromagnetic exposure are extensive. On a life event impact scale[2], exposure to electromagnetic field is ranked only slightly below situations involving physical suffering. The strong opposition to power lines in the local environment also clearly reflects this; 75% of those questioned will oppose the building of lines, and possible health effects is the main argument. Almost 80% oppose building on this basis, while only 3% are against building because of economic reasons and possible loss of value of property. However, while interpreting these results, one should bear in mind that health effects are probably a more 'legitimate' reason for opposition than purely financial or aesthetic considerations.

In situations involving known exposure to electromagnetic fields, most of the public report trying to influence the situation either by gathering information or putting up shielding against the fields from a (hypothetical) power line. More concerned persons also show a more committed engagement. In general, almost

half of the persons in the sample would consider moving house if exposed to electromagnetic fields from a newly built power line in the neighbourhood. The willingness to pay for reducing the level of exposure is also high, and again, higher electricity bills due to shielding and use of ground cables is more readily accepted among the more concerned persons. Almost 60% report that they would accept a quarterly increase up to 500 NOK (approx. 62 ECU) on electricity expenses for burying the power lines in the ground, thus at least reducing the exposure at greater distances.

KNOWLEDGE AND INFORMATION

Even though 80% of the sample report that they previously have seen, read or heard information about electromagnetic fields, the general level of knowledge is low. Different statements presented to the respondents about electromagnetic fields and possible health effects revealed this in particular. Even though the public generally overestimates the risk of cancer, very few have knowledge of the on-going (epidemiological) research in this field. Further on, the use of ground cables is also proposed as an important remedial action, but the actual effects of the cables are unknown to many.

The media, and in particular television, are the main sources of information about electromagnetic fields and possible health effects. As media are the most important channels of information, this indicates that the public only gather information on their own initiative to a lim-

Table 1. Standard derivation (SD) and margins of uncertainty at 95% confidence level, as a function of number observations in each category of answers for a representative sample of N = 1014 persons.

	Observations (%)					
	5 (95)	10 (90)	20 (80)	30 (70)	40 (60)	50 (50)
SD (%)	0.7	0.9	1.3	1.4	1.5	1.6
±1.96 SD (%)	±1.3	±1.8	±2.5	±2.8	±3.0	±3.1

Table 2. Presumed possibility for personal effects and reported concern due to exposure from electromagnetic fields. Percentages. N = 1014.

	Presumed possibility for personal effects					
	High	Rather high	Rather small	Very small	Don't know	Total (%)
Daily very concerned	1	2	1	0	0	4
Daily rather concerned	1	6	8	2	3	20
Daily less concerned	0	8	35	25	8	76
Total (%)	2	16	44	27	11	100

ited extent (partly contrasting with reported behaviour in situations of known exposure). Again there is a connection between the level of concern and involvement. Those less concerned, and those reporting a lower level of understanding regarding these matters, also report that they have fewer sources of information. At the same time we find that individuals reporting to be 'uninformed' do tend to have a lower level of education. All-in-all this indicates individual processes for selection of 'relevant' information about electromagnetic fields and possible health effects; types of information, and probably partly channels of information, are selected in accordance with expected gratifications and needs. Different sources of information are also evaluated in different ways. 'Competent' and 'independent' sources are regarded as more credible. Scientists and experts are thus reported to be well trusted by many in this matter. Representatives of local power plants as well as the media and environmental organisations are regarded as less trustworthy than the scientists. At the lower end, politicians, together with neighbours, family and friends, are considered the least reliable when it comes to questions involving exposure from electromagnetic fields.

SOURCES OF ANXIETY

A comparison of various sources of radiation and fields reveals profound differences in the public perception of the risk associated with the sources. Radioactive sources are clearly regarded most risky. While a majority report fear of radioactive waste and radioactive fallout in particular, only a fraction regard electric devices, microwave ovens or computer screens as harmful (Table 3).

Power lines, radon, and to some extent ultraviolet radiation, cause rather similar levels of anxiety. Approximately a third of the sample report that they are highly or rather frightened by these sources, while about the same number report not being frightened, or frightened to some extent. This simple comparison might indicate the importance of 'confirmed' exposure and

risk, e.g. the atomic bombs, and the harmful effects of radiation demonstrated during the last part of this century. The fear of the possible effects of nuclear accidents is often additionally strengthened by dramatic presentations in the media. In Norway radon is, on average, the most important single source of doses from ionising radiation. As the odourless and invisible gas is naturally occurring this seem to generate less concern than other sources of radioactivity, also indicating the importance of the 'unknowingness' of exposure. 'Confirmed' exposure from electromagnetic fields clearly causes more concern than 'unconfirmed' exposure. Electromagnetic fields from power lines, probably due to their massive and threatening appearance, are thus the main concern even though major parts of the Norwegian public are well aware of the electromagnetic fields surrounding electric devices in homes. Voluntariness, daily use and the feeling of higher personal control of the exposure are probably important keywords in this context.

VARIATIONS IN THE PERCEPTION

The sample is no 'homogeneous mass' when it comes to the perception of risk from electromagnetic fields, partly due to rather profound gender differences. Women regard health effects due to exposure from electromagnetic fields as more probable than men do. This tendency becomes more pronounced with education. While men with higher levels of education regard health effects less probable than men with primary and lower secondary school, the opposite effect takes place among well educated women (Table 4). Women at the university level seem to regard effects as particularly probable. Another interesting feature is the sharp decrease in the number of well educated women being insecure in these matters, as compared to the ones with lower education.

Women also respond more strongly to situations of known exposure and are more active than men at limiting the exposure, despite men reporting a more 'problem solving' attitude in general. Higher engagement can also be seen as women generally accept higher economic sacrifices to avoid the fields. Confronted with the

Table 3. Reported anxiety for different sources of radiation and fields. Percentages. N = 1014.

	Very frightened	Rather frightened	A bit frightened	Not frightened	Don't know	Total (%)
Radioactive fallout	57	24	13	5	1	100
Radioactive waste	46	27	16	10	1	100
Power lines	10	19	34	34	3	100
Radon	10	14	30	39	7	100
UV	8	20	42	27	3	100
X rays	5	9	33	51	2	100
Computer screens	3	7	27	59	4	100
Electric devices	3	5	26	64	2	100
Microwave ovens	3	5	23	64	5	100

mentioned statements about electromagnetic fields, men, and in particular men with higher education, responded more correctly, indicating a higher level of knowledge about the fields and present status of the research performed. Men also report having more sources of information: moreover, these sources seem to be 'evaluated' more critically by men. Sources of information with lower credibility in these matters, for instance neighbours and friends, are more readily 'accepted' by women, probably due to a higher interest on a daily basis.

Adults between 30 and 44 years of age are the most concerned about possible health effects. Child care could be an important factor, as we find the highest number of parents in this age group. Those between 15 and 29 years of age are least concerned and thus less active in situations of known exposure, as compared to the rest of the various age groups.

The part of the public living near to power lines also shows some special features as compared to the rest. These people consider it somewhat more probable to be personally harmed by health effects and report a slightly higher level of 'daily concern' when it comes to these matters. At the same time cancer is regarded as a less probable health effect. There seems thus to be a 'duality' in the risk perception among this group: being more 'aware' of the fields on the one hand, and simultaneously perhaps more eager to 'minimise' the risk of cancer, possibly to maintain a psychological 'defence' against the threat of electromagnetic fields. Alternatively, personal experience of living near the lines without particular problems during longer periods of time, could also influence the attitudes in a more 'positive' manner, as compared to the general perception of risk from electromagnetic fields. Or, people more concerned with health effects might have moved away from the power lines. The survey also reveals a higher willingness to buy new houses adjacent to power lines by people already living in houses neighbouring existing lines. This group of people do not, however, accept the same level of monthly economic sacrifices to get existing power lines into the ground, probably due to the prospects of a genuine increase in expenditure.

CONCLUSION

This study shows that the concern for health effects in general due to exposure from electromagnetic fields is high, while the public is less concerned with personal injuries due to the fields. Still, the presence or possible presence of electromagnetic fields might induce mental strain on parts of the public, as a significant part do report concern on a daily basis. In situations of known exposure reported reactions are extensive, both when it comes to protective actions and actions involving personal education. Women react more strongly, concordant with a higher level of anxiety for health effects, while the special features among the population living along power lines may reflect their 'adaptation' to living with a possible threat.

ACKNOWLEDGEMENT

The author would like to thank Dr philos. G. Thommesen at the Norwegian Radiation Protection Authority and Professor R. Waldahl at the Department of Media and Communication, University of Oslo, for useful comments while preparing this paper.

Table 4. Responses to the question 'Do you regard health effects probable due to the exposure from electromagnetic fields', among men and women with different levels of education. Percentages. N = 1013.

	Men			Women		
	Primary and lower secondary	Upper secondary	Higher	Primary and lower secondary	Upper secondary	Higher
Yes	56	65	59	63	64	80
No	17	17	23	8	7	8
Don't know	28	17	18	29	29	12
Total (%)	100	99*	100	100	100	100
N	127	247	128	151	272	88

*Value due to rounding off.

REFERENCES

1. Maerli, M. B. *Perception of Risk from Electromagnetic Fields*, Report No 15 (in Norwegian) (Department of Media and Communication, University of Oslo) (1995).
2. Atkinson, R. *et al. Introduction to Psychology.* (New York: Harcourt Brace Jovanovich College Publishers) (1993).

Radiation Protection Dosimetry
Vol. 68, No. 3/4, pp. 239–243 (1996)
Nuclear Technology Publishing

CULTURAL THEORY AND RISK PERCEPTION: VALIDITY AND UTILITY EXPLORED IN THE FRENCH CONTEXT

J. Brenot, S. Bonnefous and C. Mays
Institut de Protection et de Sûreté Nucléaire
Département de Protection de la Santé de l'Homme et de Dosimétrie
Laboratoire de Statistique et d'Etudes Economiques et Sociales
BP 6, F-92265 Fontenay aux Roses Cedex, France

Abstract — Explaining perceived risk can draw upon factors related to the person (e.g. demographics, personality, social/professional status, political orientation), or to the risk source (e.g. health impacts, economic effects). According to Cultural Theory risk perceptions are culturally biased. Wildavsky and Dake operationalised the Cultural Theory with questionnaire scales and found that resulting 'cultural profiles' best predict individual differences in risk perception. A French version of their questionnaire was inserted into a representative national risk opinion survey of May 1993; 1022 adults (age 18 and over) were interviewed. Major results are presented. The four cultural scales (hierarchy, egalitarianism, fatalism and individualism) show high correlations with political orientation as expected, but also with, for example, age, gender, income and education level. However, scale relationships to perceptions of risk situations (twenty, mainly technological) are not as strong as expected. Sjöberg found similar results in Sweden. The utility of the existing operationalisation of Cultural Theory for risk perception analysis is discussed.

INTRODUCTION

From individual descriptors to referentials

Sociological surveys commonly measure a number of individual characteristics, typically gender, age, area and demographic type of residence, occupation, income, educational level and orientation, and sometimes leisure habits. A cultural level is approached with items investigating political orientation, religious belief and, sometimes, level of concern expressed for societal or environmental issues. Such questions are usually received as clear and appropriate by respondents, and they allow individuals to be sorted into homogeneous groups for analysis of their replies to other opinion or behavioural measures. Because such personal characteristics are superficial traits, and offer little leverage for analysis of, for example, ideological influences on response, sociologists have developed analytic tools often called referentials.

A referential is a set of questions designed and validated to rank respondents on universal scales of psychosocial descriptors, or to sort respondents into sociological types. When properly validated, referentials can allow researchers to infer other behavioural characteristics of their respondents. When individuals' scale responses are similar, or when they belong to a same type, it may be infered that they have a same system of values or share a specific lifestyle, characteristics that may shed light on why they respond in a certain way to other study topics.

The questions included in the construction of a referential reflect sociologists' own theoretical representations of social dynamics. Some five referentials are commonly in use in France for sociological investigation, market research, etc. (see, e.g. Ref. 1). They generally are derived by factor analytic techniques. Thus such dimensions as 'preference for movement/for stability' or 'compromise/dramatisation' appear to structure peoples' opinions on societal conflict[2].

Culture as a concept for risk research

Referentials represent an attempt to identify and describe systematic links among persons that may contribute to interpreting their agreement, or lack of agreement, on survey attitude statements. The notion of culture is also one that represents an attempt to grasp what links individuals. 'Culture' is commonly understood as a determinant of how an individual views the world, interprets events, values or rejects. World views and ways of life should not, from this viewpoint, be considered as purely individual or familial, but reflect in some way belongingness to a social system which is reinforced and maintained by this participation. Culture would have its own modes of influence on the individual, relying upon our biological and psychological make-up, but distinct from the processes implied there.

A use of the concept of culture current in the nuclear world is that of 'safety culture'[3], suggesting that there exists a shared set of 'characteristics and attitudes' relating to safety in the nuclear installation which is the workplace. These are distinct from purely personal characteristics and atttiudes. It would then be possible to identify elements of this culture and develop, in a concerted way, appropriate attitudes and practices which if adhered to would maximise worker and installation safety[4].

Anthropological approaches treat culture as a more extensive system of observable practices and infered cosmology or worldview. One anthropological theorisation of culture has become of interest in recent years to risk researchers. Anthropologist Douglas and sociologist Wildavsky[5] developed a theoretical typology distinguishing social groups according to their values on the three issues of freedom, order and purity. Work in this stream[6] has attempted to define factors that prompt individuals to focus on particular risks and neglect others. Risk perceptions are held to reflect the way in which society itself is perceived; alternative views about risks (and about the world in general) flow from patterns of social order. According to so-called Cultural theorists, health and economic impacts of risk sources (as in a technical assessment approach to risk) or characteristics of risk information (as in a psychological approach to risk perception), are poor indicators. Indeed they take on relevance only within contexts of shared group views and lifestyles.

The Cultural Theory of risk attempts to describe the influence of established patterns of social relationships upon perceptions and behaviours. Social relations are seen to be characterised by four distinct patterns: egalitarianism, fatalism, individualism and hierarchy. Each pattern gives rise to a distinct 'cultural bias', or shared beliefs and values binding social groups and shaping behaviour (cultural 'code' in our view would be a better term). Theoretically each pattern designates what is a risk and what is not. Thus, risk perception is a social construction shared by adherents to a particular pattern, and is coherent with a certain world view.

Douglas' and Wildavsky's typology has been used to order different conceptions of safety in the nuclear domain[7]. Independently of that study, Cultural Theory was operationalised by A. Wildavsky and K. Dake at the end of the 1980s. They developed a set of 34 items to measure personal preferences regarding social patterns. Studies relating these preferences, or individual 'cultural profiles', to risk perception were performed in the United States and in the UK[8,9]. Reported results appeared to show that this operationalisation of the Cultural paradigm held great promise for predicting individual attitudes about risk topics. At the same time, the approach is attractive in that it seeks to relate risk perceptions to explanatory factors somewhat deeper or more highly articulated than those commonly used in survey research (e.g. demographics or education).

For these reasons, a number of studies have been undertaken to evaluate the validity and utility of Dake's Cultural Theory-grounded referential for risk perception research (e.g. Ref. 10). The present study was part of a European Commission-sponsored project involving French, Swedish and German researchers[11]. This paper presents the authors' effort to test the Cultural questionnaire in the French context and in light of risk perception research goals. The following sections describe the questionnaire itself and the French national profiles that emerged from the questionnaire (next section), risk perceptions of the national sample, and links between the 'cultural profiles' and risk perceptions identified by the questionnaire study. The final section draws conclusions as to the utility of the Cultural questionnaire tool in light of expressed study objectives.

CULTURAL SCALES

The twenty items of the questionnaire designed by Dake for his British study were translated into French (five items for each pattern or 'cultural scale'). The items consist of value statements with which individuals are asked to agree to disagree (on a five point scale ranging from 'complete agreement' to 'complete disagreement'). Examples of items for each social pattern are: egalitarianism, 'Those who get ahead should be taxed more to support the less fortunate'; fatalism, 'I don't worry about politics because I can't influence things very much'; individualism, 'In a fair system, people with more ability should earn more'; hierarchy, 'I think there should be more discipline in the youth of today'.

The French questionnaire was tested, modified and validated in a sample of psychology students, and then inserted into the May 1993 IPSN survey of public perception of 20 risk situations[12]. In this way the validity and utility of the cultural questionnaire for investigating risk perceptions were tested upon a representative French national sample of 1022 adults of 18 and over. The internal validity of the Cultural questionnaire was found to be satisfactory. Full analysis of the metric qualities of the French questionnaire may be found elsewhere[11].

Response rates to the questionnaire items were very good. Profiles of approval or rejection by the French population emerged for each social pattern as described by the questionnaire scales. Thus a strong and cohesive favour for the egalitarian viewpoint was expressed. A good degree of relatively cohesive favour was also shown for the individualistic and hierarchical patterns. In contrast, there was more dispersion in response to the fatalism scale with, on average, a rejection of this viewpoint.

Strong correlations are found between cultural scales and a number of individual descriptors. All four scales show links with political orientation. Left-wing supporters are more egalitarian than right wingers. Fatalism is stronger among people earning lower incomes, who in general belong to lower socio-professional and educational strata, position themselves to the political left and are more likely to be unemployed. A favour for individualism increases with age and religious practice; it is high among farmers, crafts and tradespeople and managers, as well as right wingers, and low among middle-level and blue-collar employees. Hierarchy is strongly favoured by older people, regular Catholic churchgoers, higher graduates, managers and right wingers. There is no difference in responses to any scale according to gender.

RISK PERCEPTION RESULTS

This section discusses results obtained on questions dealing with 20 risk situations, judged by respondents on two criteria: perceived danger to self and family, and perceived residual risk. In each case respondents were presented with a five point response scale; a 'don't know' answer, or absence of answer, could also be recorded by the interviewer.

Danger to oneself and to relatives

A five point scale (from 'not at all' to 'yes absolutely') was used to evaluate each of the twenty risk situations on the question: 'Do you think the existence of . . . endangers you or your relatives?' Figure 1 (left-hand side) shows the ranking given to the 20 risk situations from most to least dangerous (grouping the two response categories 'yes rather' and 'yes absolutely').

Water pollution (74% of respondents) and road traffic accidents (72%) are the most feared situations. Note that in spite of wide public information and prevention campaigns in recent years dealing with AIDS and with drug addiction, only 59% and 41% of the French feel personally endangered by these risks.

Residual risk

For each of the 20 situations, the question was asked: 'Existing safety and protection measures are never completely effective. For the following situations, do you think that the remaining risks are almost non-existent — low — moderate — high — very high' (plus 'don't know' or no answer). Figure 1 (right-hand side) shows the residual risk attributed to the risk situations (after grouping response categories 'high' and 'very high').

Here AIDS (82%) and drug addiction (73%) emerge, as is typical in studies of this sort, in first and second place as carrying residual risks. Radioactive waste (69%) is ranked third. A comparison of the two columns of Figure 1 shows that for each situation rated, more individuals express belief that the residual risk is high than believe they or their family are personally at risk. This commonly found pattern has been labelled 'optimistic bias'[13]. The impact upon perceptions of framing the situation as dangerous for oneself and family, or as carrying residual risk, is clearly demonstrated by the rise in perceptions of danger in the second case: drug addiction gathers 32 extra percentage points, AIDS +23, radioactive waste +15, alcohol +13, terrorism +11.

The top ranking residual risk situations are certainly perceived as 'major societal problems'. All those situations showing a sharp rise in the second frame may share other perceptual characteristics that render them more salient as problems for society than for the individual and the family. Such characteristics may stem from aspects of the risk source, or from representations given in public information campaigns; the Cultural paradigm would seek particular aspects of each such risk situation that render it appropriate to carry the definition of 'societal risk' under given social patterns of relationship.

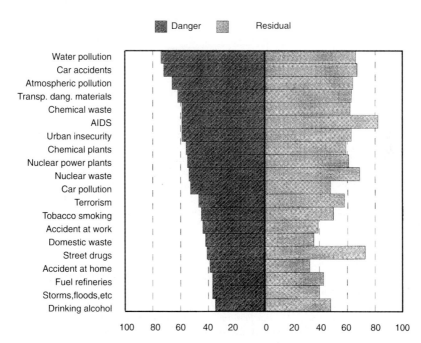

Figure 1. Perceived danger for you and your family (percentage of grouped 'yes' response) as against perceived residual risk (percentage of grouped 'high' response).

Relationships between risk perceptions and individual characteristics

Relationships between the feeling of danger to oneself and one's family, and individual characteristics were studied by applying a χ^2 test to cross tabulations. Women consistently show more concern than men, with especially strong differences in perception of daily life situations (drug addiction, AIDS, household accidents, urban insecurity, household waste, as well as terrorism). Younger people are significantly more sensitive to the AIDS risk.

Higher educational status correlates significantly with lower risk perceptions, especially for terrorism, natural disaster, urban insecurity, chemical facilities and workplace injuries. Managers also show lower concern for many risk situations (they frequently identify themselves as higher graduates).

CORRELATIONS BETWEEN CULTURAL SCALES AND RISK PERCEPTIONS

Danger to oneself and to relatives

Correlations between Cultural profiles and the perception of risks were reported by Dake[9] to be high and significant. The French data showed that fatalism and individualism are independent of the feeling of danger for any situation measured. In contrast, some significant correlations (χ^2 test) are found between certain perceived risks and egalitarianism or, especially, hierarchy.

Similar results are found in taking linear correlations between perceived danger and each cultural scale. Here we found that correlations are generally weak (under 0.20) and almost all positive. Those negative correlations found are all insignificant.

Residual risk

The correlations observed between the Cultural scales and the perceived residual risk of the 20 situations measured are in general very low and insignificant. It may be concluded that position on Cultural scales and perception of residual risk are unrelated. However, the largest of the small correlations seen link the Hierarchy position to perceptions of residual risk to society from terrorism and urban insecurity. An *a posteriori* interpret-

ation might be made that these two types of risk may be particularly abhorrent to Hierarchs in that they represent a violent rejection of established order.

DISCUSSION

The French version of Dake's questionnaire shows satisfactory internal validity. The four Cultural scales, hierarchy, egalitarianism, fatalism and individualism, show high correlations with political orientation, as expected, but also with more general personal characteristics such as age, gender, income or education level. However, relationships between Cultural profiles and perceptions of 20 mostly industrial and technological risk situations are not as high as expected in light of Dake's original results. Similarly discouraging results were obtained in Sweden by Sjöberg[14].

Some risk researchers applying Dake's Cultural items have found indications that the approach, or the theory grounding them, should not be abandoned. Marris et al[15], while finding low correlations between risk perceptions and cultural scales, see interest in the sheer number of correlations found, and in the fact that the pattern of correlations obtained was consistent with the predictions of Cultural Theory. Peters and Slovic[16] were able to demonstrate that world views as measured by Dake's Cultural items, alone and in combination with affect-laden imagery (word associations produced by survey respondents in response to the prompt 'nuclear power'), were highly predictive of perceptions of risk from nuclear power and of support for that technology.

The outcomes of the French and Swedish studies suggest that the Cultural paradigm alone, as operationalised today, is not apt to bring new insight into risk perceptions. The notion that a transverse cultural representation may be active in shaping risk perceptions, and the hypothesis of links between ideological position and risk perception, remain intuitively appealing. Further research may shed light on whether different styles of discourse may succeed in reaching particular groups, whether groups may have different behavioural responses to radiological emergencies and whether protection measures should be diversified. For the moment, however, the Cultural bias questionnaire provided by Dake does not appear to be a systematic and convincing tool for the investigation of cultural determinants of risk perception or behaviour.

REFERENCES

1. Valette-Florette, P. *Les Styles de Vie. Bilan Critique et Perspectives* (Paris: Nathan) (1994).

2. Ansel, P., Barny, M. H. and Pages, J. P. *Débat Nucléaire et Théorie de l'Opinion.* Rev. Gén. Nucl. **5**, 451–459 (1987).

3. 75-INSAG-4. *Safety Culture.* International Atomic Energy Agency (Vienna) (1991).

4. Mays, C. and Poumadère, M. *Decentralizing Risk Analysis in Large Engineered Systems. An Approach to Articulating Technical and Socioorganizational Dimensions of System Performance.* Risk Analysis **9**(4) (1989).

5. Douglas, M. and Wildavsky, A. *Risk and Culture* (University of California Press, Berkeley) (1982).

6. Thompson, M., Ellis, R. and Wildavsky, A. *Cultural Theory* (Boulder: Westview) (1990).

7. Prêtre, S. *De l'Influence de Facteurs Socio-culturels sur la Conception de la Sécurité.* Radioprotection **24**(3), 215–224 (1989).

8. Dake, K. and Wildavsky, A. *Theories of Risk Perception: Who Fears What and Why?* Daedalus **119**(4), 41–60 (1990).

9. Dake, K. *Orienting Dispositions in the Perception of Risk.* J. Cross Cult. Psychol. **22**(1), 61–82 (1991).

10. Poumadère, M., Mays, C., Slovic, P. and Mertz, C. K. *Diversity in Meaning: Risk Perceptions Compared in France and the USA* In: Proc. Risk Assessment and Management in a Global Economy, 5th Society for Risk Analysis-Europe Conf., Stuttgart (1995).

11. Brenot, J., Joussen, W. and Sjöberg, L. *Assessment and Management of Post Accidental Situations. Radiation Detriment, Risk Perception and Risk Communication. Final Report on EU Project F13P-CT930068* (Institut de Protection et de Sûreté Nucléaire, SEGR, Fontenay aux Roses) (1995).

12. Bonnefous, S. and Brenot, J. *Perception des Risques et de la Sécurité: Résultats du Sondage de Mai 1993.* Note SEGR/LSEES 93/20 (Institut de Protection et de Sécurité Nucléaire, Fontenay aux Roses) (1993).

13. Weinstein, N. D. *Unrealistic Optimism About Susceptibility to Health Problems: Conclusions from a Community-wide Sample.* J. Behav. Med. **10**, 481–500 (1987).

14. Sjöberg, L. *Explaining Risk Perception: An Empirical and Quantitative Evaluation of Cultural Theory.* Rhizikon Risk Research Reports no. 22 (Center for Risk Research, Stockholm School of Economics, Stockholm) (1995).

15. Marris, C., Langford, I. and O'Riordan, T. *Integrating Sociological and Psychological Approaches to Public Perceptions of Environmental Risks: Detailed Results from a Questionnaire Survey.* CSERGE Working Paper GEC 96-07, University of East Anglia (Norwich) (1996).

16. Peters, E. and Slovic, P. *The Role of Affect and Worldviews as Orienting Dispositions in the Perception and Acceptance of Nuclear Power.* Decision Research Report no. 95–1 (Eugene, Oregon) (1995).

Radiation Protection Dosimetry
Vol. 68, No. 3/4, pp. 245-249 (1996)
Nuclear Technology Publishing

MULTIPLE CAUSES OF STRESS IN THE CONTEXT OF RADIATION RISK

P. T. Allen
Robens Institute, University of Surrey
Guildford, GU2 5XH, UK

Abstract — In the presence of a threat from radiation, such as that posed by exposure to contamination caused by the Chernobyl accident, people are actually confronted with a variety of 'threats'. These include a mixture of components having objective and subjective elements. The management of countermeasures, in particular, contributes to the definition of the situation which labels the threats people encounter. Some findings from the affected areas in the former Soviet Union are discussed to demonstrate the impact of several factors on the affect response of the population.

INTRODUCTION

Some of the results from a number of social psychological investigations carried out in the regions affected by the Chernobyl NPP accident are reported. The research was part of a collaborative programme between the European Commission and the State Committee for Chernobyl Affairs in Belarus, Russia and Ukraine. The social and psychological characteristics of the situation in the aftermath of the accident have been under investigation for several years[1,2]. The focus for many such studies has been to examine affect response to the situation, including the incidence of clinical symptoms. In this regard the work continues the tradition which identified long-term stress reactions to the much less severe NPP accident at TMI[3].

The present approach made the assumptions that the characteristics of individuals, the ways in which they dealt with problems or, in general, their response to the accident and its sequelae, including countermeasures, would constitute strains which would result in higher levels of referred somatic complaints, anxiety, social dysfunction and possibly severe depression. In the most general formulation the threat from radiation, when perceived by people, is assumed to induce some kind of stress reaction which, for some individuals, may be severe enough to cross the clinical threshold.

However, the nature of the threat actually perceived by people in the affected regions does not appear likely to reflect the dose accountancy which is employed by the radiation protection community. The latter is based on the rational analysis of phenomena so that, for example, a saving of dose due to one situation can be combined with an increase in another to give a net dose. If people were fully aware of this approach it is conceivable that they might react to it, and their affect reactions, such as stress, might then reflect the favoured criterion of radiation protection scientists, namely dose.

In the real post-accident situation people are confronted with a range of information, some of it incorrect, which reflects not merely dose but policies, actions taken to reduce dose and other facts relating to the accident. It seemed likely that people would react to these different possible indicators in a complex way. In other words it was assumed that people would become stressed by learning of contamination in general, by learning of possible food contamination and as a result of actions. There would thus be multiple causes of stress in the situation, the analysis of which might suggest different emphases in policy.

Some of the earliest findings confirmed variations in stress due to apparently objective phenomena and to policies[4]. For example, higher levels of stress were associated with the existence of contamination and, in some areas, with the policy of relocation. The assumption was made that the association with contamination was a reflection of knowledge about that contamination whereas, in the case of the policy, there may be issues about the implementation of the policy, or its adequacy and effectiveness.

After initial pilot work a number of surveys with quasi-experimental designs were conducted to confirm the effects which seemed to be indicated. Analysis of variance models confirmed the expectation that stress was higher in contaminated areas but also showed that, for example, relocation in Russia was differentially effective. In the Russian relocated population stress was at the same level as in unaffected areas, in the other republics there was no stress reduction.

Because affect response is only one component of the way people respond to a threat it was clearly necessary to begin to measure other psychological aspects of the situation. Results from the first experimental designs pointed to the importance of the role played by beliefs about typical outcomes in life, as measured on a Locus of Control scale[5-7]. This distinguishes between 'internal' control, where life is seen as the responsibility of the person, and 'external' control, where events are seen as the result of forces beyond individual control[8-11]. The differences in the scores on this scale for groups in the contaminated and clean areas were statistically significant, which confirmed that relocation had had psychological effects that were not limited to stress. Thus in order to provide a better understanding of the situation it was necessary to turn to multivariate modelling, to measure a wider variety of psychological responses and, specifically, to include some of the main elements of contemporary social psychological theory.

There are many factors that can be readily identified as potential variables in the prediction of stress. For example, men and women tend to have different levels of stress as do people of different ages, or in different family circumstances. In addition to such factors, and in this very complex situation, it was useful to turn to models of social cognition in order to select, and put some reasonable ordering on, the more important variables.

There are several 'social cognition' models within social psychology which have been applied in recent years to health related problems. These include the health belief model[12,13], the theory of reasoned action[14], later refinements such as the theory of planned behaviour[15,16] and developments such as the precaution adoption process[17,18]. These theories have in common the attempt to predict health related behaviours and have usually been used to examine protective behaviours. In most such approaches, affect response does not feature or, it features as merely one component in models designed to predict behaviour.

Very recently Schwarzer[19] has offered the 'health action process' approach which provides a simplification of these models to include the four components: self-efficacy expectations, outcome expectancies, threat and intention. These components describe a first phase concerned with motivation, which then leads to the formation of intention to act. A second, or action, phase includes planning, behavioural and situational components. In his review of these approaches Schwarzer makes a number of points which have particular relevance. For example, he notes that 'cognitive processes, in particular expectancies, have been identified as the crucial determinants of changes in health practices'.

As an example a parallel study conducted in the affected areas found that the population believed themselves to have a considerable 'health problem'[5]. But the investigation of Locus of Control revealed that these people were unlikely to believe in the effectiveness of taking responsibility for their own health. Despite their claims that their health condition was a major problem they tended to argue for more attention to be paid to this 'problem' by the authorities and were unlikely to have taken action to protect themselves from radiation or to decrease their ingestion dose. This highlights the importance of expectancies in the post-accident situation.

The expectancies fall into three types: situational outcomes (what will happen without personal agency); outcome expectancies (what will happen normally); and self-efficacy expectations (perceived competence to carry out appropriate actions). The latter are implicated across a wide range of response situations and high self-efficacy is counted as a psychological resource success-

fully brought to bear on cognitive stressors in coping responses[20].

The structuring of the independent variables followed the general logic of social cognition approaches, as suggested by Schwarzer. However, the nature of the generic interaction between perceived severity of outcome, perceived vulnerability and the resulting threat is not yet clear in the literature. It may be that perceived threat is less important in understanding the processes that lead people to take, or not to take, particular sorts of actions than is an understanding of expectancies and situational constraints. Once processes of interpretation have begun, and expectancies are aroused, the consequent arousal of affect and/or the taking of actions seems more likely to be explained by reference to these cognitions and constraints.

In the survey work reported here most situational characteristics could not be specified in detail, thus one implication of the design is that the measures needed to refer to general tendencies. For example, it is generalised outcome expectancy that is relevant in this situation and general self-efficacy.

METHOD

Stress was to be examined in regression analyses including personal, attitudinal and behavioural characteristics and controlling for locality variations. Generalised outcome expectancy was measured by Fatalism[21] which refers to a range of behavioural outcomes and excludes specific radiation relevant behaviours. General self-efficacy was measured by a scale of Personal Mastery[22]. Threat was represented by the inclusion of two variables based on self-estimates of contamination and dose received. These were Perceived Dose (a simple low-medium-high self-estimation) and Perceived Food Contamination, which was a composite measure based on beliefs about the contamination levels in meat, fish, milk, vegetables, fruits, poultry, curd cheese and mushrooms and berries.

Demographic details were requested, including Sex, Age, and the presence or not of Dependent Children (defined as people under 18 years). People were also asked about their knowledge of local radiological information, and, as measures of action, their self-reported changes in behaviour since the accident and whether or not they follow official advice, including food advice.

The situation element was represented by a choice of settlements having different levels of contamination and countermeasures. The results discussed below were drawn from ten settlements, two in Russia and eight in the Ukraine. Average contamination levels varied from 52 kBq.m^{-2} (1.4 Ci.km^{-2}) to 973 kBq.m^{-2} (26.3 Ci.km^{-2}) and in half of these settlements rather more severe countermeasures, such as cattle slaughter, were in force. Because the situational characteristics could not be specified in detail, and because both contamination and countermeasures were confounded in the two Russian settlements, any differences in effects due to the situation of the settlements in Russia were to be revealed by a dummy variable for Location included in the multivariate analyses. In the Ukraine the greater number of settlements enabled the role of contamination to be examined more thoroughly, independent of any effect due to stronger or more numerous counter-measures.

Control samples were taken in unaffected areas to provide quasi-experimental comparisons for the main independent variable which were all entered into multi-variate regression analyses. The dependent variable was the General Health Questionnaire, 28-item version (GHQ-28)[23,24]. Further details on all these measures appear elsewhere[25].

FINDINGS

There were no significant differences between the selected groups within republics with respect to age. There was a difference between the overall average age in the Russian samples (44.8 years) and that in the Ukraine (39 years; F = 17.3; df 2,962; p < 0.001). There were similar proportions of men and women in each of the groups in all samples ($\chi^2 = 43.7$; df 32; ns). The overall proportion of men was 43.2%. The samples appear to be a reasonable reflection of the actual population.

A preliminary analysis was conducted of the clean area samples. As expected the personal characteristics had significant effects on the GHQ-28 score (at least p < 0.05). The standardised beta coefficients were: Sex 0.19; Age 0.17, Dependent Children 0.14. A dummy variable for Republic also had a strong effect (0.24) indicating systematic differences in stress levels between republics. This had also been found in previous surveys. However, the effect for republic dropped out of the subsequent equations, which were built on data solely from the contaminated regions.

Hierarchical step-wise regressions were conducted in blocks representing the main stages common to most versions of social cognition theories. In the first block were the demographic variables (age, sex, dependent children). These were followed by Personal Mastery, then Fatalism and then threat (Perceived Dose and Per-ceived Food Contamination). Reported change in behav-iour was then included and, finally, situational aspects were added (average local contamination level and level of countermeasures in the Ukraine, or, in Russia, Location).

Most of the variables had very significant effects and, in both republics, the final equations were fairly efficient. After removal of variables with missing values the equations were based on 158 cases in Russia and 219 in Ukraine. In Russia the variables explained 50.2% of the variance in GHQ-28 score and in the Ukraine 44.9%. The results from the two republics were broadly similar but the personal characteristics accounted for 24% of the variance in Russia and only 4% in Ukraine. Nevertheless the perceived threat factors accounted for similar proportions of the variance; in Russia 13% of the total and in the Ukraine 9%.

The results for Russia were as follows (standardised beta values and significance level in parenthesis): Age (0.24; p < 0.001), Sex (−0.11; p < 0.07), presence of Dependent Children (0.19; p < 0.005), Personal Mas-tery (−0.25; p < 0.005), Fatalism (0.11; p < 0.15), Per-ceived Food Contamination (0.24; p < 0.000), Per-ceived Dose (0.11; p < 0.08), reported change in behaviour (0.22; p < 0.000) and Location (0.14; p < 0.05).

Interpretation of these results is that older people and those with dependent children had higher levels of stress, just as in the control areas. Women had higher levels of stress than did men, but this effect was weak-ened by subsequent inclusion of the factors concerned with radiation. Personal Mastery, that is the extent to which people feel that they can cope with situations, had a considerable effect in reducing stress, whilst the other factors tended to increase stress. This is partly a consequence of the design of the study but it does high-light the impact of some of the independent effects of threat, since, for example, beliefs about contamination in food and subjective estimates of the dose of radiation together exceeded the reduction associated with Per-sonal Mastery.

General outcome expectancy, represented by fatalism, reduced the positive benefit due to beliefs about per-sonal mastery but its effect was marginal. Fatalism is related to stress but the relationship is not entirely clear. For example, the zero order correlations between Fatal-ism and GHQ-28 in the clean areas were highly signifi-cant (Russia 0.32; Ukraine 0.51). In the contaminated areas they were lower but still significant (Russia 0.33; Ukraine 0.35; p < 0.01). Earlier results suggest that two relationships may be at work here. In one fatalism reflects a negative outlook with respect to outcome expectancies and therefore contributes to stress. In the other fatalism is actually a response to high stress and acts as a coping strategy.

Interpretation of the result for reported change in behaviour is not conclusive because, as with other aspects of this approximate methodology, several fac-tors may be responsible. Any sort of change in life is likely to be associated with stress and the changes in behaviour measured here may include changes due to personal attempts to limit dose or responses to counter-measures, or both. In any event those who reported more change in behaviour were recording higher levels of stress and this again underlies the multiple impacts of the accident.

The significant effect of location may be due to contamination, or to differential countermeasures im-plementation, or both. Interpretation of the finding is that the settlement with the higher average level of con-tamination (and with the more severe countermeasures) had higher levels of stress. If the effect is due to contamination this cannot be a direct influence. It must be the case that there is either a set of intervening social cognition variables, which represents the knowledge and interpretation of the contamination level, or that the contamination level has its effect through the differential implementation of countermeasures.

The results for the Ukraine were as follows: Age (0.12; $p < 0.05$), Sex (-0.09; ns), presence of Dependent Children (0.07; ns), Personal Mastery (-0.29; $p < 0.000$), Fatalism (0.10; $p < 0.08$), Perceived Food Contamination (0.08; ns), Perceived Dose (0.25; $p < 0.000$), reported change in behaviour (0.25; $p < 0.000$), local average contamination level (0.24; $p < 000$) and countermeasures (-0.05; ns).

These results are similar to those obtained in the case of the two Russian settlements but with the following differences: in the Ukraine the presence of dependent children had little effect and the effects due to Perceived Dose and Perceived Food Contamination were reversed in scale in the Ukraine.

The results for the Ukraine also include a very strong effect of average local contamination level which, following the logic of the step-wise regression procedure, is independent of the measured subjective assessments and of countermeasures. Over and above the effects which could be detected due to the subjective estimates of contamination and dose, therefore, there remain the possible additional effects of contamination. Whatever people attribute in the way of contamination, it is the case that well publicised official zones exist based on contamination ranges and locally measured contamination levels. Knowledge of these zones, and other information relating to contamination, will have found its way into the awareness of people through a multiplicity of routes. Presumably the detected effect of actual contamination level on stress represents a proxy for these other sorts of information. Furthermore there was no residual effect due to differential countermeasures implementation. This suggests that the Location effect found in Russia was also due to contamination level, rather than differential countermeasures.

DISCUSSION

These results indicate something of the complexity of human response to the continuing situation following the Chernobyl accident. They show that the 'threat' experienced by people is qualitatively different from that which the dose calculus of the radiation protection specialist would suggest. In particular people seem to respond to each category of indicator in an additive way. Thus their concerns are not limited to perceived dose or to the perceived levels of contamination in foods; as is revealed by the residual effect of local average contamination level, which remains once the effects of subjective dose estimate and perceived food contamination have been taken into account.

It is likely that the actual mean levels of contamination in a given locality are known approximately by people. Certainly the bands are known because they serve as legal boundaries. In the Russian data, for example, there was a small but statistically significant relationship between subjective dose estimate and local average measured contamination ($r = 0.24$; $p < 0.001$; $N = 195$). This may be because a 'passport dose' (official measured dose recorded for individuals) was available to inhabitants, and for the settlement with the higher level of contamination this dose was just below the $5 \, \text{mSv.y}^{-1}$ criterion for compulsory relocation. In the other settlement the average was not near this important level and seems less likely to have been of special significance to the inhabitants. However, there was no such correlation in the Ukrainian data.

These findings especially underline the ways in which policy, and the definitions of the situation on which it is based, contribute to the perception of threat. Effective policies and countermeasures depend in part on a better understanding of the ways in which people are likely to respond to such definitions.

ACKNOWLEDGEMENT

The research described in this paper was partially funded by the Radiation Protection Research Action of the European Commission.

REFERENCES

1. International Advisory Committee. *International Chernobyl Project* (Vienna: International Atomic Energy Agency) (1991).

2. Rumyantseva, G. M. and Martyushov, A. N. *Risk of Psychic Dysadaptation in Nuclear Accidents: Chernobyl Accident as a Model.* Paper presented to Third Conf. of the Society for Risk Analysis, European Branch, Paris, December, 1991.

3. Baum, A., Gatchel, R. J. and Schaeffer, M. A. *Emotional, Behavioural, and Physiological Effects of Chronic Stress at Three Mile Island.* J. Consult. Clin. Psychol. **51**(4), 565–571 (1983).

4. Allen, P. T. *Annual Report of EC Joint-Studies Project 2.* Robens Institute Report, University of Surrey (1994).

5. Allen, P. T. *Stress and Locus of Control in the Chernobyl Region.* Paper presented at the EC Joint Studies Program Workshop, Paris, October, 1993.

6. Rumyantseva, G. M., Allen, P. T., Melnichuk, T. N., Margolin, S. A. and Plyplina, D. V. *Locus-of-control in the Population Suffering from the Chernobyl Disaster and Living under Conditions of Chronic Ecological Stress.* Bekhterev Rev. Psychiat. Med. Psychol. **3**, 34–40 (1994).

7. Bazhin, E. F., Golynkina, E. A. and Etkind, A. M. *Methods and Methodology of Research: the Method of Researching the Level of Subjective Control.* Bekhterev Rev. Psychiat. Med. Psychol. **5**(3), 153–162 (1984).

8. Butterfield, E. C. *Locus of Control, Test Anxiety, Reactions to Frustration and Achievement Attitudes*. J. Pers. **32**(3), 355–370 (1964).

9. Rotter, J. B. *Generalised Expectancies for Internal versus External Control of Reinforcement*. Psychol. Monogr. **80**(1) (1966).

10. Levenson, H. *Attitudes Towards Others and Components of Internal-External Locus of Control*. Psychol. Rep. **36**, 209–210 (1974).

11. Lefcourt, H. M. *Locus of Control: Current Trends in Theory and Research*. 2nd edn (London: Lawrence Erlbaum Associates) (1982).

12. Becker, M. H. *The Health Belief Model and Personal Health Behaviour*. Health Educ. Monogr. **2**(4) (1974).

13. Janz, N. K. and Becker, M. H. *The Health Belief Model: a Decade Later*. Health Educ. Q. **11**(1), 1–47 (1984).

14. Ajzen, I. and Fishbein, M. *Understanding Attitudes and Predicting Behaviour* (Englewood Cliffs, NJ: Prentice-Hall) (1980).

15. Ajzen, I. *The Theory of Planned Behaviour*. Organ. Behav. Hum. Decis. Processes **50**, 179–211 (1991).

16. Ajzen, I. and Madden, T. J. *Prediction of Goal-directed Behaviour: Attitudes, Intentions, and Perceived Behavioral Control*. J. Exp. Soc. Psychol. **22**, 453–74 (1986).

17. Wienstein, N. *The Precaution Adoption Process*. Health Psychol. **7**, 355–386 (1988).

18. Wienstein, N. and Sandman, P. M. *A Model of the Precaution Adoption Process: Evidence from Home Radon Testing*. Health Psychol. **11**, 170–180 (1992).

19. Schwarzer, R. *Self-efficacy in the Adoption and Maintenance of Health Behaviours: Theoretical Approaches and a New Model*. In: Self-efficacy: Thought Control of Action, Ed. R. Schwarzer (Washington: Hemisphere) (1992).

20. Bandura, A. *Self-efficacy Conception of Anxiety*, Anxiety Res. **1**, 77–98 (1988).

21. Dake, K. *Myths of Nature: Culture and the Social Construction of Risk*. J. Soc. Issues **48**(4), 21–37 (1992).

22. Pearlin, L. I. and Schooler, C. *The Structure of Coping*. J. Health Soc. Behav. **19**, 2–21 (1978).

23. Goldberg, D. and Hillier, V. F. *A Scaled Version of the General Health Questionnaire*. Psychol. Med. **9**, 139–145 (1979).

24. Goldberg, D. and Williams, P. *A User's Guide to the General Health Questionnaire*. (Windsor: NFER-NELSON) (1988).

25. Allen, P. T. and Rumyantseva, G. *The Contribution of Social and Psychological Factors to Relative Radiation Ingestion Dose in Two Russian Towns Affected by the Chernobyl NPP Accident*. In: Proc. Society of Risk Analysis (Europe) Conf., Stuttgart (in press).

Radiation Protection Dosimetry
Vol. 68, No. 3/4, pp. 251–255 (1996)
Nuclear Technology Publishing

CHERNOBYL CLEAN-UP WORKERS' PERCEPTION OF RADIATION THREAT

N. Tarabrina†, E. Lazebnaya†, M. Zelenova† and N. Lasko‡
†Laboratory for Traumatic Stress Studies, Institute of Psychology
Russian Academy of Science
Yaroslavskaya Str. 13, 129366, Moscow, Russia
‡VA Research Service, Psychophysiology Laboratory
Harvard Medical School
228 Maple St, Manchester, NH 03103, USA

Abstract — The goals of this study were: (1) to compare the psychometric profiles of male Chernobyl liquidators who met DSM-III-R criteria for current PTSD with those who did not, and (2) to explore liquidators' perception and assessment of the 'invisible' stressor of the radioactive hazard. Results of t-test comparisons between the PTSD and non-PTSD groups for the various psychometric measures are shown. Both diagnostic groups were similar in regard to their mean ages and education levels. The PTSD group scored significantly higher than the non-PTSD group on all the measures of PTSD and general psychiatric symptomatology, state and trait anxiety, depression. On the whole, results of this study demonstrate the determining role of individual perception and assessment of radioactive hazard in the development of post-traumatic stress and place this problem among the most important in studying the psychological consequences of experiencing radioactive threat. The real working conditions and the level of information also affected workers' estimate of the severity of the radiation hazard in Chernobyl.

INTRODUCTION

The 1986 explosion of the Chernobyl reactor represents the largest source of potential invisible trauma. Vyner[1] has suggested that the experience of exposure to radiation and invisible contaminants involves uncertainty, adaptational dilemmas, hyper-vigilance, and non-empirical belief systems about the exposure, which can lead to the development of 'traumatic neuroses'. Post-traumatic psychiatric syndromes have been described in survivors of exposure resulting from radioactive accidents at Three Mile Island[2], Goiania, Brazil[3], and Chernobyl[4,5] as well as in populations suffering from toxic contaminants[6]. However, experts disagree as to whether an event not involving the direct, sensory perception of danger meets the DSM 'A' (stressor) criterion for post-traumatic stress disorder (PTSD). As the list of potential stressors allegedly capable of leading to PTSD expands, it becomes an important issue whether or not their inclusion is supported by empirical evidence.

Traumatic stress endured by Chernobyl disaster workers (liquidators) during post-explosion clean-up work has its specific features. First, the intensity of perception of a radiation hazard depended on the individual level of workers' knowledge, usually inadequate, about harmful effects of radiation and on their subjective vision of the radioactive situation during their work in a contaminated area. Second, the main stressors were 'invisible' so they could not have been comprehended, estimated and experienced with a reasonable level of objectivity. Third, workers had to stay in a traumatic situation for a continuous period of time (1–6 months), thus cumulative effects of the stress may be presumed.

The above mentioned factors, along with other stressful events that occurred in the specific conditions of the disaster zone, may be referred to as the primary stress factors. After coming back liquidators had experienced effects from the secondary stress factors. Among these an 'information' factor is especially significant. 'Glasnost' brought about an outpouring of publications about the true scale of the catastrophe and the harmful effects of radiation exposure. This information served as a main secondary stress factor that caused and is still causing a traumatic effect on a liquidator's mental health.

Additional post-Chernobyl secondary stress factors were: (1) health problems, subjectively associated with participation in a clean-up work; (2) fear of developing radiation disease and a sense of foreshortened future as a consequence; (3) increased anxiety at work due to hyper-vigilance in regard to possible accidents and their consequences; (4) psychological problems in the family associated with their reproductive ability.

In addition, neither at the time of their work in Chernobyl nor afterward, were liquidators provided with accurate information about the level of radiation to which they were exposed. Their perception of radiation hazard depended on the level of the liquidator's individual knowledge and/or subjective belief about the degree of radioactive contamination in the work area.

Therefore, it may be hypothesised that an individual's perception and assessment of a particular traumatic situation plays a crucial role in development of PTSD among the population studied and should be considered as one of the most important problems in studying the psychological consequences of experienced radioactive threat.

SUBJECTS AND METHODS

Subjects (n = 65) were medication free male ex-disaster workers who participated in the Chernobyl reactor clean-up. Excluded were subjects with a radioactive illness in any stage, or any kind of a cerebral pathology. The dose of radiation they may have received in Chernobyl according to medical records did not exceed the authorised level. Demographic and psychometric data appear in Table 1. All subjects experienced a similar, allegedly traumatic event, viz., one to two months' exposure to radiation during clean-up of the nuclear power station in Chernobyl in 1986.

In order to assess presence or absence of PTSD, Russian-language versions of the Structured Clinical Interview for DSM-III-R (SCID)[7] and the Clinician-Administered PTSD Scale (CAPS)[8] were administered to each subject. Both evaluate the PTSD syndrome based upon seventeen DSM-III-R symptoms as 'recollections, dreams, distress, diminished interest, detachment, estrangement, emotional numbing, hyperarousal,' etc.

In addition, Russian-language versions of following widely used and validated psychometric instruments were used:

(1) Mississippi Scale for Civilian PTSD[9]
(2) Impact of Event Scale (IOES)[10]
(3) Minnesota Multiphasic Personality Inventory (MMPI)
(4) State Trait Anxiety Inventory (STAI)[11]
(5) Beck Depression Inventory (BDI)[12]
(6) Symptom Check List 90-revised (SCL90-R)[13]
(9) Radioactive Threat Perception Questionnaire (RTPQ)[14] that was developed on the basis of initial interviews and contained 30 questions answered on five-point Likert scale.

RESULTS AND DISCUSSION

According to DSM-III-R criteria incorporated into

Table 1. Demographic and psychometric data.

	PTSD (n = 21)		non-PTSD (n = 44)			
	M	SD	M	SD	t	p
Demographics						
Age (y)	35.4	(5.8)	38.3	(7.2)	1.6	0.1
Education (y)	12.1	(2.5)	12.9	(2.6)	1.1	0.3
MMPI						
L	47.5	(10.3)	49.2	(7.2)	0.7	0.4
F	84.6	(20.0)	69.1	(10.0)	3.8	<0.001
K	48.6	(9.2)	50.2	(7.5)	0.7	0.4
HS (1)	83.9	(14.2)	68.3	(18.4)	3.3	0.002
D (2)	89.5	(16.3)	73.0	(17.0)	3.6	<0.001
HY (3)	73.5	(11.7)	61.8	(12.4)	3.5	<0.01
Pd (4)	74.5	(11.6)	60.1	(13.6)	3.8	<0.01
Mf (5)	63.9	(7.7)	63.3	(11.2)	0.2	0.83
Pa (6)	74.3	(13.0)	59.8	(10.7)	4.6	<0.001
Pt (7)	83.1	(12.7)	67.9	(13.3)	4.3	<0.001
Sc (8)	90.7	(19.4)	69.3	(15.0)	4.7	<0.001
Ma (9)	71.4	(12.2)	63.9	(12.0)	2.3	0.03
Si (0)	61.5	(8.3)	58.1	(8.7)	1.5	0.4
Pk (PTSD Keane)	75.6	(15.4)	62.7	(14.1)	3.3	0.02
PS (PTSD Schlenger)	73.1	(11.8)	61.5	(12.6)	3.5	0.001
IOES Intrusion	5.9	(3.9)	2.5	(2.6)	4.1	<0.001
Avoidance	8.0	(6.7)	2.9	(3.9)	3.8	<0.001
Mississippi Scale for Civilian PTSD	95.2	(13.9)	81.6	(14.3)	3.6	<0.001
CAPS Frequency	23.3	(6.2)	6.0	(5.7)	11.1	<0.001
Intensity	23.9	(6.4)	6.2	(6.4)	10.4	<0.001
STAI State	46.0	(8.8)	41.0	(8.9)	3.7	0.03
Trait	52.5	(7.9)	44.9	(7.4)	3.7	<0.001
SCL-9-R Gen. Sympt. Index (GSI)	1.0	(0.5)	0.6	(0.4)	3.4	0.001
BDI	17.3	(7.4)	9.9	(7.4)	3.7	0.001

SCID and CAPS, subjects (n = 65) were classified into PTSD (n = 21) and non-PTSD (n = 44) groups. Results of t-test comparisons between the PTSD and non-PTSD groups for the various psychometric measures are presented in Table 1. Both diagnostic groups were similar in regard to their mean ages and education levels. The PTSD group scored significantly higher than the non-PTSD group on all the measures of PTSD and general psychiatric symptomatology, state and trait anxiety, depression.

The MMPI profile of the Chernobyl PTSD group is in accord with previously published data on PTSD[9,15–19]. The three-point MMPI code configuration was 8-2-F for the entire profile, and 8-2-1 for the clinical scales. This profile 'type individuals are characterised by extreme inadequacy in all areas of their lives, varied somatic complaints, confused thinking, flat affect and inability to concentrate'[20]. Several studies have suggested that the clinical scale configurations associated with PTSD diagnosis include: F-2-8/8-2[9,19,21], 8-2-7[22], 2-8-7, and F-8-7[23]. In the present study, the PTSD group scored significantly higher on the MMPI F-scale as well as on most of the clinical scales. Furthermore, this profile bears a striking similarity to that reported by Orr et al[15] for Vietnam combat veterans with PTSD. The only notable differences are found on the F and Hs scales, on which the Chernobyl subjects were more elevated. The Hs elevation suggests that Chernobyl PTSD subjects were manifesting substantial concern about their physical health, not surprising given their exposure to a serious radiation hazard with its associated health implications.

Although the PTSD and non-PTSD groups differed significantly on the specific PTSD psychometric measures, viz., CAPS, IOES, and Mississippi Scale for Civilian PTSD, the magnitudes of the Chernobyl PTSD group's scores on each of these instruments fell well below the PTSD cut-offs established by research in other traumatised populations, mainly combat veterans. These latter results echo the negative results of psychophysiological testing for PTSD previously reported in Chernobyl subjects[24]. It would seem that if PTSD does exist in victims of the 'invisible trauma' of Chernobyl, it is milder than that resulting from other, more visible traumatic experiences.

Chernobyl liquidators response to the Radioactive Threat Perception Questionnaire (RTPQ) revealed that when they were in Chernobyl, those with PTSD experienced anxiety and fear more frequently and were more likely to worry about their health than non-PTSD subjects. Of PTSD subjects 92.2% relative to only 41% of non-PTSD thought that they had been harmed by radiation so much that they felt compelled to talk about their health problems with someone (item 28) (t = 2, 50; p < 0.05). In contrast to non-PTSD subjects, PTSD subjects reported that their work stations were located closer to the nuclear reactor and that they worked in the dangerous area more frequently and for longer periods than was assumed to be safe. They were also more often engaged in dangerous situations that required a higher level of potential resources of the organism (both physical and psychological), and experienced anxiety and fear of sudden increase in radiation level more frequently than did non-PTSD subjects. In addition, as a result, liquidators with PTSD were more likely to worry about their reproductive ability.

Factor analysis revealed that the content and structure of disaster workers' perception and assessment of the radiation hazard were determined mostly by individual differences in their experience of situational stress endured in the disaster zone[14,25–27]. Also shown was a transformation of the above experiences into a new attitude about the work in Chernobyl. For most of the liquidators who developed PTSD, Chernobyl per se became a significant event in their life that brought a feeling of personal alteration, becoming a different person. This feeling is especially apparent in workers' attitudes toward their health, which they believe has deteriorated due to radiation exposure. Therefore, the post-Chernobyl behaviour of workers who considered their participation in the Chernobyl disaster clean-up as the most significant event of their lives, was greatly affected by the subjective feeling of endured psychological stress. Most noteworthy is the fact that objective difficulties and conditions had less impact on the post-Chernobyl behaviour. The real working conditions and level of information also had an effect on workers' estimate of the severity of the radiation hazard in Chernobyl.

In order to develop a brief version of RTPQ for screening large populations of Chernobyl liquidators a correlation analysis was performed between the results of each of the 30 questions of the RTPQ and SCID's PTSD diagnosis for each subject. This analysis identified ten RTPQ questions that had the strongest correlations (p < 0.01) with SCID diagnosis:

(2) How frequently did you work within an area of severe destruction of a building, equipment, or communications?

(3) How often were you placed in dangerous situations due to somebody else's ignorance or mistakes?

(5) How often were you placed in situations that required unusual courage, fortitude, or endurance?

(8) How much did you work in an area that was considered unsafe?

(13) To what degree have you felt that your health has worsened?

(15) To what degree do you consider participation in Chernobyl disaster work to have been a significant event in your life?

(18) To what extent do you feel that since Chernobyl you have become a different person, or that something has changed in your behaviour, feelings, emotions, or attitudes?

(24) How much do you worry about developing a radiation disease?

(27) In your conversations, how frequently do you go back to the subject of health in connection with radiation?

(28) To what degree do you consider yourself to be suffering as a result of your work in Chernobyl?

The means of RTPQ-10 scores (max. 50) were 33.55 (6.53) for subjects with PTSD and 23.75 (6.2) for non-PTSD individuals. Therefore, according to the frequency distribution of the individual scores of RTPQ-10 the diagnostic cut-offs (DC) were set at >32 for PTSD diagnosis and at <25 for non-PTSD. Between these scores the probability of the correct diagnosis was less than 50%. Discriminant analyses (Table 2) indicated

Table 2. RTPQ-10 discriminant function subject classification.

	Responders	Non-responders	
Chernobyl PTSD	15	5	Sens = 67.5%*
Chernobyl non-PTSD	13	27	Spec = 75.0%*

*p = 0.05

that RTPQ-10 successfully classified 15 PTSD subjects out of 20 (sensitivity 67.5%) and 27 non-PTSD out of 40 (specificity 75%).

The validity of the diagnostic cut-offs was tested through a comparison of the psychometric data in two groups of subjects: those with RTPQ-10 score >32, (n = 16) and those with RTPQ-10 score <25, (n = 33) '(Table 3). Subjects (n = 16) with scores in between diagnostic cut-offs (26–31) were not included in this analysis. It is clear that these two groups significantly differ on most of the measures, with the exception of two scales from SCL-90-R. In other words, the psychometric profile of the group with DC > 32 looks similar to that of Chernobyl liquidators with PTSD[23]. Therefore, the RTPQ-10 may prove useful and valid instrument to screen large populations of the Chernobyl clean-up workers.

On the whole, results of this study demonstrate the determining role of individual perception and assessment of radioactive hazard in the development of post-traumatic stress and place this problem among the most important in studying the psychological consquences of experienced radioactive threat. The real working conditions and the level of information also affected the workers' estimate of the severity of the radiation hazard in Chernobyl.

Table 3. Psychometric profile of clean-up workers with the differences in DC level.

Psychometrics		Diagnostic areas					
		RTPQ score >32 (n = 16)		RTPQ score <25 (n = 33)			
		M	(SD)	M	(SD)	t	p
IOES	Avoidance	6.44	(4.43)	2.06	(2.62)	4.35	***
	Intrusion	5.19	(3.89)	2.24	(2.68)	3.10	**
Mississippi Scale for Civilian PTSD		91.69	(18.74)	76.36	(13.59)	3.26	**
BDI		16.75	(9.59)	7.64	(6.49)	3.93	***
SCL90-R							
	som	1.44	(0.70)	0.69	(0.55)	4.10	***
	o–c	1.13	(0.67)	0.65	(0.57)	2.64	*
	int	0.85	(0.54)	0.54	(0.42)	2.24	*
	dep	1.12	(0.63)	0.53	(0.47)	3.70	**
	anx	1.14	(0.66)	0.45	(0.37)	4.67	***
	hos	0.83	(0.49)	0.63	(0.61)	1.14	
	phob	0.48	(0.59)	0.22	(0.39)	1.80	
	par	0.83	(0.51)	0.43	(0.52)	2.55	*
	psy	0.73	(0.48)	0.25	(0.31)	4.24	***
	oth	1.00	(0.47)	0.49	(0.62)	2.91	**
	GSI	1.01	(0.46)	0.51	(0.38)	4.02	***
STAI	State	46.38	(9.28)	40.97	(7.90)	2.12	*
	Trait	50.94	(8.69)	43.58	(6.56)	3.31	**

*p < 0.05
**p < 0.01
***p < 0.001

REFERENCES

1. Viner H. M. *The Psychological Dimensions of Health Care for Patients Exposed to Radiation and the Other Invisible Environmental Contaminants.* Soc. Sci. Med. **27**, 1097–1103 (1988).

2. Dew, M. S. and Bromet, E. J. *Predictors of Temporal Patterns of Psychiatric Distress during 10 Years following the Nuclear Accident at Three Mile Island.* Soc. Psychiat. Psychiat. Epidemiol. **28**, 49–55 (1993).

3. Collins, D. L. and de Carvalho, A. B. *Chronic Stress from the Goiania ^{137}Cs radiation accident.* Behav. Med. **18**, 149–157 (1993).

4. Alexandrovski, J. A., Rumjanzewa, G. M., Jurow, W. W. and Martiuschow, A. A. *The Dynamics of Psychological Maladjustment States of Chronic Stress in Inhabitants of Areas Involved in the Chernobyl Nuclear Accident.* Psychiatr. Prax. **19**, 31–34 (1992).

5. Torubarov, F. S. and Chinkina, O. V. *Psychological After Effects of the Disaster at the Chernobyl NPS.* Klin. Med. (Moscow) **69**, 24–28 (1991).

6. Simon, G. E., Katon, W. J. and Sparks, P. J. *Allergic to Life: Psychological Factors in Environmental Illness.* Am. J. Psychiatr. **147**, 901–906 (1990).

7. Spitzer, R. L., Williams, J. B. W., Gibbon, M. and First, M. D. *Structured Clinical Interview for DSM-III-R* (Washington: American Psychiatric Press) (1989).

8. Weathers, F. W. and Litz, B. T. *Psychometric Properties of the Clinician-Administered PTSD Scale, CAPS-1.* PTSD Res. Q. **7**(1), 2–6 (1994).

9. Keane, T. M., Malloy, P. F. and Fairbank, J. A. *Empirical Development of an MMPI Subscale for the Assessment of Combat-related Posttraumatic Stress Disorder.* J. Consult. Clin. Psychol. **52**, 888–891 (1984).

10. Horowitz, M. J., Wilner, N. J. and Alvarez, W. *Impact of Event Scale: A Measure of Subjective Stress.* Psychosom. Med. **41**, 209–218 (1979).

11. Spielberger, C. D., Gorsuch, R. L. and Lushene, R. E. *Manual for the State-Trait Anxiety Inventory (self-evaluation questionnaire)* (Palo Alto: Consulting Psychologists Press) (1970).

12. Beck, A. T., Ward, C. H., Mendelson, M., Mock, J. E. and Erbaugh, J. *An Inventory for Measuring Depresssion.* Arch. Gen. Psychiatr. **4**, 561–571 (1961).

13. Derogatis, L. R. *SCL-90-R: Administration, Scoring and Procedures Manual-II for the Revised Version* (Towson, MD: Clinical Psychometric Research) (1983).

14. Tarabrina, N. V. and Petrukhin, E. V. *Psychological Features of Radiation Danger Perception.* Psykhol. Zh. **15**(1), 27–41 (1994).

15. Orr, S. P., Claiborn, T. M., Altman, B., Forgue, D. F., de Jong, J. B., Pitman, R. and Herz, L. *Psychometric Profile of PTSD, Anxious and Healthy Vietnam Veterans: Correlations with Psychophysiologic Responses.* J. Consult. Clin. Psychol. **58**, 329–335 (1990).

16. Fairbank, J. A., Keane, T. M. and Malloy, P. F. *Some Preliminary Data on the Psychological Characteristics of Vietnam Veterans with PTSD.* J. Consult. Clin. Psychol. **51**, 912–919 (1983).

17. Merbaum, M. and Hefez, A. *Some Personality Characteristics of Soldiers Exposed to Extreme War Stress.* J. Consult. Clin. Psychol. **44**, 1–6 (1976).

18. Roberts, W. R., Penk, W. E., Gearing, M. L., Robinowits, R., Dolan, M. P. and Patterson, E. T. *Interpersonal Problems of Vietnam Combat Veterans with Symptoms of Post-traumatic Stress Disorder.* J. Abnorm. Psychol. **91**, 444–450 (1982).

19. Wolfe, J., Quinn, S., Stewart, J., Vielhauer, M., Clum, G., Kamen, D. and Brown, P. *MMPI-2 Profiles in Males and Females with PTSD: A Retrospective Analysis.* Poster at Ann. Meeting Int. Soc. for Traumatic Stress Studies, San Antonio, TX, October 1993.

20. Gilberstadt, H. and Duker, J. *A Handbook for Clinical and Actuarial MMPI Interpretation* (Philadelphia: W. B. Saunders) pp. 74–75 (1965).

21. Blanchard, E. B., Hickling, E. J., Taylor, A. E., Loos, W. R. and Gerardi, R. J. *The Psychophysiology of Motor Vehicle Accident Related Post-traumatic Stress Disorder.* Behav. Ther. **25**, 453–467 (1994).

22. Burke, H. R. and Mayer, S. *The MMPI and the Post-traumatic Stress Syndrome in Vietnam Era Veterans.* J. Clin. Psychol. **4**, 152–156 (1985).

23. Blue, B. A., Fama-Collins, L., Blake, D. D. and Gusman, F. *Psychometric Norms for a Combat-related PTSD Inpatient Sample.* Poster at Ann. Meeting Int. Soc. for Traumatic Stress Studies, Los Angeles, CA, October 1992.

24. Tarabrina, N. V., Lazebnaya, E. O., Zelenova, M. E., Lasko, N. B., Orr, S. P. and Pitman, R. K. *Psychophysiological Reactivity in Liquidators of the Chernobyl Disaster.* Psykhol. Zh. **17**(2), 30–45 (1996).

25. Petrukhin, E. V., Kharkovskaya, T. A., Selkova, V., Tarabrina, N. V. and Lasko, N. B. *Chernobyl Disaster Workers' Perception of the Radioactive Threat.* Poster at Ann. Meeting Int. Soc. for Traumatic Stress Studies, San Antonio, TX, October 1993.

26. Tarabrina, N. V., Lazebnaya, E. O. and Zelenova, M. E. *Psychological Features of Post-Traumatic Stress States among Chernobyl Disaster Workers.* Psykhol. Zh. **15**(5), 67–78 (1994).

27. Lazebnaya, E. O., Zelenova, M. E., Petrukhin, E. V. and Tarabrina, N. V. *Psychological Characteristics of "Invisible" Stress Victims.* Poster at Ann. Meeting Int. Soc. for Traumatic Stress, Chicago, IL, November 1994.

Radiation Protection Dosimetry
Vol. 68, No. 3/4, pp. 257–259 (1996)
Nuclear Technology Publishing

THE SOCIAL AND CULTURAL CONSTRUCTION OF RADIOLOGICAL RISK: A CASE STUDY

D. Van Nuffelen
Radiation Protection Service,
Cité Administrative de l'Etat, Quartier Vésale
B–1010 Brussels, Belgium

Abstract — Man, society or culture, considered as objects, cannot be measured in the same way as one would measure gravity or a hyperbola. In these conditions, how can one isolate the socio-anthropological aspects from the overall perception of radiological risks, thus the nuclear question? This paper deals with an empirical study derived from some fundamental research conducted in order to explain how different social actors conceive the nuclear question by means of different social constructions of reality. It fits into the sociological scheme of knowledge posing a set of methodological and theoretical questions that have as the object the study of the social determinants of knowledge related to the nuclear question. The present survey, carried out in Belgian agricultural workers, makes clear how such determinants interact to form one social construction of the radiological risk. It allows us to presume that the perception of the radiological risks cannot be reduced to some laypeople's measurable psychic (mis)perceptions.

INTRODUCTION

In this paper, the hypothesis is formulated according to which the nuclear question — especially the radiological risk — is socially constructed[1] by social actors. This hypothesis is taken from a socio-anthropological study[2] carried out in Belgium about two years ago, during eight months, using a sample of agricultural workers, to make clear how the reality of radiological risk is socially and culturally built. Note that the question is not to know what these people think about nuclear risk, but to seek the way they conceive it, to explain how they make sense of it. Such research implies very sophisticated methods for analysing the system of thought commonly used by the members of a given social group on a given subject.

METHODS

On the whole, its methodology is based on a participant observation: the *monographic approach*, more precisely the *crossed life narrations* method. Investigators went to the farms. They had interviews of about ninety minutes with the members of each extended family at the farms. The respondents did not know the actual aim of the survey. Nobody told them it was related to nuclear issues and nobody told them it was a socio-anthropological study. The interviewers were introduced by agronomists as members of the Ministry of Health who were preparing an information booklet for the farmers and, therefore, needed to know the agricultural world better. The interviews were semi-directive: the respondents did not have to fill in a questionnaire nor to answer any closed question, but were asked to speak according to one common reading grid used by the interviewers. This grid contained the same elements of discussion, in the same order, for each farm of the sample. This means that the introduction of nuclear issues

into the discussion occurred at an equally unexpected moment for each respondent.

In doing so, the risk of inducing their responses is very low. This point is fundamental, because their talk, in such conditions, is expected to represent their normal way of conceiving radiological risk. Note that, if necessary, the investigators revive the discussion. Furthermore, they note most of the reactions of the members of the extended families.

The interviews are recorded and, later, written down in their entirety, as well as all the observations and notes. As a result, a complete monograph is obtained for each farm of the sample. The treatment of these monographs consists in a content analysis. This permits one to draw the pattern of the social and cultural construction of radiological risk used by the agricultural workers. It would take too long to explain here each step of this analysis — the monographs are just divided in different semantic topics. These must be clearly unequivocal. Then they are compared one by one in each monograph. Computer programs are used for these comparisons and the statistical analysis that they imply. Perhaps it is important to note that such research does not separate quantitative and qualitative techniques of investigation. This study consists of statistical and semiological analyses.

The *saturation level*, in other words the number of monographs after which the semantic topics become redundant, is reached after ten monographs (twelve monographs are considered in the study). This point must be explained. If we consider the size of the sample, which contains about sixty individuals, it is clear that such a sample is not a representative cross section of these workers. But it is possible to carry on the study on a representative sample of this population. According to calculations, we should take a random sample of a little more than one thousand individuals. On the other hand, in considering a word as a statistical unit, the size of the sample is here about thirty eight thousand. In terms of content analysis, it may be enough to provide good hypotheses on a given system of thought related to radiological risk. Consequently, the next step of the present research would consist in analysing these hypotheses on a larger scale.

RESULTS AND DISCUSSION

In the present state of the study, the redundant semantic topics observed lead to the idea that a common way of conceiving radiological risk may be found in farm workers. To consider this point, a few words about some results of the study are given.

A first interesting result is the proportion (p) of nuclear issues expressed in the monographs. An effective number of words (n) equals about thirty eight thousand, and a sample error (α) of five per cent represents more or less seventeen per cent only. It is thus obvious that nuclear issues do not interest the farm workers a great deal. However, in this ratio are found very interesting common semantic topics.

As can be seen, the range of common semantic topics meaning that 'nuclear technology is a problem of society' has the highest relative frequency (Figure 1). Then comes the range of topic two: 'nuclear questions are not under citizen control'. These topics are an interesting discovery. For farm workers, indeed, radiological risk, firstly, is thought of in terms of political debate.

Then, in topics three and four, radiological risk is associated with the deep gap which exists between the traditional culture of farm workers and the very different way of life of nuclear workers. It would take too long to explain here, but employees in the nuclear industry are described by farm workers as 'maniacs', 'outsiders' (even if they come from the country, even if they are relatives), 'profiteers', 'wasters', 'liars' and 'corrupt individuals'. Furthermore, their activity is regarded as a very mysterious and very hidden thing. Lastly, as can be seen in topics five and six, farm labourers are not interested in nuclear issues. As some of them said, they have no time to worry about such 'lucubrations'. To conclude, note that topic seven represents only five per cent, and yet, it is the only case in which radiological risk is thought of in terms of biological effect; and then only with respect to cattle.

Hypothetical explanation

To explain such topics, the following hypothesis may be taken into account. The everyday life of farm labourers is made of clear relationships between commonplace elements of significance, such as the farm, the family, the earth, the cattle and so on. In this semantic set, making sense depends on agricultural activity. It is through their everyday activities that these people bring some sense to their existence. This semantic set appears as a kind of matrix of significances. That means that all the

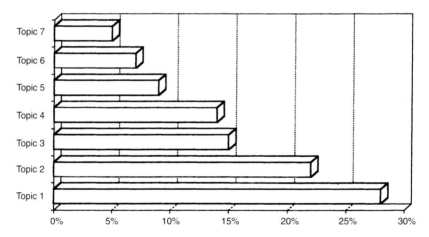

$$\frac{\sigma}{\bar{x}} = 0.56$$

$$n = 37,952$$

$$\alpha = 0.05$$

$$p \in \left[16.6 \times 10^{-2} ; 17.4 \times 10^{-2} \right]$$

Topic 1 . Nuclear technology is a problem of society.
Topic 2 . Nuclear questions are not under citizen control.
Topic 3 . Nuclear workers are abnormal people.
Topic 4 . Nuclear energy is a taboo.
Topic 5 . Nuclear issues do not concern the farm workers.
Topic 6 . Nuclear issues are not known at all.
Topic 7 . Nuclear risk concerns the cattle only.

Figure 1. Common semantic topics.

events which may occur are related to it and interpreted through it. A deeper analysis shows that this particular system of thought depends on the successive socialisations the members of the peasant class have received, and it is a quite rare occurrence to find any socialisation of radiological risk in the workers' semantic set. Their primary socialisations define basic social determinants of knowledge — such as values, roles or norms — which are common to all agricultural workers. Their secondary socialisations and re-socialisations, on the other hand, define particular social determinants of knowledge which are not common to all such people. Thus, the question is not only to identify such determinants, but mainly to explain how they interact to form one social construction of the radiological risk, in other words how they provide a coherent system of thought which remains in compliance with a collective definition of the nuclear question.

The semantic set of the workers is in relationship to rural society. In this one, making sense depends upon a *typifying* process. The elements of the rural society are defined as *types*, in other words persons or things whose existence, function and usefulness are wholly defined (for instance, 'the vet', 'the agronomist', 'the dairy', 'the sugar refinery', 'the country', 'the village'). Note that all these *types* are always associated with one of

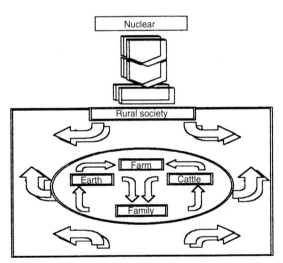

Figure 2. Pattern of social and cultural construction.

the elements of significance of the semantic set. So, it may be supposed that the *typifying* process is the extension of the semantic set. In fact, it forms with it a complex system of references. Both agricultural activity and the typifying process seem to form an agricultural *ethnoknowledge*. This concept is taken from ethnomethodology[3]. It represents knowledge that a social group needs for itself. This implies a reduction of reality for the use of the group's members. It consists in a dialogue for everyday use between the members of the group and an object, more precisely a *negotiation* on the large number of possible ways of thinking of and talking about this object.

Such a concept may explain the processes of risk selection and risk definition observed in agricultural workers: any ethnoknowledge, indeed, provides its members with one plausible explanation of reality and eliminates all others. It must be pointed out that nuclear issues are quite outside the normal ethnoknowledge of agricultural labourers. As can be seen, according to the pattern of social and cultural construction, nuclear reality is thought of as something imposed from the outside, with no sensible relation to everyday life nor to rural society (Figure 2). The explanation is clear: there is no typifying of nuclear issues and these are not tied to normal agricultural activity. Consequently, radiological risk is regarded, if at all, as a very distant worry. Furthermore, it never appears as a fear because of the dangerous effects of ionising radiations on human beings, but because of the danger it represents for the society, in particular the democracy. Indeed, what the peasants consider as a 'radiological risk' is the fact that nuclear knowledge, decisions, facilities, policies and effects are not under their intellectual nor social control; in other words, radiological risk is nucleocracy.

So, the *radiological fear* must be associated with the type of society in which the nuclear question is posed. In fact, the radiological risk is an excellent revealer of the oscillations between fear and knowledge, uncertainty and decision, science and technology, reason and morality, and so on, which constitute an important peculiarity of our modern societies. In this context, socio-anthropology allows us to explain the nuclear question in terms of a societal problem, to understand the different systems of thought constructed by different social actors, to clarify the problematic relationships between some sectors of the society, and to restore the social actor's place in the techno-scientific world.

REFERENCES

1. Berger, P. and Luckmann, T. *La Construction Sociale de la Réalité* (Paris: Méridiens Klincksieck) (1986).

2. van Nuffelen, D. *L'agriculteur et le Nucléaire. Etude de Sociologie Compréhensive* (Bruxelles, Conseil Supérieur d'Hygiène) (1993).

3. Garfinkel, H. *Studies in Ethnomethodology* (New Jersey: Prentice Hall) (1967).

Radiation Protection Dosimetry
Vol. 68, No. 3/4, pp. 261–266 (1996)
Nuclear Technology Publishing

PERSONAL USE OF COUNTERMEASURES SEEN IN A COPING PERSPECTIVE. COULD THE DEVELOPMENT OF EXPEDIENT COUNTERMEASURES AS A REPERTOIRE IN THE POPULATION, OPTIMISE COPING AND PROMOTE POSITIVE OUTCOME EXPECTANCIES, WHEN EXPOSED TO A CONTAMINATION THREAT?

A. Tønnessen†, L. Skuterud†, J. Panova‡, I. G. Travnikova‡, P. Strand† and M. I. Balonov‡
†Norwegian Radiation Protection Authority
PO Box 55, 1345 Østerås, Norway
‡Russian Institute of Radiation Hygiene
8 Mira Str, 197101 St Petersburg, Russia

Abstract — The appraisal and use of countermeasures in a rural district of Russia with quite high deposition after the Chernobyl accident is studied from a coping perspective. The field work was done during the summer of 1994, in the Bryansk region. There are important methodological shortages in the study, the sample of respondents is not a random sample and therefore not necessarily representative for the villages covered, and in some parts of the questionnaire the frequency of 'don't know/missing' responses is too high. With these limitations in mind the current study tries to expand the knowledge about reactions to diffuse environmental threats by studying populations as they continue their daily lives living in a contaminated area. The data from interviews with the final net sample of 163 respondents shows that about one in four were users of countermeasures such as, refraining from consumption of natural foods, or radiometric inspection of the food. Of the different countermeasures that were included in the questionnaire, the renunciation of natural products was most frequently employed. Findings indicate that the respondents who used countermeasures had lower levels of radiocaesium content in their bodies, they felt more able to influence possible health effects of the accident, and at the same time answered that they were more afraid of possible health effects than the non-users of countermeasures. This higher emotional concern is seen in a perspective of 'realistic anxiety', and the use of countermeasures is related to perceived control and outcome expectancies.

INTRODUCTION

In both the short and long term perspective after a nuclear accident, the active utilisation of coping measures in the affected population will greatly affect the dose received and how the population comes to grips with the problem, and thus affects the health consequences in a broad sense. As for the Chernobyl accident, nuclear power plant accidents are not acute, time limited events such as the more traditional industrial accidents. Rather, the Chernobyl accident started a sequence of events that continued to unfold over several years, thereby creating a situation of uncertainty and chronic stress for many people. Nuclear accidents may be without a clearly defined low point, from which 'things will gradually get better'[1]; also the accidents may contaminate populated areas, and if so people will have to live with this contamination for many years to come in their daily life. After the initial phase in which external exposure is more prominent, the internal dose becomes an increasingly more important contributor of radiation dose to man. The behaviour of the exposed population when it comes to dietary habits and use of countermeasures will be important for the internal dose through ingestion pathways. The factual day to day behaviour of individuals, families and social groups as they live on in contaminated areas will greatly affect the doses

they receive. Interventions applied after an accident must not only be sound from a 'pure' radiation protection point of view, but advice and countermeasures offered to the population must also be viewed in the context of how to optimise the coping of the population affected.

THEORETICAL CONSIDERATIONS

Events that are characterised as uncontrollable, unpredictable, not meaningful, and challenging our views of ourselves, tend to be experienced as stressful. The Chernobyl accident, as well as other possible future nuclear accidents, will all be highly charged with just those characteristics. The contamination event has a great potential for causing psychological stress and anxiety in the population, reactions which often are not related to what the experts view as the 'actual' radiation effects and consequences. The strong public reactions to nuclear accidents, from the authorities point of view, are often seen as undesirable as they may cause greater health consequences. Often 'experts' view the anxiety created as not in proportion to the health risk caused by the radiation situation[2–4]. It can be argued that much of the public reaction may indeed be viewed as 'realistic anxiety', and that the question of what degree of an anxiety reaction is an expedient response to a radiation accident is a key element in this field. Sigmund Freud's considerations about 'realistic' versus 'neurotic anxiety' as discussed in the *Introductory Lectures on Psycho-Analysis* in 1916–17 may form an important theoretical basis. There, realistic anxiety is described as a reaction to the perception of an expected or foreseen injury from an external danger[5]*: Freud goes on in this lecture to a discussion about what part of the anxiety reaction may be viewed as expedient. Freud emphasises the 'preparedness' part of the anxiety situation as expedient: a part of the situation which manifests itself in increased sensory attention and motor tension.

'This expectant preparedness can be unhesitatingly recognised as an advantage; indeed its absence may be made responsible for serious consequences. From it there then proceeds on the one hand motor action-flight in the first instance at a higher level *active defence* — and on the other hand what we feel as a state of anxiety.'

(p. 394–395 of Reference 5, our italics). We will postulate that for optimal coping in a radiation accident situation the population must be supplied with the possibility of using 'higher level active defence' in the form of different countermeasures. These countermeasures must come across as possible and meaningful to be employed at an individual level. The individuals that constitute the population must be supplied with a 'repertoire of responses' and intervention actions that give them a possibility of reducing the perceived threat. If the population has such measures available and learn that this is the case, positive outcome expectancies may be developed[6,7].

On the other hand, in a situation where people are

living in a contaminated area after an accident and if they feel that there really is nothing they can do that will reduce the health consequences of the accident, many may develop withdrawal and apathy. This may be related to Seligman's concept of 'Learned Helplessness'[8]. The original theory of learned helplessness was developed after animal experimentation studies[9], and has of course important limitations when generalised to humans. For instance, it has been shown that some people are invigorated by the challenge of uncontrollable events[10]. In the literature about psychosocial reactions after Chernobyl there are many descriptions about asthenia, apathy and fatalistic reactions[11–13]. May some of this be understood as a reaction to an aversive uncontrollable event, and could better coping be achieved by offering expedient countermeasures that may establish positive outcome expectancies in the population?

This study has an explorative hypothesis generating character. The attitudes toward the use of countermeasures, and the reported application of countermeasures were studied. The results were also related to the respondents whole-body content of radiocaesium. The issue was also addressed of the degree to which the respondent feared possible health consequences of the accident, and to what extent such fear could be seen as a 'realistic anxiety' that served as a motivational basis for applying countermeasures. To increase our understanding of coping mechanisms in populations exposed to environmental hazards the importance is stressed of interviewing people living with the contamination problem on a daily basis, as compared to survey studies where people are responding about reactions on a more hypothetical basis[14].

---

*Lecture XXV, page 393: 'It is possible at the start to work upon the subject of anxiety for quite a time without thinking at all of neurotic states. You will understand me at once when I describe this kind of anxiety as 'realistic' anxiety in contrast to 'neurotic' anxiety. Realistic anxiety strikes us as something very rational and intelligible. We may say that it is a reaction to the perception of an external danger — that is, of an injury which is expected and foreseen. It is connected with the flight reflex and it may be regarded as a manifestation of the self-preservative instinct. On what occasions anxiety appears — that is to say, in the face of what objects and in what situations — will of course depend to a large extent of a person's knowledge and on his sense of power *vis-à-vis* the external world. We can quite understand how a savage is afraid of a cannon and frightened by an eclipse of the sun, while a white man, who knows how to handle these instruments remains without anxiety in these circumstances. On other occasions it is actually superior knowledge that promotes anxiety, because it makes an early recognition of the danger possible. Thus the savage will be terrified by a trail in the jungle that tells an uninformed person nothing, because it warns him of the proximity of a wild animal; and an experienced sailor will look with terror at a small cloud in the sky that seems trivial to a passenger, because it tells him of an approaching hurricane.'

MATERIALS AND METHODS

The present study was made together with the ECP9 project under the EC/CIS Chernobyl Programme[15] that performed dietary surveys, sampling and measurements of radiocaesium in foods, and whole-body monitoring of about 400 persons in rural areas in the Russian Federation and Ukraine during the summer and autumn of 1994. As a bilateral addition to the ECP9 project questions were also included about the use of different measures to reduce intake of radionuclides (countermeasures), perceptions of risks and other psychosocial issues. Most of the adult population at both sites are employed at the local collective farms. Traditionally the population has small private farms producing most of the food they need themselves, covering nearly all the basic food products (with bread as a major exception), this includes animals producing milk and meat.

Initially, it was intended that the population at both the Russian and Ukrainian sites should be studied. However, at the Ukrainian site the population was informed relatively late about the high radiocaesium levels in locally produced foods, and it is therefore difficult to compare these people with the interviewed Russian population. This paper therefore summarises only results from the Russian site. The Russian study site was two villages in the Novozybkov district of the Bryansk region. The villages, Shelomi and Korchi, received high fallout levels from the Chernobyl accident ($230 \, \text{kBq.m}^{-2}$ — $1500 \, \text{kBq.m}^{-2}$, as a typical range of measurements from ^{137}Cs deposition, May 1994), and was defined as a 'control area' by the authorities[16]. One implication of being a control area was that in 1986 all private animals were purchased by the state in order to reduce the levels of radioactivity in the food consumed by the inhabitants. During the past couple of years a few of the inhabitants have again acquired privately owned animals.

The interviews involved 188 adult persons (112 females and 76 males above 16 years). The respondents were asked if they had been living in the area all the time since the accident, and about the use of countermeasures in different time periods after the accident. On the basis of this 25 respondents were excluded from the analysis because they had not been living in the area for the whole period.

The average age of the respondents was about 49 years, with the female respondents being, on average, 5 years older than the males. A sampling procedure to ensure a representative sample of the population in the villages of Shelomi and Korchi was not employed. Village inhabitants were invited and encouraged to participate. The interviews were conducted both by visiting people in their homes, or people were asked by the head of the collective farm to show up for the interview in the town/village hall.

Especially in the more psychosocial part of the interview there is a large percentage of 'don't know/no answers' to questions. There are several possible explanations for this, it may be related to language problems, i.e. questions that function in an English/Norwegian setting but not in the Russian language and cultural setting, insufficiencies in interview technique, lack of motivation for participation in the study, a reflection of general apathy, a result of the fact that respondents were given the possibility of an easy way out by offering the option of 'don't know', etc. The high proportion of 'don't knows' adds further to this study's 'explorative' approach, but some of the answers given are nevertheless interesting. Also the methodological problems encountered will be a concern for any researcher doing work in this area.

The different countermeasures about which the respondents were asked, were:

(i)   abstain from milk consumption,
(ii) abstain from meat consumption,
(iii) refrain from vegetables and/or fruit consumption,
(iv) refrain from consumption of natural/wild food products,

(v)   refuse to keep cattle,
(vi) change methods of cooking,
(vii) radiometric inspections of food.

Some advice about the use of these countermeasures had been given by the authorities. As an indication of the respondents general coping style, they were asked to rate their own typical coping pattern with an item related to Rotter's concept of 'locus of control'[17]. They were asked: 'When you face difficult problems, do you try to: influence the situation, adapt to the situation, avoid the situation, or do you wait and hope that the problem will eventually disappear?' There had been experience with the use of this single item from surveys in Norway where it was found to be significantly correlated to such background variables as education and income level[14].

RESULTS AND DISCUSSION

Use of the different countermeasures in 1994

In 1994, 16% of the males and 33% of the females answered that they used one or more of the seven listed countermeasures, about 8% of all respondents used more than one of the countermeasures (the expression users/non-users will in the rest of the text imply users/non-users of countermeasures in 1994). Most of the users reported themselves as being consistent users in all years since the accident. It seems to be very important to understand the respondents use of countermeasures in 1994 as a result of not stopping the application of countermeasures. The most frequently used measure in 1994 was 'refraining from natural food products consumption', followed by 'changed method of cooking'. Renunciation of natural products was also reflected in the percentage of the population answering that they did not consume wild mushrooms; in 1994–1995 it was about 50%, whilst in 1985 (before the Chernobyl accident) only about 20% of adult rural inhabitants of Bryansk region did not consume wild mushrooms[16]. The renunciation of natural products is a more frequently applied countermeasure among the female respondents, while more males use radiometric inspection of food as a countermeasure. Convincingly, it was found that the users had significantly lower radiocaesium activity concentrations in their bodies ($P < 0.01$ for females, $P < 0.05$ for males), on average only about 50% of the level in those who did not use any measures (see Figure 1). Obviously the less frequent consumption of wild mushrooms was an important contributor to lower body burdens as the study also showed that there was a significant correlation between mushroom consumption and radiocaesium activity concentrations in people[17].

Considerations regarding the use of countermeasures

When it comes to attitudes toward the application of countermeasures, about one in five of the respondents answered that they did have the possibility of applying such measures, twice as many respondents (about four out of ten) answered that it was *not* possible, while the rest responded 'don't know' to the question. The respondents who did not feel they had a possibility of applying countermeasures were asked about different possible explanations for this. The respondents were offered six different possible explanations they could confirm as an explanation, including 'don't know'. Insufficiencies in availability and trust in information, and shortage of money and resources were among the most frequent of the explanations given, whereas about 50% checked out 'don't know' as a response.

The respondents were asked to judge their present knowledge about countermeasures and radioactivity (e.g. contamination level, health consequences etc.). In accordance with the finding that shortcomings in information is one explanation variable for differences between users/non-users, the users rated their own knowledge to be better than the non-users.

The respondents were also asked to give a numerical ranking to the different countermeasures in accordance with their importance, but unfortunately this item did not function in the interview. The same result was experienced when asking the respondents about their reactions to different difficult situations: asking them to respond by applying a scale from 1 to 6, where 1 represents a very weak reaction and 6 a very strong one.

When it comes to outcome expectancies and the use of countermeasures the respondents were asked if they felt that countermeasures gave them the possibility of influencing the health impact of the Chernobyl accident on themselves and their families. The main response was that about half of the respondents felt that use of countermeasures gave them no possibility of influencing the health impact, and 15% felt it was only possible to a small extent. But, interestingly, of the 15% that indicated a possibility for influencing impact through application of measures, the users are over-represented. In particular, female users more often responded it was possible, to some extent, that countermeasures provide the possibility of influencing the impact of the accident.

In accordance with general findings from stress research[19-21], the working hypothesis used in our research is that the respondents experience of controllability is one important variable that determines the severity of the stress people experience while living in a contaminated area. The fallout pattern from the Chernobyl accident is, of course, something over which respondents cannot experience any control, but the responses to the question about the expedient of countermeasures used could indicate important differences when it comes to the degree of positive outcome expectancies that respondents held when considering whether they could influence possible health effects of the accident. The variation of control experienced will be related both to the individual's general coping style and to the dynamic of the specific threat, in this context a man-made environmental threat undetectable by our senses. One of the many special features of contamination as an environmental threat is that the population will be living with the threat in their environment for decades, and their coping and behaviour in the long term in a contaminated area will greatly influence the dose received as well as their psychological well being.

When it comes to the item regarding respondents'

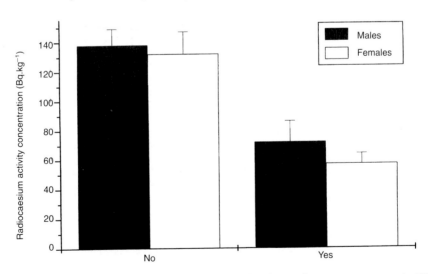

Figure 1. Content of radiocaesium in the population depending on whether they used any countermeasures in 1994 (arithmetic mean ± standard error).

general coping pattern the respondents find the question hard to answer and about 40% have responded 'don't know'. Among those (15%) that indicate a more active coping style (e.g. more internal locus of control) users of countermeasures are over represented (46% of them are users). This can be seen as an indication of how people's general coping style is also a determination variable for their behaviour when confronted with such an environmental threat. Generally, coping is defined as the process by which a person tries to manage stressful demands, and it is often categorised in the two forms of problem-focused and emotion-focused coping[22,23]. Most people are found to use both forms of coping, but with more uncontrollable problems like a fallout situation, emotion-focused coping may be the more available option. Some researchers believe that emotion-focused coping with its emotional preoccupations may get in the way of good problem solving[24]. We take as a starting point that emotional reactions to stressful events have a functional value. As was mentioned in the Introduction it is believed that the old theoretical distinction between realistic anxiety, and a neurotic anxiety touches a core element of this field. When it comes to low doses and dose rates, what is the 'actual danger', and by what certainty can the 'actual danger' be determined? What is the 'right' level of anxiety when a population is affected by radioactive fallout, and with what kind of 'higher level defences' has the population been supplied from authorities and experts? Some researchers have viewed the strong reactions among the public to the Chernobyl accident as an indication of reactions out of proportion, and have even used the term 'radiophobia'. The strong

reactions could also be viewed in the context that the accident had the important features of events that tend to be experienced as stressful, especially the elements of unpredictability and lack of perceived control[25]. In this study the respondents were asked how afraid they currently were of the possible health consequences of the radioactive pollution on themselves and their family, the response categories were; very afraid, afraid, not so afraid and not at all afraid. As illustrated in Figure 2, there were 60% that responded that they were not at all afraid of the health consequences, and of them only 15% were users, while about 50% of the 15% that responded very afraid were users of countermeasures.

CONCLUSIONS

The current study has very important limitations due to methodological shortcomings, e.g. lack of representative sample, and a high 'don't know' or missing response on many variables. Results must therefore be interpreted very cautiously. Regardless of this the present study examines the respondents *feelings*, attitudes, and repertoire regarding countermeasures, and how interventions also must be viewed in the perspective of improving the coping of a population facing an environmental threat. The respondents that applied countermeasures had a significantly lower whole-body content of radiocaesium, they were more afraid of the health effects of the accident, and viewed the application of countermeasures as a vehicle for reducing health effects and thereby perhaps promoting the feeling of positive outcome expectancies.

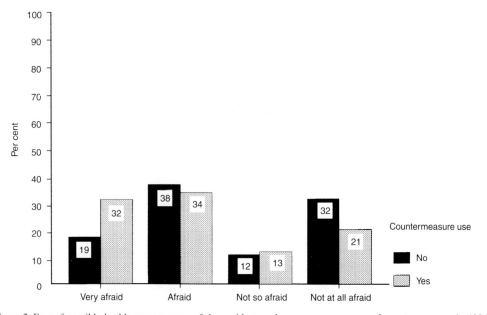

Figure 2. Fear of possible health consequences of the accident, and user versus non-user of countermeasures in 1994.

REFERENCES

1. Weisæth, L. *Psychosocial Reactions in Norway to Nuclear Fallout from the Chernobyl Disaster*. In: Communities at Risk. Collective Responses to Technological Hazards. Eds S. R. Couch and J. S. Kroll-Smith. (New York: Peter Lang Publishing) pp. 53–80 (1991).

2. Michell, R. C. *Rationality and Irrationality in the Public's Perception of Nuclear Power*. In: Public Reactions to Nuclear Power: Are there Critical Masses? Eds W. R. Freudenburg and E. A. Rosa (Westview Press) pp. 137–179 (1984).

3. Daglish, J. *Radiophobia and Radiation Protection*. Atom **383**, 14–17 (1988).

4. Oberhofer, M. *Thoughts of the Phenomena of Radiophobia*. CD-NA-12056-EN-C (Luxembourg: Directorate General Commission of the European Communities) (1989).

5. Freud, S. *Lecture XXV, Introductory Lectures on Psycho-Analysis (1916–17, Part III)*. In: The Standard Edition of the Complete Psychological Works of Sigmund Freud, Volume XVI. Ed. J. Strachey (London: Hogarth Press) (1963).

6. Hytten, K. *Studies on Stress and Coping: Psychosocial and Physical Dangers: Establishment and Manifestations of Negative and Positive Response Outcome Expectancies* (University of Oslo) (1989).

7. Ursin, H. and Hytten, K. *Outcome Expectancies and Psychosomatic Consequences*. In: Personal Coping: Theory, Research, and Application. Ed. B. N. Carpenter (Westport: Praeger Publishers/Greenwood Publishing Group) pp. 171–184 (1992).

8. Seligman, M. E. P. *Helplessness* (San Francisco: Freeman) (1975).

9. Overmeier, J. B. and Seligman, M. E. P. *Effects of Inescapable Shock upon Subsequent Escape and Avoidance Responding*. J. Comp. Physiol. Psychol. **63** (1967).

10. Wortman, C. B. and Brehm, J. W. *Responses to Uncontrollable Outcomes: An Integration of Reactance Theory and the Learned Helplessness Model*. Adv. Exp. Soc. Psychol. **8**, 236–279 (1975).

11. Viinamäki, H., Kumpusalo, E., Myllykangas, M., Salomaa, S., Kumpusalo, L., Komakov, S., Ilchenko, I., Zhukowsky, G. and Nissinen, A. *The Chernobyl Accident and Mental Wellbeing — a Population Study*. Acta Psychiatr. Scand. **91**, 396–401 (1995).

12. Drottz Sjöberg, B. M., Rumyantseva, G. M., Martyvshov, A. N., Arkhangelskaya, H. V., Nyagu, A. and Ageeva, L. A. *Public Reactions to the Chernobyl Accident. Report from a Data Collection in 1993 in Russia, Belarus and Ukraine*. In: Social and Psychological factors. The Joint Study Project 2 (JSP-2), January 1994 (1994).

13. Spivak, L. I. *Psychiatric Aspect of the Accident at the Chernobyl Nuclear Power Station*. Eur. J. Psychiatr. **6**, 207–212 (1992).

14. Tønnessen, A., Reitan, J. B., Strand, P., Waldahl, R. and Weisæth, L. *Interpretation of Radiation Risk by the Norwegian Population*. In: Biomedical and Psychosocial Consequences of Radiation from Man-made Radionuclides in the Biosphere. Ed. G. Sundnes (Trondheim: Tapir) pp. 251–278 (1995).

15. Strand, P., Howard, B. and Avery, V. (Eds) *Transfer of Radionuclides to Animals — their Comparative Importance under Different Agricultural Ecosystems and Appropriate Countermeasures*. Final Report EUR 16539. Experimental Collaboration 9 — International Scientific Collaboration on the Consequences of the Chernobyl Accident 1991–1995 (Luxembourg: Office for Official Publications of the European Communities) (1996).

16. Balonov, M. I. and Travnikova, I. G. *Importance of Diet and Protective Actions of Internal Dose from ^{137}Cs Radionuclides in Inhabitants of the Chernobyl Region*. In: The Chernobyl Papers. Eds S. E. Mervin and M. I. Balonov (Richland: Research Enterprises) pp. 127–166 (1993).

17. Skuterud, L., Travnikova, I. G., Balonov, M. I., Strand, P. and Howard, B. J. *Importance of Fungi for Intake of Radiocaesium by Populations in Russia*. (Submitted).

18. Glass, D. C. and Singer, J. E. *Urban Stress: Experiments on Noise and Social Stressors* (New York: Academic Press) (1972).

19. Averill, J. R. *Personal Control over Aversive Stimuli and its Relationship to Stress*. Psychol. Bull. **80**, 286–303 (1973).

20. Miller, S. M. *Controllability and Human Stress: Method, Evidence, and Theory*. Behav. Res. Ther. **17**, 287–306 (1979).

21. Rotter, J. B. *Generalized Expectancies for Internal versus External Control of Reinforcement*. Psychological Monographs: General and Applied **80** (1966).

22. Lazarus, R. S. and Folkman, S. *Stress, Appraisal, and Coping* (New York: Springer) (1984).

23. Lazarus, R. S. *Emotion and Adaption* (New York: Oxford University Press) (1991).

24. Nolen-Hoeksema, S. and Morrow, J. *A Prospective Study of Depression and Distress Following a Natural Disaster: The 1989 Loma Prieta Earthquake*. J. Pers. Soc. Psychol. **61**, 105–121 (1991).

25. Drottz Sjöberg, B. M. and Persson, L. *Public Reaction to Radiation: Fear, Anxiety or Phobia?* Health Phys. **64**, 223–231 (1993).

Radiation Protection Dosimetry
Vol. 68, No. 3/4, pp. 267–271 (1996)
Nuclear Technology Publishing

THE ROLE OF SOCIAL AND PSYCHOLOGICAL FACTORS IN RADIATION PROTECTION AFTER ACCIDENTS

M. Morrey† and P. Allen‡
†National Radiological Protection Board
Chilton, Didcot, Oxon, OX11 0RQ, UK
‡Robens Institute, University of Surrey
Guildford, Surrey GU2 5XH, UK

Abstract — The inclusion of social and psychological factors in the justification and optimisation of intervention after an accident requires identification of the relevant factors and their appropriate quantification. Recent studies suggest a possible approach. Some social and psychological factors either influence the consequences of radiation protection countermeasures, or are direct consequences of those measures. Such factors can be grouped into those that alter the dose-effectiveness of a countermeasure, those that extend the need for countermeasures in time or space, and those that fall into neither of the first two categories. Factors of the first two types can be quantified in terms of changes to the anticipated averted dose and monetary cost of a countermeasure. Quantification of the third type is currently difficult, but the existence of structural models for applications in social psychology suggests that such models could be developed for radiation protection in the future.

INTRODUCTION

Even before the accident at the Chernobyl nuclear power plant in 1986, it was recognised that the overall response to accidents involving a potential public radiation exposure needed to take account of social factors[1]. The difficulties for those involved in radiation protection are to determine the extent to which these factors should be taken into account when justifying and optimising the radiation protection aspects of the response and how to take account of them.

In 1990, the National Radiological Protection Board (NRPB) developed advice on emergency response in the UK which included an explicit conceptual treatment of some postulated social and psychological factors. These were the reassurance provided, and the anxiety induced, by introducing countermeasures, together with the disruption which countermeasures cause to individuals and society[2]. Subsequently, the relevance of social and psychological factors to the setting of intervention levels has been reaffirmed by both the International Commission on Radiological Protection (ICRP) and the International Atomic Energy Agency (IAEA)[3,4]. All three organisations have recommended multi-attribute decision-aiding techniques[5,6] as a means of incorporating such factors into the optimisation process. However, no further detailed guidance has been provided on which factors to include, their likely influence on the response, or how they might be quantified for inclusion in the optimisation.

A number of studies have been carried out in Russia, Belarus and Ukraine with the purpose of better understanding the role and significance of social and psychological factors in accident response. These studies were part of an international collaborative programme agreed between the Commission of the European Communities (CEC) and the Commonwealth of Independent States (CIS) following the accident at the Chernobyl nuclear power plant[7]. These studies are focused on the extent to which such factors should be included in the optimisation of radiation protection after an accident. This paper summarises the key findings so far and draws some preliminary conclusions regarding both the role of social and psychological factors in radiation protection after accidents and how they could be quantified for inclusion in the justification and optimisation of countermeasures.

IMPORTANCE OF SOCIAL AND PSYCHOLOGICAL FACTORS IN ACCIDENT RESPONSE

As indicated above, it is widely accepted that social and psychological factors are important for accident response in their own right. In the context of the Chernobyl accident they have played an even more important role than might have been expected in the West. This is partly due to the coincidence of the accident with the movement towards freedom of information and the increasing economic and political instability in the affected republics. Research in Russia, Belarus and Ukraine has quantified many aspects of the social and psychological response and demonstrated the increased stress experienced by individuals, the disruption to their lives and the fear induced by the situation[8]. In a series of decision conferences organised by the CEC in 1990 as part of the IAEA Chernobyl Project[9], it was judged that the illnesses caused by increased stress within the affected populations would far outweigh the anticipated radiation health effects[10]. Further findings within the CEC/CIS collaborative programme are reported in detail by Allen and Marston[11] and summarised below.

It was found that in 1991/2 people in the contaminated territories were suffering from a degree of general psychological distress. This seemed partly to be because they felt there was nothing they could do about their situation. Consequently, feelings of helplessness and fatalism dominated the survey responses. Medical examinations were felt to have been superficial and the lack of information tended to cause further mistrust and feelings of pointlessness. Most people still ate food from their own allotments, either because there was no 'clean' food available, or because it was too expensive. Many still went into the forests because they felt that they could not live without such a 'paradise'. People reported having become passive, living from day to day in an atmosphere of uncertainty and hopelessness. Other effects of the accident included: employment problems, including a decrease in the workforce as people relocated to 'clean' areas; disruption of children's education; break up of family and other social networks due to relocation; and, frustration that humanitarian aid was promised but often not received.

The heightened anxiety, inadequate provision of information and mistrust of official representatives resulted in disbelief in the efficacy of countermeasures. Many people thought that there were no food controls, particularly in smaller markets. At the same time, their villages were suffering from a general food shortage. Little was known about radiation monitoring and protective measures, except for the tarmacking of some surfaces. This specific measure was perceived to have been poorly carried out, probably because during the dying years of the Soviet regime people had learnt that little was ever done properly. Responses by the authorities to the accident were seen in this light. People were particularly concerned about: the health effects of the radiation; the effects on the next generation; the lack of uncontaminated food and the poor supply of food in general; the limited implementation of countermeasures, particularly relocation; and, the lack of clear relevant information. Psychologically, people seemed to need both national and international attention, to feel they were being told the truth, and to feel that they could have some control over their situation.

From this summary it is clear that decision makers, particularly at a political level, need to take account of social and psychological factors when developing strategies for response to accidents, particularly in the long term. The task for the radiation protection community is to identify which of these factors should be incorporated in the optimisation of the radiation protection aspects of accident response, and how they might be quantified to achieve this.

SOCIAL AND PSYCHOLOGICAL FACTORS IN RADIATION PROTECTION

To determine which social and psychological factors should be included as radiation protection factors it is useful to refer to the ICRP definition which states that 'radiological protection factors are those which are related to the level of health protection sought'[3]. ICRP makes it clear that, provided the primary aim of the intervention is to reduce doses, all consequences of that intervention, including social and psychological consequences, are to be treated as radiation protection factors and included in the justification and optimisation of the measure. It follows that all factors which influence these consequences should also be included. In other words if, for example, informational or economic aspects influence social and psychological outcomes, and subsequently are likely to influence the effectiveness of countermeasures, then these aspects are relevant to decisions on radiological protection. ICRP gives as examples of radiation protection factors the reassurance provided by, and the anxiety and disruption caused by, an intervention.

In order to include relevant social and psychological factors in countermeasures decisions it is necessary to identify and measure the key factors and to determine their manner of influence. Ideally such a quantification should be achieved using appropriate structural models of behaviour. However, whilst a variety of such models have been proposed and tested in a number of applications (see, for example, Ref. 12), considerable further research is required to develop and validate such models in the context of radiological accidents. The conclusions drawn from present research can therefore only be preliminary. Despite this, the studies carried out so far have been able to identify some important factors and to quantify their influence on the consequences of countermeasures.

Studies of stress in the affected republics have shown that there is a systematic difference between the levels in contaminated areas compared with those in the uncontaminated areas[13]. There is also a systematic difference between the stress in each republic, presumably reflecting the different political and economic situations, and national attitudes. Further studies were carried out to look at the changes in stress brought about by the relocation of populations, compared with those remaining in the contaminated areas[14]. It might be expected that taking people out of the contaminated areas would reduce their stress. However, whilst this was indeed the case in Russia, the relocations studied in Belarus and Ukraine were found to have had no measurable impact on the level of stress. More detailed examination of the implementation of the strategies in the three republics revealed that the Russians were given more opportunity for self-determination over the timing and manner of their relocation. They were also provided with a better economic package than their counterparts in the other republics[15]. Studies such as these show that it is possible to quantify the influence of both the accident and subsequent countermeasures on some social and psychological factors. In particular, such studies can provide key information for optimising the implementation of countermeasures[16].

A separate study revealed that official advice in Belarus to avoid the known most highly contaminated foods (private milk and local forest produce and game) had only been partially sucessful in reducing doses[17]. Whilst the detailed reasons for this were not explored, it is likely that the worsening economic situation, the lack of availability or knowledge of alternative food supplies, mistrust of official statements and a desire to resume pre-accident lifestyles all contributed. Since some of these reasons are social psychological, this raises the possibility that social and psychological factors have the potential to reduce the dose-effectiveness of countermeasures.

One problem with which the governments of the three CIS republics are currently grappling is that of the resistance of settlement populations to the lifting of countermeasures. For example, Rumyantseva[18] reports that most people, when asked for their views, said that countermeasures already taken should be continued, and that further measures were also necessary. This indicates that although the doses received in many areas are now small, settlement populations are unwilling to relinquish their status as 'victims' of the Chernobyl accident. Since many of the contaminated settlements receive direct or indirect financial assistance it is likely that economic pressures have contributed significantly to this resistance; another probable factor is mistrust of the authorities. However, a further finding from the CEC/CIS studies suggests that such resistance may also result because those living in the contaminated territories do not perceive dose to be an adequate sole measure for their total harm from the accident. It was found that, independent of their 'perceived dose', the measured average level of contamination in the studied settlements also contributed significantly to the stress individuals experienced in Ukraine, and may have done so in Russia[19,20]. In other words, people were concerned about living in contaminated areas, irrespective of their perceived dose, and irrespective of the countermeasures that had been implemented to protect them.

The above examples illustrate the complexity of the interaction between some social and psychological factors and radiation protection decisions. Whilst the previously identified factors of reassurance, anxiety and disruption are clearly implicated in these studies, more is now known about the manner in which they affect and are affected by countermeasure decisions, particularly in the longer term. Further research is required to improve modelling and quantification of the radiation protection factors that are also social and psychological factors. However, based on what has been learned, it is useful to explore possible ways forward with respect to the quantitative inclusion of such factors in the justification and optimisation of intervention strategies.

INCLUDING SOCIAL AND PSYCHOLOGICAL FACTORS IN THE JUSTIFICATION AND OPTIMISATION OF INTERVENTION

The studies summarised in the preceding section indicate that it is possible to devise research programmes which can identify those social and psychological factors that either influence the consequences of radiation protection countermeasures, or are direct consequences of those measures. As was also indicated in that section, the quantification of these influences and consequences requires the development of appropriate structural models. The existence of such models for other applications (e.g. Ref. 12) suggests that assuming the development of appropriate models is not unreasonable. However, it is important that such models quantify the impact of social and psychological factors in appropriate terms. This section therefore addresses the quantification of social and psychological factors in terms that can be related to other key factors, in particular dose averted and monetary cost.

The reported studies have shown that relevant social and psychological factors can be divided into three types: (i) those that alter the dose-effectiveness of a countermeasure; (ii) those that tend to extend the temporal or spatial boundaries of an intervention; and (iii) those that, whilst influencing or being a consequence of the intervention, fall into neither of the first two types. An example of each type is given in the previous section: the reduced effectiveness of food countermeasures in Belarus illustrates the first type, the pressure for further countermeasures in settlements where doses are now low is an example of the second type, and the differences in stress in the three republics due to relocation represents the third.

The distinction between these three types is useful because it reflects the manner in which each factor can be quantified for incorporation in the justification and optimisation of an intervention strategy. If the optimisation is seen in its simplest form, that of a balance between the aggregated costs (monetary value) and benefits (dose averted) of a protective strategy, then the action of each of these types of factor can be viewed as follows. Factors of the first type act to alter the benefit anticipated from averting dose. Therefore, they could be quantified in terms of the amount by which they are expected to modify the anticipated dose-effectiveness of a countermeasure. Factors of the second type act to alter the level of resource required for a countermeasure. These, therefore, could be quantified in terms of the consequent change in anticipated monetary cost.

Factors of the third type form a cost or, in limited cases, a benefit, in their own right. At present, it is difficult to suggest how these might easily be aggregated for inclusion in the justification and optimisation of a countermeasure. As a first step, a more qualitative approach could be used. Descriptive information on the likely direction and magnitude of the social and psychological outcomes generated by different intervention options could be provided to the policy maker. For example, with respect to food interdiction, strategy options might include combinations of the following: providing advice to avoid certain food sources; legally banning certain food sources; physically preventing the local production of certain foods; and, providing uncontaminated supplies for purchase or free distribution. Each option would be associated with consequent social and psychological outcomes. Providing policy makers with such information would at least enable an intervention strategy to be developed which took account of these factors. To test the usefulness of this approach, a preliminary module providing information on the implications for stress of different methods of implementing relocation policies has been incorporated within the computer decision support system PRANA, developed within the CEC/CIS collaboration programme[21]. A more quantitative approach might be to define some form of unit collective social and psychological detriment in a manner reminiscent of the assignment of a monetary value to unit collective dose in some decision aiding approaches[22]. However, further understanding of the range and interdependency of social and psychological outcomes would be required in order to define an appropriate quantity.

CONCLUSIONS

In the context of response to major radiological accidents social and psychological factors are important in their own right. However, some such factors are also radiation protection factors, in that they directly influence or are influenced by interventions aimed at reducing doses from the accident. Preliminary studies carried out in Russia, Belarus and Ukraine as part of a CEC/CIS collaborative programme following the accident at Chernobyl, have begun to elucidate and quantify the interaction between these social and psychological factors and radiation protection measures.

One of the difficulties in incorporating relevant social and psychological factors into justification and optimisation procedures is the need to quantify their consequences in terms that can readily be related to the other factors being considered, in particular dose and monetary cost. Based on the findings of the preliminary

CEC/CIS studies, it is suggested that social and psychological factors that are radiation protection factors can be divided into three types: those that alter the dose-effectiveness of a strategy; those that tend to prolong or extend the area of an intervention; and those that, whilst being a consequence of the intervention, do not fall into either of the first two categories. Factors of the first two types, once quantified, can be fairly readily incorporated into an optimisation procedure, since, respectively, they simply modify the anticipated radiological benefit and the monetary cost.

Factors of the third type are not so straightforward to include. As a first step, information on the likely direction and magnitude of the strain generated by different countermeasures could be provided to the decision maker. This would at least enable a strategy, once decided upon, to be implemented in the best way with respect to stress. A more quantitative approach might be to define some form of unit collective social and psychological detriment.

It is recognised that the inclusion of social and psychological factors that are radiation protection factors into the justification and optimisation of countermeasures decisions assumes the development of appropriate social psychological structural models for estimating their consequences. However, the existence of such models for other applications argues that it is not unreasonable to presume such quantitative modelling ability will be developed in the future.

ACKNOWLEDGEMENT

The authors wish to acknowledge the contribution made to the ideas in this paper by Dr Neil Higgins of the National Radiological Protection Board through his research on the role of social and psychological factors in so-called indirect countermeasures, and on their incorporation within computer decision support systems. They also wish to acknowledge the support of the Commission of the European Communities for the part-funding of this work.

REFERENCES

1. International Commission on Radiation Protection. *Protection of the Public in the Event of Major Radiation Accidents: Principles for Planning* (Oxford: Pergamon Press) ICRP Publication 40, Ann. ICRP **14**(2) (1984).

2. National Radiological Protection Board. *Emergency Reference Levels of Dose for Early Countermeasures to Protect the Public* (London: HMSO) Doc. NRPB **1**(4), 7–33 (1990).

3. International Commission on Radiation Protection. *Principles for Intervention for Protection of the Public in a Radiological Emergency* (Oxford: Pergamon Press) ICRP Publication 63, Ann. ICRP **22**(4) (1991).

4. International Atomic Energy Agency. *Intervention Criteria in a Nuclear or Radiation Emergency.* Safety Series no 109 (Vienna; IAEA 1994).

5. Merkhofer, M. W. *Decision Science and Social Risk Management* (Dordrecht: D. Reidel Publishing Company) (1987).

6. International Commission on Radiation Protection. *Optimization and Decision-making in Radiological Protection* (Oxford: Pergamon Press) ICRP Publication 55, Ann. ICRP **20**(1) (1989).

7. Stather, J. *International Collaboration after Chernobyl.* Radiat. Prot. Bull. **149**, 19–21 (1994).

8. Drottz-Sjoberg, B.-M., Rumyantseva, G. M., Arkhangelskaya, H. V., Nyagu, A. and Ageeva, L. *Public Reactions to the Chernobyl Accident. Report from a Data Collection in 1993 in Russia, Belarus and Ukraine* (Center for Risk Research, Stockholm School of Economics, Stockholm) (1994).

9. International Atomic Energy Agency. *The International Chernobyl Project: Technical report* (Vienna: IAEA) Report by an International Advisory Committee (1991).

10. French, S., Kelly, N. and Morrey, M. *Decision conferencing and the International Chernobyl Project.* J. Radiol. Prot. **12**(1), 17–28 (1992).

11. Allen, P. T. and Marston, J. *Social and Psychological Factors of the Chernobyl Aftermath: a Qualitative Analysis of Interview Responses in One Affected Area of Russia.* Robens Institute Report R193/PSY/002, University of Surrey (1993).

12. Schwarzer, R. *Self-efficacy in the Adoption and Maintenance of Health Behaviours: Theoretical Approaches and a New Model.* In: Self-efficacy: Thought Control of Action. Ed. R. Schwarzer (Washington: Hemisphere) (1992).

13. Allen, P. T. *Stress and Locus of Control in the Chernobyl Region.* Paper presented at the EC Joint Studies Project 2 Workshop, Paris, October 1993.

14. Rumyantseva, G. M., Allen, P. T., Melnichuk, T. N., Margolin, S. A. and Plyplina, D. V. *Locus-of-control in the Population Suffering from the Chernobyl Disaster and Living under Conditions of Chronic Ecological Stress.* Bekhterev Rev. Psychiat. Med. Psychol. **3**, 34–40 (1994).

15. Rumyantseva, G. M. *The History of Relocation Caused by Chernobyl Accident in Russia.* (Moscow: Serbsky Institute) (1994).

16. Higgins, N. A. and Morrey, M. *Social Intervention and Risk Reduction — Indirect Countermeasures.* Radiat. Prot. Dosim. **68**(3/4), 213–217 (1996) (This issue).

17. Skryabin, A. M., Masyakin, V. B., Osypenko, A. N., Vlasova, N. C., Savkin, M. N., Grinev, M., Lebedev, A., Androsova, A., Konstantinov, Y. O., Erkin, V. G., Korelina, N. F., Moskalev, O. S., Robinson, C. A., Prosser, S. L., Jones, K. A. and Morrey, M. *The Distribution of Doses Received in Rural Areas Affected by the Chernobyl Accident.* NRPB-R277 (London: HMSO) (1996).

18. Rumyantseva, G. M. *Trends in Stress and Views on Countermeasures in the Region of Russia Affected by Chernobyl.* Paper presented at the EC Joint Studies Project 2 Workshop, Paris, October 1993 (Available from P. T. Allen).

19. Allen, P. T., Ferents, V., Kasyanenko, A., Plipina, D., Prilipko, V., Rumyantseva, G. and Skryabin, A. *Two Roles for Psychological Variables in the Aftermath of Chernobyl: Inputs and Outcomes.* Presented at an Int. Conf. in Kiev, May 1995.

20. Allen, P. T. *Multiple Components of Stress in the Context of Radiation Risk.* Radiat. Prot. Dosim. **68**(3/4), 245–249 (1996) (This issue).

21. Morrey, M., Dovgiy, S., Yatsalo, B., Higgins, N. A., Likhtariov, I., Dreicer, M., Lochard, J., Savkin, M., Demin, V., Khramtsov, M., Grekov, L. and Utkina, T. *Decision Support Systems for the Post-emergency Management of Contaminated Territories.* In: Proc. First International Conference on the Radiological Consequences of the Chernobyl Accident. EUR 16544, 453–464 (Luxembourg: CEC) (1996).

22. National Radiological Protection Board. *Values of Unit Collective Dose for Use in the 1990s.* Doc. NRPB **4**(2), 77–80 (London: HMSO) (1993).

Radiation Protection Dosimetry
Vol. 68, No. 3/4, pp. 273–278 (1996)
Nuclear Technology Publishing

RADIATION RISK AND SCIENCE EDUCATION

H. M. C. Eijkelhof
Centre for Science and Mathematics Education
University of Utrecht
PO Box 80.008, 3508 TA Utrecht, The Netherlands

Abstract — Almost everywhere the topic of radioactivity is taught in the physics or chemistry classes of secondary schools. The question has been raised whether the common approach of teaching this topic would contribute to a better understanding of the risks of ionising radiation: and, if the answer is negative, how to explain and improve this situation? In a Dutch research programme which took almost ten years, answers to this question have been sought by means of analyses of newspaper reports, curriculum development, consultation with radiation experts, physics textbook analysis, interviews and questionnaires with teachers and pupils, class observations and curriculum development. The main results of this study are presented and some recommendations given for science teaching and for communication with the public in general as regards radiation risk.

INTRODUCTION

In science classes in senior secondary schools all over the world the topic of radioactivity is taught. The usual approach is to start with the structure of the atom and the nucleus, followed by concepts such as half-life, activity, nuclear fission and fusion. Towards the end of the series of lessons some applications are usually mentioned, such as carbon dating, irradiation and the nuclear reactor. Safety issues are dealt with only superficially.

Such a teaching approach may be defended from the viewpoint that this would be the best way to prepare students for higher education in the sciences. If this proposition is true or not, an objection to the exclusive use of this viewpoint is that nowadays most students in Europe are not in school to prepare themselves for future studies in the physical sciences, but to be educated for life in modern society. One may wonder whether this common approach to teaching the topic contributes to a better understanding of the risks of ionising radiation, a topic often covered in the newspapers and on TV.

In order to explore this field, in the early eighties as part of the large Dutch physics curriculum development project PLON[1] a physics unit was developed which had as its main aim the improvement of student understanding and reasoning abilities regarding the risks of ionising radiation[2]. In this unit a number of safety aspects were added to the traditional nuclear concepts and a great deal of attention was given to medical applications, nuclear arms and the nuclear fuel cycle.

Evaluation showed that such new contents were strongly appreciated by the students (especially the girls), but that their reasoning ability hardly improved. In fact, by asking them to argue about the risks of new applications (such as food irradiation) a number of lay ideas appeared[3] about which, in those days, only limited knowledge was available in the field of science education[4,5]. This was in contrast to other fields of physics, such as mechanics, electricity, light and heat, for which, worldwide, a large number of studies had revealed the existence of lay ideas, more commonly called children's ideas, alternative conceptions or misconceptions[6,7]. These kinds of commonsense ideas which students have before they enter science classes have proved to be rather resistant to change by common teaching strategies in which the existence of these ideas is ignored. However, results were available from risk perception studies[8–10], confirming that many people today hold strong beliefs about the danger of anything nuclear. Weart[11] claims that public ideas in this field are based on a complex web of social and political considerations, on old myths about pollution, cosmic secrets, mad scientists and apocalypse, and on the threat of nuclear war.

As the aim of the PLON materials (improving understanding and reasoning abilities regarding the risks of ionising radiation) had not been achieved satisfactorily, questions were raised about the suitability of the contents of the unit, the role of lay ideas and risk perception, and possible ways to improve the effectiveness of teaching. A study programme was designed to find answers to the following research question:

'Which curricular and other teaching conditions must be fulfilled in order to promote thoughtful risk analysis and assessment as regards applications of ionising radiation, through physics lessons in senior high school?'

The main results of this study are presented and some recommendations given for science teaching and for communication with the general public about radiation risks.

OUTLINE OF THE STUDIES

The assumption was made that such an answer could not be given by means of a single study and that the knowledge and experience of radiation experts should be used as one of the bases to improve teaching and learning. It was assumed that radiation experts could advise about:

(i) suitable contents and applications,
(ii) the nature of lay ideas and their consequences for risk assessment, and
(iii) dealing with risk aspects in teaching.

For this purpose a Delphi study[12] was held with 63 radiation experts who worked in a variety of fields: nuclear energy, health care, industry, radiation protection, environment and the civil service. Each expert had at least four years of work experience in his or her field. They completed questionnaires in three rounds, each questionnaire raising issues which could be seen as conclusions from previous rounds.

It was also expected that newspapers would be a source to detect lay ideas about radiation risks. Shortly after the start of collecting newspaper cuttings about ionising radiation, the accident at Chernobyl took place which resulted in an abundance of news reports. For instance, the British newspaper The Guardian carried over 160 separate articles dealing with Chernobyl, as well as several cartoons and over 30 readers' letters. Over 1000 articles from three Dutch (Volkskrant, NRC-Handelsblad and Utrechts Nieuwsblad) and eleven British newspapers (The Times, The Guardian, The Daily Telegraph, The Daily Mirror, The Sunday Mirror, The Sun, The Daily Mail, The Daily Express, The Star, The Sunday Times and The Observer) were collected and analysed.

A third source of information in our research programme was formed by students in secondary schools. Firstly, 312 form IV students completed open questionnaires about Chernobyl, six months after the accident. Next, another thirty form IV students from five different schools were interviewed in depth about their ideas regarding radiation risks around Chernobyl, nuclear waste, medical application, food irradiation and background radiation. Finally, 138 form VI students completed questionnaires after lessons about radioactivity (using traditional or PLON books) testing their insight into radioactivity and ionising radiation.

MAIN RESULTS OF THE STUDIES

Curriculum contents

In the Delphi study general agreement amongst the radiation experts was reached about changes in content of the science syllabus. The way this consensus was reached has been elaborated by Eijkelhof (ch. 2 of Ref. 13). Table 1 presents the subject matter items recommended by the participants as being important for learning to assess the risks of ionising radiation.

Compared with current practices of teaching more attention should be given to contamination with radioactive substances and to basic knowledge about radiation protection.

The participants also agreed on criteria for the selection of a set of applications which should be dealt with in physics lessons. These criteria are:

(1) A large part of the total collective dose should be covered by the set.
(2) Applications which are most likely to be encountered by citizens should be included.
(3) The set should reflect the variety of applications in society.
(4) The applications with the most important social implications should be included.

Table 2 contains the recommendations of the radiation experts regarding the set of applications.

The table shows that to deal with radiation risk it is recommended that a wide variety of applications be used, such as background radiation, medical applications, fallout, storage of nuclear waste and tracer applications in industry and research.

Common lay ideas

In the press reports about radiation issues terms such as 'radiation', 'radioactivity', 'dose' and 'radiation level' are often used. Analysis shows that these reports frequently use these terms with different meanings from those used by scientists[14,15].

A common example is the term 'radiation', which is often used in press reports when scientists would use the term 'radioactive material'; for instance, in quotations such as:

'Radiation is still pouring into the air from a fire raging at the plant.'

Table 1. Subject matter items recommended by radiation experts.

A. *Basic knowledge about atomic and nuclear physics*

   Structure of the nucleus: nucleon, proton, neutron, atomic number, mass number, (Z,N) diagram, isotope, atomic mass unit.
   Radioactive sources: stable and unstable nuclei, energy levels of a nucleus, disintegration, activity (Bq), radioactive decay curve, half-life.
   Ionizing radiation: alpha, beta, gamma and neutron radiation, X rays, nature and properties of these types of radiation, X ray spectrum.
   Detection of radiation: Geiger counter, photographic plate, cloud chamber.
   Nuclear energy: nuclear reactions, nuclear fission, chain reaction, principles of a nuclear reactor.

B. *Basic knowledge about radiation protection*

   Irradiation: absorption, dose (Gy), interaction with living matter, dose equivalent (Sv), influence of distance and medium.
   Contamination: spreading of radioactive substances in the environment and in the human body.
   Effects of ionising radiation: early and late effects of low and high doses, somatic and genetic effects.
   Safety aspects: film badge, lead apron, radiation norms, ALARA principle, safety measures.

'The wind is carrying the radiation over Scandinavia.'

'Students . . . were contaminated by radiation.'

'We have recently collected examples of fresh standing rainwater and tests showed they contained fairly high levels of short-lived radiation.'

Similarly, the term 'radioactivity' is often applied to situations in which scientists would use the terms 'radiation' or 'radioactive material'.

Related to the lay use of the term 'radiation' is the common idea in the press reports that it is in one way or another conserved after it has entered an object or a person. Examples of this idea are:

'Spinach has been exposed to too much radiation.'

'Radiated crops would not be saleable.'

'In case of a nuclear disaster our water purifying installations could only remove 30 to 50% of the radiation.'

Indeed, the lay idea of radiation makes it impossible to make a proper distinction between situations of irradiation and contamination.

Also related to this is the lack of scientific distinction in news reports between 'activity' and 'dose', for example:

'Accidents at which large doses of radiation are being released.'

'The Germans thought a radiation dose of 1000 Bq acceptable.'

'We need more information about the radiation dose that escaped.'

Both types of terms, of which the latter is most commonly used, seem to indicate a quantity of radiation contained by food, air, water or the human body. In combination with safety levels, they are used to indicate the dangerousness of the situation.

As part of the Delphi study the radiation experts were also asked to formulate lay ideas often found in their professional contacts with the public, to discuss the importance of these lay ideas in view or risk assessment and to participate in the identification of common ideas about the risks of ionising radiation[16]. The lay ideas which the experts most often encountered in their contacts with the public were similar to those found in the news reports. They could be classified according to the lack of insight into the scientific meaning of concepts (such as radiation, radioactive material, contamination, irradiation, activity and dose) and to common ideas about the risks of radiation. Such common ideas are:

(i) radioactivity and radiation are always dangerous (association with cancer);

(ii) radiation for medical purposes is less dangerous than that used for other purposes;

(iii) radiation standards indicate a safety level, safe below, dangerous above;

(iv) a nuclear power station is as dangerous as a nuclear bomb.

According to the participants of the Delphi study some lay ideas have more serious consequences for risk estimation than others. In particular, the importance of the lack of distinction between irradiation and contamination was illustrated with a number of examples from a variety of context domains (Table 3).

These examples show that people are often worried, either too much and sometimes too little, due to their lay conceptions of radiation and risk.

Table 2. Recommended radiation applications for a physics curriculum.

Category I (important)

1. Background radiation: from the cosmos, food, rocks, building materials, etc.
2. Medical applications: diagnostic and therapeutic uses of X rays and nuclear radiation.
3. Nuclear energy: emission of radioactive substances, normally and after an accident.
4. Storage of nuclear waste: underground, above ground, on the ocean floor.
5. Fallout (as a consequence of nuclear weapons explosions).
6. Some applications of ionising radiation in scientific and industrial research (e.g. tracers).

Category II (fairly important)

7. Other industrial applications (materials research, sterilisation, measurement and control).
8. Immediate consequences of nuclear weapons explosions.
9. Radioactivity from coal fired power plants.

Table 3. Examples of cases reported by radiation experts.

A. Reluctance to buy irradiated food for fear of radiation.

B. The idea that walls of a medical X ray department are full of radiation and therefore should be treated as radioactive waste.

C. Some workers who look after animals which are irradiated by X rays in experimental settings had a feeling of being neglected: they had not been issued dosemeters and did not get regular blood tests in contrast to personnel who irradiate the animals, although the latter personnel had less contact with the animals.

D. A nurse who does not place herself behind a wall when taking X rays because 'the radiation would reach me anyhow through the open door'.

E. The social isolation of an industrial worker who received an extra radiation dose by accident: he was considered by his colleagues and neighbours to be suffering from radioactive contamination.

Students' ideas

The interviews with students focused on their ideas about radioactivity, ionising radiation and risk in the contexts of Chernobyl, medical use of radiation, radioactive waste disposal, food irradiation and background radiation. Students' ideas within these contexts show that commonsense and information from the media dominate many of the students' views. Scientific notions play a small or non-existent part. Reasoning appears to be centred around the perceived risk of radiation for people. The nature of the effects of radiation is quite well known and does not differ from context to context, in spite of the perceived seriousness of the radiation hazard in each context.

Students seem to be less concerned with the nature and origin of the radiation. They often make analogies. These analogies are based on the characteristics of the contexts, especially the function of radiation and the saliency of safety measures. Propagation of radiation is only seen as relevant if the source is at a large distance and is considered dangerous (for example, Chernobyl and radioactive waste). When sources are nearby and inside buildings (for example, food irradiation, health applications and radon from building materials), ventilation is considered to be useful. The scientific notion of absorption was seldom found.

Students seem to have conservation ideas about radiation, which could be summarised as: 'When an object (such as food or a wall) receives radiation, the radiation will accumulate in the object. When the amount of radiation is large enough, the object will itself start emitting radiation'.

Students also appear to attribute meanings to the terms 'radiation', 'contamination', 'radiation standards' and 'radioactivity' which differ from the accepted scientific meanings.

Indiscriminate use of the terms contamination and irradiation was very common. Many students spoke of contamination when someone or something has received a certain amount of radiation, sometimes specified as 'a surplus' of it or 'more than normal'. Analysis of the answers also showed that students seem to have different meanings for 'radiation standards'. Four distinct views were recognised:

(1) A *regulation* view, expressing the idea that standards are what the regulatory bodies consider to be acceptable. This would apply to contamination of food and air, and to irradiation of people.
(2) A *threshold* view suggesting that there will be zero risk below a certain standard level. The body is expected to be able to cope with small amounts of radiation.
(3) A *probabilistic* view in which the risks are seen as more or less directly proportional to the received dose. Below the standards the risk is generally seen as small.

(4) A *distrust* view. Standards are seen as meaningless as all radiation is dangerous.

Finally, in the interviews forms of reasoning were identified which were labelled 'commonsense reasoning'. Students draw conclusions which seem logical to them because the conclusions are based on the uses of radiation, on personal experience or on the existence of safety measures or protests about safety. Examples of such reasoning are:

'If you look at how the workers in a food irradiation plant have to be protected with special clothing, it could not be right for an apple to receive a dose of radiation.'
'Food irradiation is not dangerous, otherwise they wouldn't do it'.'

A number of the lay ideas found with students appeared to persist despite instruction. Table 4 lists those lay ideas which were found with a majority of the senior secondary students after several weeks of instruction on the topic of ionising radiation.

No significant difference in the presence of these lay ideas was found between the PLON students and the students who worked with traditional books. In both learning materials no attention was given to the existence of lay ideas. Apparently, teaching the topic of ionising radiation without paying attention to lay ideas has little effect on students in altering those ideas.

RECOMMENDATIONS

The results about lay ideas appear not only to apply to Dutch students but have been confirmed in England[17-19], Norway[20] and Poland[21].

The studies described in this paper have led to conclusions which should have consequences for science education. If the main aim of science education in secondary schools should be to prepare students for coping with life in modern society, the purpose of teaching the topic of ionising radiation should be shifted from

Table 4. Examples of persistent lay ideas.

A.	Radioactive contamination means that someone is contaminated with radiation.
B.	The period in which nuclear radiation from an external source remains active in a cancer patient depends on half-life or length of irradiation.
C.	Radiation might accumulate in the human body.
D.	After an accident in a nuclear power station, the radiation might be spread by the wind.
E.	Radiation might be stored in food which is irradiated, so it is dangerous to eat that food for some time.
F.	X rays have effects on the human body which are very different from those of nuclear radiation.
G.	X rays should be extracted from air in order to reduce radiation risks.

'understanding nuclear physics' towards 'being able to understand radiation risk information'. This should have effects on curriculum contents and teaching strategies. Such changes are not easily implemented: it requires changes in current practices of teaching which could be characterised as (i) focusing on closed sources and on processes in the nucleus, (ii) paying low attention to risk concepts, (iii) using a limited range of applications, and (iv) ignoring the role of lay ideas and lay ways of reasoning. In our experience, support from the field of radiation experts could be very helpful in this respect.

One should acknowledge, however, that this is a sensitive issue. Some teachers might fear that radiation experts want to trivialise radiation risks or to prescribe ways of teaching. The basis of cooperation should be formed by a common goal: making science education more relevant and interesting for students. Input from the teachers into such cooperation is their teaching experience with the age group and their knowledge of the curriculum. Input by the radiation experts should be their knowledge of the radiation field as regards contents and applications. Synthesising both types of expertise could be very fruitful and of benefit for a large number of young people.

What could be learned from our studies for radiation risk communication in general? One should realise that the public has a lot of knowledge and beliefs about radiation risks which in the experts' view may be wrong and inconsistent, but which are not so perceived by the audience. The public's ideas have served them well so far[22,23] and could well be interpreted in a coherent way[24,25]. Any risk communicator should be familiar with the general public's ideas, and try to understand the meanings which are commonly ascribed to terms. It is likely that communication with the public is more effective when it starts from the common knowledge base of lay people and experts[25].

Of course, the best way to communicate about radiation risk depends on the audience. When dealing with lay people, it may be wise to avoid unnecessary use of micro-meanings of concepts such as radiation, activity, dose and half-life. Macro-interpretations of these concepts are usually sufficient and are better understood by many people[25,26]. It is also advisable to emphasise the distinction between irradiation and contamination, and open and closed sources, which no doubt is only sensible once one understands the need to distinguish between radiation and radioactive matter. With people who are more familiar with the field of nuclear physics such micro-meanings of concepts could well be used, but one should not be surprised to find lay ideas even among those!

REFERENCES

1. Eijkelhof, H. M. C. and Kortland, K. *Broadening the Aims of Physic Education*. In: *Development and Dilemmas in Science Education*. P. Fensham, Ed. (London: Falmer Press) pp. 282–305 (1988).

2. PLON. *Ioniserende Straling* (Universiteit Utrecht). (1984). English version: *Ionizing Radiation* (Monash University, Faculty of Education, Melbourne, Australia) (1988).

3. Eijkelhof, H. M. C. *Dealing with Acceptable Risk in Science Education: the Case of Ionizing Radiation*. In: *Ethics and Social Responsibility in Science Education*. M. J. Frazer and A. Kornhauser Eds. (Oxford: Pergamon Press) pp. 189–199 (1986).

4. Riesch, W. and Westphal, W. *Modellhafte Schülervorstellungen zur Ausbreitung radioaktiver Strahlung*, PhU. **9**(4) 75–85 (1975).

5. Strauss, K. A. *A Layman's Perspective*. Am. J. Roentgenol. **140**, 597–598 (1983).

6. Helm, H. and Novak, J. D. (eds) *Proceedings of the International Seminar on Misconceptions in Science and Mathematics* (Cornell University, Department of Education, Ithaca, NY, USA) (1983).

7. Driver, R., Guesne, E. and Tiberghien, A. *Children's Ideas in Science* (Milton Keynes: Open University Press) (1985).

8. Slovic, P., Lichtenstein, S. and Fischhoff, B. *Images of Disaster: Perception and Acceptance of Risks from Nuclear Power*. In: *Energy Risk Management*. G. Goodman and W. Rowe Eds (London: Academic Press) pp. 223–245 (1979).

9. Slovic, P., Fischhoff, B. and Lichtenstein, S. *Informing the Public about the Risks from Ionizing Radiation*. Health Phys. **41**(4), 589–598 (1981).

10. Van der Pligt, J., Eiser, J. R. and Spears, R. *Attitudes towards Nuclear Energy, Familiarity and Salience*. Environ. Behav. **18**(1), 75–93 (1986).

11. Weart, S. R. *Nuclear Fear. A History of Images* (Harvard University Press) (1988).

12. Linstone, H. A. and Turoff, M. *The Delphi Method: Techniques and Applications* (Reading, Mass.: Addison-Wesley) (1975).

13. Eijkelhof, H. M. C. *Radiation and Risk in Physics Education*. Doctoral dissertation (Utrecht: CD-β Press) (1990).

14. Eijkelhof, H. M. C. and Millar, R. H. *Reading about Chernobyl: the Public Understanding of Radiation and Radioactivity*, School Sci. Rev. **70** (251), 35–41 (1988).

15. Lijnse, P. L., Eijkelhof, H. M. C., Klaassen, C. W. J. M. and Scholte, R. L. J. *Pupils' and Mass-media Ideas about Radioactivity*. Int. J. Sci. Educ. **12** (1), 67–78 (1990).

16. Eijkelhof, H. M. C., Klaassen, C. W. J. M., Lijnse, P. L. and Scholte, R. L. J. *Perceived Incidence and Importance of Lay-ideas on Ionizing Radiation: Results of a Delphi-study among Radiation Experts*, Sci. Educ. **74**(2), 183–195 (1990).

17. Millar, R. H. *School Students' Understanding of Key Ideas about Radiation and Radioactivity*. Science Education Research Paper 93/01 (Science Education Group, University of York, UK) (1993).

18. Millar, R. H. and Gill, J. *Irradiation and Contamination: School Students' Understanding of Two Key Ideas about Radioactivity.* Science Education Research Paper 93/02 (Science Education Group, University of York, UK) (1993).

19. Boyes, E. and Stanisstreet, M. *Children's Ideas about Radioactivity and Radiation: Sources, Mode of Travel and Dangers.* Res. Sci. Technol. Educ. **12** (2), 145–160 (1994).

20. Henriksen, E. K. *Laypeople's Understanding of Radioactivity and Radiation.* Radiat. Prot. Dosim. **68**(3/4), 191–196 (1996) (This issue).

21. Strugala, E. *Students' Attitude to the Risk of Ionizing Radiation.* In: *Atoms in our Hands.* Ed. G. Marx (Budapest: Roland Eötvös Physical Society/IUPAP) pp. 172–186 (1995).

22. Sjöberg L. *Strength of Belief and Risk.* Policy Sci. **11**, 39–57 (1979).

23. Zajonc, R. B. and Markus, H. *Affective and Cognitive Factors in Preferences.* J. Consumer Res. **9**, 123–131 (1982).

24. Lijnse, P. L., Klaassen, C. W. J. M. and Eijkelhof, H. M. C. *Developmental Research as a Way to an Empirically Based 'Didactical' Structure of Physics: the Case of Radioactivity.* AERA/NARST-paper. ERIC-document no. 363496 (1993).

25. Klaassen, C. W. J. M. *A Problem Posing Approach to Teaching the Topic of Radioactivity.* Doctoral dissertation (Utrecht: CD-β Press) (1995).

26. Millar, R. II., Klaassen, C. W. J. M. and Eijkelhof, H. M. C. *Teaching about Radioactivity and Ionising Radiation: an Alternative Approach.* Phys. Educ. **25**, 338–342 (1990).

Radiation Protection Dosimetry
Vol. 68, No. 3/4, pp. 279–281 (1996)
Nuclear Technology Publishing

INFORMATION ON RADIATION PROTECTION: AN ANTHROPOLOGICAL APPROACH

D. Van Nuffelen
Radiation Protection Service
Cité Administrative de l'Etat, Quartier Vésale
B-1010 Brussels, Belgium

Abstract — It is necessary to prepare the messages on radiation protection before a nuclear accident arises, i.e. in a normal radiological situation. The approach discussed in this paper is based on the hypothesis that any communication is a relationship between different actors (such as a transmitter and a receiver) whose semantic frames of reference, mainly defined by social and cultural determinants of knowledge, cannot be completely identical. To work out messages correctly intended for a given receiver, one has consequently to bring out the common semantic references to both the transmitter and the receiver. That means that actual communication never exists between a transmitter who wants to be seen as the guardian of an exclusive knowledge and a receiver who is generally thought of as being dependent on an exclusive ignorance.

INTRODUCTION

The hypothesis discussed here is that any communication is a relationship between different actors (such as a transmitter and a receiver) whose semantic frames of reference cannot be completely identical. Consequently, the more the different actors have semantic references in common, the more the communication between them will be effective. A problem is the fact that these actors are not individuals but social and/or cultural groups. Thus, the semantic frames of reference involved are of a sociocultural nature. In other words, it is necessary to bring out the systems of thought, the norms, the values, the roles, etc., of each actor. A way to study these social and cultural determinants of knowledge is the socio-anthropological approach.

A SOCIO–ANTROPOLOGICAL MODEL

The model of communication discussed here according to this approach concerns the normal radiological situation only. Indeed, data on nuclear accidents are poor and contradictory. It is hard, in these conditions, to get theoretical conclusions from them. For instance, the way a nuclear accident is posed to a society, and consequently the way the different actors react, is different in Three Mile Island, Chernobyl and Goiania. T.M.I.: 200,000 people in the streets, malfunctioning of the communication systems and accusations against the operators. Goiania: progressive adaptation to the situation. Chernobyl: no communication before exterritorial reactions, accusations against the eastern style of society and segregationist reactions.

Not only the available data, but the theoretical models also present difficulties. In sociology, of the major techno-scientific accidents, for example, two opposite theses are presented. According to one, such disasters reinforce the social links. The disasters, in this view, are considered as the normal consequences of a style of society[1]. According to the other, on the contrary, the major techno-scientific accidents cause social and cultural destabilisation. The disasters, here, are considered as crises[2].

The aim of the present paper is not to come to a decision. Its main purpose is to show how a correct comprehension of the communication in a normal radiological situation may lead to preparation of effective messages about radiation protection. The social and/or cultural groups for which such messages are intended can be determined and studied before a new nuclear accident arises.

THE MEANING OF COMMUNICATION

To understand correctly what communication means, a short theoretical review may be needed. Nowadays, most research workers agree with a systemic theory on communication. Nevertheless, it was not the case some decades ago, and even now such a theory is not always well understood. According to an 'old' classical model which is still used by some communicators, communication simply consists of the transmission of a message from a transmitter to a receiver by means of a channel, reducing noise — in other words, physical and semantic characteristics that affect the transmitting process — with maximum efficiency[3]. Such a theory implies a single linear causality, from which one cause produces one effect: the receiver reacts necessarily and only after an action of the transmitter (Figure 1). That may seem

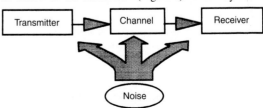

Figure 1. Classical model of transmitting information.

obvious, but the reality is more complicated. Indeed, this theory cannot explain a lot of phenomena that are, however, related to any communicating process, such as the context (which is the main point), the gatekeepers, the distortion, the opinion leaders or else the feed-back[4].

Feedback

In any system of communication, feed-back occurs. That is a very important process. It implies that a modification in an output variable reacts on an input variable[5]. In a few words, the feed-back is positive when the modification in the output is in accordance with the input. In this case, the transformation operated by the system reinforces the input. The state of the system is changing. The feed-back is negative when the modification in the output is opposed to the input. In this case, the system is regulated. Any communication between a transmitter and a receiver is determined by these processes. Thus, the transmitter and the receiver are interacting. Consequently, the systems of communication are not determined by a single linear causality but by a cybernetic causality, which is circular. In communicating on nuclear issues, this means that not only the viewpoint of the experts must be taken into account, but also that of the social group being informed.

Opinion leaders

The linear model does not take into account the important role played by the opinion leaders. These are relays between the transmitter and the receiver. Their function is to reinforce certain messages into local areas of a social group[6]. Unfortunately, working with opinion leaders has been done most often to influence public attitudes, not to communicate with social groups on radiological risk (cf. antinuclear lobbies).

Distortion

Another important fact that the linear model does not explain is the distortion of information. This process depends upon the elements of the system of communication and their relationships, in particular the cultural distance from the transmitter to the receiver[7]. Even if 'noise' is reduced, it does not mean that distortion disappears. That is why studies on the cultural perception of radiological risk should be generalised. Indeed, processes such as the selection and the construction of radiological risk may deeply affect the exchange of information between the scientific groups and the other social groups.

Gatekeepers

Other important elements that cannot be analysed by the linear model are the 'gatekeepers'. Those are actors who select the messages[8]. It should be stressed that both transmitter and receiver are always gatekeepers[9]. The selection of nuclear information, as of radiological risk itself, is dependent upon cultural and social factors, such as the respect for certain values, the adherence to a group or a class, the representation of society, science and technology. Moreover, in observing most of the public nuclear information over a little more than ten years, it clearly appears that only a few subjects are popularised on a large scale. *Mutatis mutandis*, the messages are always related to some effects of the radioactivity on living beings, to some aspects of nuclear safety, to some descriptions of how a nuclear reactor works or what is an atom. It is not said that such questions are not important, but one has to note that many other important questions — as, for instance, social, economic, political or legal aspects of the nuclear reality — are often not popularised. Furthermore, it seems hard to believe that people who receive any nuclear information from the nuclear industry or Greenpeace do not feel that it may be tailored to influence them.

Context

Finally, in analysing the context within which any communication on radiological risk takes place, it clearly appears that two actors — a techno-scientific organisation and a lay population — are concerned with the exchange of one semantic frame of reference only: the transmitter's one. That represents an ethnoknowledge, in other words a reductive definition of the reality for the use of one given sociocultural group[4]. Indeed, according to the dominating values in occidental societies, the techno-scientific view on the nuclear question (thus, the radiological risk) is generally regarded as the one truth and imposed on the others. In these conditions, the exchange of nuclear knowledge is often a one-way process. That is the main reason why this kind of communication fails. Indeed, really to communicate with any receiver, the transmitter would have to share the semantic experiences common to both[10] (Figure 2). Because of the reduction implied by any ethnoknowledge, there is an infinitude of possible talks about radiological risk: each social group is expected to define its own discourse (socially constructed and culturally

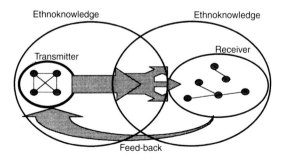

Figure 2. General context of a communication.

selected) on such an issue. Consequently, communicating it supposes a negotiation on the topics in which are put together the claims, the systems of thought, the cultural patterns and the questions related to each actor involved[11].

Information test

Last but not least, information worked out this way can be tested. That permits us to measure how it is correctly intended for and understood by the receiver. In the case of the Belgian agricultural workers, for instance, information was tested on the studied sample and a control group. The results were very encouraging.

CONCLUSION

In conclusion, the communication is not the production of statements supposed to represent the knowledge and the truth that the public must accept as they are. What matters is that we should study the cultures for which the messages are intended. The communication is creative of social links only if it is governed by a logic of equity[12]. Actual communication never exists between a transmitter who wants to be seen as the guardian of an exclusive knowledge and a receiver who is generally thought of as being dependent on an exclusive ignorance.

REFERENCES

1. Duclos, D. *La Peur et la Savoir. La Société face à la Science, la Technique et leurs Dangers.* (Paris: Ed. La Découverte) (1989).

2. Lagadec, P. *La Civilisation du Risque. Catastrophes Technologiques et Responsabilité Sociale.* (Paris: Seuil) (1981).

3. Shannon, C. and Weaver, W. *The Mathematical Theory of Communication* (Urbana) (1949).

4. Van Nuffelen, D. *Prolégomènes à une Théorie de l'Echange d'un Savoir Nucléaire* (Paris: Committee on Radiation Protection and Public Health) (1995).

5. Wiener, N. *Cybernetics* (Paris) (1948).

6. Katz, E. and Lazarsfeld, P. F. *Personal Influence* (Glencoe) (1954).

7. Van Nuffelen, D. *La Communication en Question: le Point de Vue du Sociologue* (Bruxelles: Association Belge de Radioprotection) (1993).

8. White, D. M. *The Gatekeepers: a Case Study in the Selection of News.* Journalism Quarterly **27** (1950).

9. Van Nuffelen, D. and Balieu, M. *Informer: un Temps de Réflexion.* (Paris, Agence de l'Energie Nucléaire) (1993).

10. Schramm, W. *The Process and Effects of Mass Communication* (Urbana) (1954).

11. Van Nuffelen, D. *Anthropologie et Information Nucléaire* (Paris: Agence de l'Energie Nucléaire) (1994).

12. Zonabend, F. *La Presqu'île au Nucléaire* (Paris: Odile Jacob) (1989).

Radiation Protection Dosimetry
Vol. 68, No. 3/4, pp. 283–286 (1996)
Nuclear Technology Publishing

THE COMMUNICATION OF RADIOLOGICAL RISK TO POPULATIONS EXPOSED TO A RADIOLOGICAL ACCIDENT: CONSIDERATIONS CONCERNING THE ACCIDENT IN GOIÂNIA

M. P. Curado
Associação de Combate ao Câncer em Goiás
Rua 239 No 181 Setor Universitário
P.O. Box 871, CEP 74.605-070 Goiânia, Brasil

Abstract — The main purpose of this paper is to describe the reactions of a population subjected to the effects of a radiological accident and receiving information about radiation effects for the first time. The behaviour of the victims during various phases of the accident is discussed.

INTRODUCTION

In 1987 a serious radiation accident occurred in Goiânia in Brazil. An abandoned 50.9 TBq ^{137}Cs radiotherapy source was broken, it seriously irradiated around 250 persons externally and internally (including fatalities), and gave rise to widespread contamination[1–4]. The author participated in the acute phase activities, and has later been engaged in continued work in the area, both relating to somatic and psychosocial issues, and humanitarian efforts. The perception of a radiological risk in a population victimised by an accident of this nature creates expectations which overturn the balance of the individual, social, economic and family context of the group involved. The population living in areas close to the accident also suffer from a process of social destabilisation at the time of the accident. It must be assumed that the adaptation of the population has at least been influenced by the information they received.

A risk is not the same as an accident, nor the same as a disaster. Risk in general refers to a probability of some harm (in technology defined as the product of probability and consequences). Accidents may be defined as serious mishappenings affecting few or several people, and which may be dealt with using emergency plans and available resources. Disasters or castastrophies refer to sudden events with substantial injury, damage and social structure disruption[5]. It is often believed that disasters are big accidents only, and that previous accident preparedness plans can be used. However, a disaster surpasses the available resources for mitigation and calls for a much broader cooperation between a greater number of different parties than estimated before the disaster occurs[6]. Thus, the Goiânia accident may well be regarded as a disaster.

Most studies on radiation risk information deal with general information more than crisis and disaster information. There are both differences and similarities between a potential risk of radiation as an environmental hazard and a real radiation accident. The former is generally concerned with low radiation doses comprising a risk of late effects such as cancer, whereas in acci-dents, people must also be given advice on avoiding large radiation doses with possible acute effects. Moreover, in a pre-accident situation, authorities may plan the information and largely decide if and how information shall be released. In an accident, the population and mass media will demand information immediately and to an extent surpassing the capacity. The purpose of this paper is to describe some of the features of a real and severe accident situation, the scenario to which any information or communication must be tailored.

ACUTE EMERGENCY PHASE

The radiotherapy source was removed by scavengers, partially damaged, and eventually transported to a junkyard. By disassembling, blue glowing particles were found, powdered and offered to friends, relatives and other individuals. Two weeks after the initial removal the radioactive nature of the accident was realised. At that time several persons had developed clinical symptoms of radiation sickness and widespread contamination had occurred, and large parts of the population were assembled for screening at the Olympic Stadium. A total of 112,000 persons were monitored during a fortnight.

When radiation was mentioned widely for the first time in the Goiânia accident, the whole of society, because of this accident, became aware of radiation as one more factor of social and economic risk. This apparently caused tendencies to panic and hypochondria both among the victims and the professionals involved in the treatment and mitigation. Not least was the collective fear often interpreted by the media as a state of panic[1].

Some social destabilisation occurred, mainly in the emergency phase of the accident. The individuals felt generally insecure for many reasons, among which one can mention the introduction of a completely new vocabulary in their daily lives, previously unknown to them. The initial feeling of insecurity of the groups at risk was apparently partly generated by the massive dissemination of information by the press through interviews with technicians, scientists and national/state authorities. They answered the questions raised by the society, by the affected groups of people, by the population as a whole and by the local scientific community. All the communication with the community was handled exclusively by official spokesmen. This attitude led to the formation of non-authority parallel groups who were ready to criticise to the press the quality of the technical work. At this emergency stage an immediate reaction on the part of the most diverse social segments, demanding a definitive answer, could be verified.

Credibility of spokesmen seems to be a major factor, with the assumed motivation of the sender to present a correct message, not to have interests in distorting or manipulating the facts, and with no special, e.g. economic, interests in the issue[7]. The professionals engaged in the accident management were seen as tied in with radiation agencies as such. The population of Goiânia did not always believe the official spokespeople because they represented the authorities, and what they relayed was perceived as manipulated information.

The debates which took place between the official authorities and the non-governmental scientists reflected the engagement of society in the search for a better understanding of the facts and for the safety of the population subjected to immediate danger. A population exposed to a radiological accident functions as a receptor of information on the risks and effects of radiation. The communication of these risks and effects begins with the many different official and non-official means of communication available in the given population.

During this phase the beginning of a process of social and structural adaptation is seen, both within the risk groups and the population as a whole. This constitutes the initial phase of reaction after an accident of this sort. The language used in the communication should be as close as possible to the facts and to the social level of the exposed group of people[8]. The cultural distance between the groups which represent technical knowledge and the social groups affected by the accident should be decreased. Both the technicians and the scientists should limit themselves to inform on the facts, within their capacity of predicting them. However, they should not under- or over-rate the questions that may arise. They should always be ready to listen and not just answer dogmatically with pre-established theories, because the technological understanding of risk does not necessarily match the apparently broader risk concept of the public[9]. The difference between information as a one-way and communication as a two-way process is obvious.

The identification of a leader within the directly affected group is the starting point for a dialogue with the official authorities and the scientists. (In the case of the accident in Goiânia, the natural leader was identified because she started questioning authorities through the media on behalf of the group of victims about the consequences of the accident, and she demanded from the authorities compensation for the economic losses caused by the accident.) This leader will handle the requests for quality medical treatment along with a series of other social and economic demands. At this moment the group already has an idea of the risk and has attained a definite personality. This is the phase in which the social and economic losses are assessed and reparation is asked for.

Communication has a greater impact in the emergency phase and thus the communication system must act fast and well. The continuous presence of an official spokesperson with credibility, ready to answer questions posed both by the population and the scientists from other areas, is crucial to lower the level of stress of the risk groups. The presence of a continuous and always updated source of information will help form a basis for the understanding of the radiological risks which can be predicted over time.

INTERMEDIATE PHASE

This perception of risks is slowly incorporated into the daily life of the victims, and with the passing of the years there is a tendency for life to settle, in a situation which can be described as of apparent calmness. However, half a year after the accident, two thirds of the Goiânia residents reported to have suffered discrimination and curtailment of social relations. About a year after the accident around 20%, both victims and neighbours, still reported life changes affecting work, emotion and social life[1]. The professionals were the ones that suffered the most serious discrimination from their working colleagues. Thus, the apparent calmness may hide psychosocial sequelae, reflecting transposition in the psychological sense, or some kind of depression. In Hiroshima, survivors felt thrown back upon several potential deadly impairments, and outsiders saw them as tainted with death, adding stigma to the stressful situation[10].

However, if new facts connected to the late effects of the radiation, such as the death of one of the victims, come up and are widely publicised by the press, the level of stress increases among the people who make up the risk group. They start to fear death and diseases such as cancer and everyone starts to question the authorities on the late effects of radiation. The communication of each new fact, whether positive or negative should be made to all who make up the risk groups. The authorities, community leaders, teachers and anyone who is interested in this kind of information should have access to it. A need for close contact between different parties has also been reported from the Three Mile Island accident[11].

There are always internal differences of opinion among specialists that often generate some tension between the spokespeople and the scientists. The technical group and the official institutions should, at least in the opinion of many, come up with joint final conclusions and should be able to control the information that is published by the press in order to prevent contradiction and to lend credibility to the facts. However, control of the press by authority carries serious problems in relation to press freedom. The possibility of cooperation and turning the press into a constructive force in mitigating the effect of disasters should be considered important. The role of the press in maladaptive processes of the public may be a result of faulty cooperation[5,12]. Continuous training sessions should be encouraged and clear information should be given to members of the families of the victims and to the professionals who work with these victims and in the accident area.

LATE PHASE

The effects of the radiation are soon forgotten by the population if no new fact — which could be considered as suspect of having originated from accident — comes up and is published by the press. The scientists' search for victims for the sake of research has created a feeling of dissatisfaction. The high risk group has, to some extent, isolated itself and has developed its own basic social and survival needs. Information may add to the remaining stress of isolation and alienation mentioned earlier[1].

Today the sequelae of the accident in Goiânia in the short, medium and long term are frequently questioned, especially cancer and other degenerative chronic diseases. Even though the information on the probable long-term sequelae with which the population is confronted do not emphasise such diseases in the risk group during the acute phase, these diseases should be assessed and traced through the adoption of a medical follow-up programme[13]. Would we be more technically prepared to answer these questions in the emergency phase of a radiological accident than in the later

phases of the accident? Probably quite the contrary, because appropriate assessment of contamination levels, doses to the public, and effectiveness of countermeasures, will take time to establish. Incorrect information about late effects during the acute phase may leave serious misunderstandings. The late impact of diseases such as cancers start to be seen as chronic problems that do not interfere, directly, with the population. The creation of parallel study groups that dedicate themselves to divulging information which conflicts with that published by the official channels generates controversy, but does not destabilise the social status which the population attain after the accident, with the passing of the years up to the present time.

CONCLUSION

In Goiânia, the high risk group has isolated itself and has developed its own basic social and survival needs. It has by this means re-acquired a position in the social context which is family centred. This *status quo* is only destabilised when diseases (which affect the direct victims) appear, especially if they are in any way connected to the family group. The scientists' search for victims for the sake of research has created a feeling of dissatisfaction among these people because they feel they have become guinea pigs for the benefit of science for which the risks of radiation are not yet well known and which still has many questions without answers.

The people who make up the risk group of a radiological accident have to be respected at all costs, through an increased knowledge of the social structure of the group involved in the problem. Communication and information from authorities and through the media must be guided by the perspective of the affected population[8,9]. Their cultural and religious beliefs should also be preserved as far as possible.

REFERENCES

1. Curado, M. P., Costa, Neto, S. and Helou, S. *Psychological Aspects of the Radiation Accident in Goiânia: A General Overview on Victims and Population*. In: The Medical Basis for Radiation-accident Preparedness. The Psychological Perspective. Eds R. C. Ricks, M. E. Berger and F. M. O'Hara. pp. 143–154 (New York: Elsevier) (1991).

2. Oliveira, A. R., Hunt, J. G., Valverde, N. J. L., Brandão-Mello, C. E. and Farina R. *Medical and Related Aspects of the Goiânia Accident*. Health Phys. **60**, 17–24 (1991).

3. Oliveira, A. R., Brandão-Mello, C. E., Valverde, N. J. L., Farina R. and Curado, M. P. *Localized Lesions Induced by ^{137}Cs during the Goiânia Accident*. Health Phys. **60**, 25–29 (1991).

4. Rosenthal, J. J., de Almeida, C. E. and Mendonça, A. H. *The Radiological Accident in Goiânia: The Initial Remedial Actions*. Health Phys. **60**, 7–15 (1991).

5. Kreps, G. *Research Needs and Policy Issues on Mass Media Disaster Reporting*. In: Disasters and the Mass Media. Proceedings. pp. 35–74 (National Academy of Sciences, Washington, DC) (1980).

6. Quarantelli, E. L. *Radiation Disasters: Similarities to and Differences from other Disasters*. In: The Medical Basis for Accident Preparedness. Eds R. Ricks, M. E. Berger and F. M. O'Hara. The Psychological Perspective. pp. 15–24 (New York: Elsevier) (1991).

7. Waldahl, R. *Public Information Strategies*. Radiat. Prot. Dosim. **62**, 107–111 (1995).

8. Baker, F. *Risk Communicating about Environmental Hazards*. J. Public Health Policy **11**, 341–359 (1990).

9. Otway, H. *Experts, Risk Communication, and Democracy*. Risk Anal. **7**, 125–129 (1987).

10. Lifton, R. J. *Death in Life: Survivors of Hiroshima*. (New York: Random House) (1967).

11. Wald, N. *Decontamination Advisory Panel and Public Stress Mitigation*. In: The Medical Basis for Accident Preparedness. The Psychological Perspective. Eds R. Ricks, M. E. Berger and F. M. O'Hara. pp. 253–262 (New York: Elsevier) (1991).

12. Smyser, R. D. *The Role of the Media in Minimizing Anxiety in Radiation Accidents*. In: The Medical Basis for Accident Preparedness. The Psychological Perspective. Eds R. Ricks, M. E. Berger and F. M. O'Hara. pp. 243–251 (New York: Elsevier) (1991).

13. Curado, M. P. *Health Care for Cesium 137 Accident Victims in Goiânia — Brasil*. In: Proc. Int. Symp. of the 50th Year of the Atomic Bombing. pp. 88–96 (Hiroshima) (1995).

Radiation Protection Dosimetry
Vol. 68, No. 3/4, pp. 287–291 (1996)
Nuclear Technology Publishing

THE MEDIA'S RECEPTION OF THE RISK ASSOCIATED WITH RADIOACTIVE DISASTERS

S. Vettenranta
Norwegian University of Science and Technology
Faculty of Social Sciences, Department of Education
N-7055 Dragvoll, Norway

Abstract — There is an urgent need to develop methodologies to examine the response by the media to radioactive disasters. 'Reception study' is a new research approach in the field of mass communication, studying how the viewers construct meaning from TV news. This ongoing reception study explores how fifteen respondents, all involved in the Chernobyl disaster in 1986, recall and interpret TV news coverage nine years after the accident. The main aim is to discover how the news affects the recipients' interpretations of a disaster and what kind of thoughts, reactions and associations risk messages provoke in retrospect, in the present and in the beliefs about the future. The initial findings indicate that the Chernobyl news on TV was mainly based on technical rationality, while viewers construct meaning founded on symbolic, cultural rationality. The transmission of catastrophe news is not just a matter of responding to the information needs of the public. Denotative risk messages simultaneously convey connotative, symbolic resonance of risk on a metaphysical level.

INTRODUCTION

Nuclear power, environmental hazards, health threats, and technical disasters have kept risk issues in the headlines. The media set these topics on the daily agenda, and the question of risk arises as one of the important matters in the public-policy debate[1]. Risk communication, however, is a relatively new concept in the field of mass communication research. Early social science studies of risk communication in the mass media on radioactive disasters were carried out in the late 1980s. The Chernobyl disaster increased the interest in risk communication research. There are neglected domains in the field, such as the development of methods and the formation of theories[2]. Risk communication is still misleadingly viewed as crisis information, transfer of messages from experts to lay people. This concept reflects linear, one-way information from the authorities to the public. The receiver's role is passive and obedient. Risk communication is a two-way interactive process of exchange of information among individuals, groups and institutions. It involves also messages which express recipients' concerns, opinions and reactions to risk messages[3].

The research has mostly focused on the sender's perspective, not the recipients'. There are very few studies which shed light on recipients' construct of meaning of disaster news from a cross-cultural perspective. Traditionally, the study of media audience response has been based on studying behavioural effects of exposure to mass media messages. This approach is still pursued in the USA and Canada where mass media research has been influenced by psychological agenda and experimental studies. In the Nordic Countries, England, the Netherlands and Australia the 'perception tradition' has been superseded by the more recent audience research approach called 'reception studies' in the field of mass communication. This approach has been developed in the past decade and derives from literary criticism and cultural studies. 'Reception' is a wider concept than 'perception'. According to Höijer, reception analysis includes viewers' interpretations, decodings, readings, meaning productions, perceptions or comprehension of programmes[4]. Media studies on radioactive accidents have mostly been based on quantitative content analyses or surveys on the comprehension of news and brochures, issued in connection with major accidents. The content of the message in these studies consists of 'information', the manifest meaning of the text. The 'effects' of the message are primarily measured through questionnaires. These transmission models are regarded as insufficient and inadequate by many media scientists today. The media are an integral part of a cultural process through which meanings are produced[5,6]. Media messages are complex discourses composed of verbal and visual signs with meanings encoded into them through culturally specific communicative codes. All texts, included TV news, are polysemic, open to many different interpretations. The ways in which individuals construct the meaning of news are functions of the particular context within which they live[6]. While content analysis is a useful way measuring the manifest content of the text, it does not reveal the latent meanings or the context in which they are placed[5,7].

As the chief information officer in the Directorate for Nature Management in Norway during the Chernobyl disaster, the author experienced the problems of transmitting risk messages. She had the operational responsibility for editing and transmitting information about radioactive waste in vegetation, wild game (reindeer) and freshwater fishes. The conflict between risk information supplied by the authorities and the insatiable demand of lay people was prevalent. This gave the author some misgivings which were not allayed by the studies which followed the Chernobyl disaster as they did not address the problems she had found. There was more than just misleading information, the lack of information and too difficult language, as contact with the public over several months indicated. Moreover, the author's position as mediator between the authorities, the media and the audiences allowed her to gain insight into risk communication during a catastrophe. This insight will be put to good use in the current doctoral study and will be presented in the final section of this paper.

TECHNICAL AND SYMBOLIC RATIONALITY

Risk communication has emerged from earlier studies in risk perception. According to Otway and Wynne[8], the simplistic models of risk perception have obscured the view of the social interactions and contexts which define authentic risk communication. An important contribution from risk perception research is that the concept of risk is defined differently by lay people and experts. When experts judge risk, their responses correlate highly with technical estimates of annual fatalities, accident probabilities, annual mortality rates, and losses of life expectancy. For lay people the perception of risk is determined by other characteristics such as benefits, uncertainty, controllability, catastrophic potential, equity, and threat to future generations[8–11]. Plough and Krimsky[12] claim that the present discourse on risk relies on quantitative models and cognitive typologies of perception. It does not take into consideration underlying value controversies in the social context of risk communication. The power of qualitative reception study methods lies in their sensitivity to the contexts of everyday life, and their ability to explore the structures of meaning among different groups[5,7].

The concept of risk communication has both a conventional definition and a symbolic definition[12]. The former term derives from risk management, while the latter originates from political discourse. The conventional definition neglects cultural themes and symbolic meanings, which are included in the symbolic definition, and may be of equal or of greater importance to the understanding of a risk message. Plough and Krimsky[12] distinguish two forms of rationality applied to risk: technical and cultural. To understand cultural rationality, anthropological and phenomenological issues must gain equal interest with behavioural ones. Technical rationality is based on explicitly defined principles and scientific norms including hypothetico-deductive methods and quantification of risk events. This means that the risk can be studied independently of context. Cultural rationality incorporates technical knowledge within a broader framework. To understand the symbolic meaning of risk communication, it must be studied in its social context[12]. The initial findings of the current study indicate that risk messages on TV about the Chernobyl disaster were founded on technical rationality while the respondents' concepts of risk mainly were founded on cultural rationality.

APOCALYPTIC RHETORIC

The media have been accused of biased and sensationalised reporting of risks. It has been argued that trivial or inappropriate dimensions of risky situations have been exaggerated to intensify the worry about a risk. Journalists have been blamed for playing on public fears by the improper use of symbols (e.g. showing a nuclear explosion while reporting about an accident in a nuclear reactor), by giving too prominent space or time to rather unimportant events or by emotionalising an event by focusing on the victims. Reporting from the Three Mile Island and the Chernobyl accidents is an example of this[13]. The author, previously a TV journalist herself, was astonished by this remarkable change in news reporting since 1986, an aspect which was also commented upon by every one of the 15 respondents.

Apocalyptic rhetorics, a new journalistic genre, which describes disasters as infernos and nuclear holocausts has emerged. Giddens[14] states that it is not surprising that people who hold to religious beliefs are inclined to see the potential for global disaster as an expression of the wrath of God. An example: soon after the accident it was discovered that Chernobyl in the Ukrainian language means wormwood, a bitter herb, mentioned in Revelations in connection with apocalyptic prophesies. This unfortunate coincidence could be interpreted as a sign of a prophesy[15]. Many of the respondents in my study referred to metaphysical thoughts without any introductory questions, after all collective destruction has been mentioned in the Bible. In the respondent sample, several individuals mentioned radioactive disasters within the context of Revelations and also evoked comparisons with deliberate radiation damage, specifically Hiroshima. An example:

'And then Chernobyl ... became a term over time. You know it means 'wormwood' ... That was a bit exciting, because people took this to mean Wormwood falling down from heaven, as it says in Revelations ... Well, at best, or perhaps at least, it could be a small hint ... And we also know that we can poison our drinking water like it says in Revelations ...' (Male researcher, Ph.D., age 48).

Some scholars claim that catastrophes are covered as single events, taken out of context, and that journalists often fail to put risks in perspective. They cover nuclear hazards by using inflammatory and value-laden language (deadly, fatal, lethal, mortal, killing). The television discourse utilises symbols, photographs, music, facial expressions and body language to dramatise the news[16,17]. Wilkins and Patterson[18] argue that news follows certain cultural patterns where disaster news tends to be portrayed as a melodrama and a predictable stereotype with heroes and villains. In my study the hero is the Geological Survey of Norway, and the two villains are the directors from the Directorate of Health and the Norwegian Radiation Protection Agency.

Media coverage of the Chernobyl accident, according

to some studies, made both rhetorical and pictorial connections to the underlying nuclear terror[19]. Lifton, who developed the concept 'atomic angst', claims that nuclear fear is intensified by the unknown — by the amorphousness, mystery, and totality of impact we associate with nuclear weapons. Nuclear fear does not occur in isolation but interacts with everyday life's 'more ordinary struggles'[20]. As one of my respondents put it:

'... we all have a fear or a phobia of something or other and therefore some of us need to channel this more than others. Some manage to live with it and sweat a little at night (laughs), and others ... must in one way or another find a concrete place to hang their fears ... something outside of themselves ... this is like doomsday ... philosophy, that one must have something that is threatening. And it is clear that when you get a radioactive cloud and it is also ... invisible, and you don't know if it's dangerous, a certain number of people will quite automatically be drawn to it and turn their anxiety in that direction' (Female executive, B.A., age 38).

IMMORAL SECRETS

Risk information about nuclear energy is connected to energy politics and economic, political and moral arguments which complicate the transmission. The media often look at risky events as primarily political stories with scientific and technological underpinnings[18]. During disaster coverage, journalists tend to release information they believe will not lead to improper public reaction[21]. In this study, a female journalist told that when she wrote an interview in which children expressed their fear and dread during the Chernobyl disaster, she was 'strictly controlled' by her editor in order to avoid causing anxiety in the public. Suppression of information can, according to Elliot[21], promote feelings of helplessness by allowing people to learn too little too late and by focusing on chaos and trauma. My initial findings, though, do not primarily reveal a sense of helplessness, but the respondents' anger, fury and hostility towards authorities. They contended that the authorities were withholding vital information and considered this deceitful and treasonous. As Günther and Luckmann[22] note 'Secrets are considered to be morally suspect and more than that, downright immoral, surrounded by an aura of danger and evil'. They claim that the existence of societies depends on sharing a common stock of knowledge between their members. Withholding relevant knowledge from those who feel they are entitled to share it, may cause harm and damage to the reciprocal relation. Nohrstedt and Nordlund[23] claim that an information crisis during the Chernobyl disaster may have developed because the public felt itself disadvantaged regarding information. This led to a spiral of increased suspicions of hidden

agendas, and that the authorities were withholding information and abusing power. The preliminary findings in this study indicate that this withholding of information, the 'immoral secrets', will be one of the most important ruptures which was produced by the Chernobyl process, studied in retrospect.

SYMBOLIC RESONANCE IN DISASTER NEWS

There have been few reception studies based on televised catastrophe news. Corner et al[17] have explored how viewers made sense of the nuclear power debate from its televised or video representation after the Chenobyl disaster. Programmes representing various genres and perspectives on nuclear energy were shown to three respondent groups with different social and occupational backgrounds. The study revealed clearly how doubts and anxieties about the nuclear industry were shared by all groups. The programmes brought to light an interpretative context of deep uncertainty which was supplanted by confidence, based upon faith and hope, rather that factual knowledge. They[17] concluded that the mediations of the environment on TV is often characterised by a strong element of threat and risk. Often the programmes are reinforced by affective visualisation, dramatic simulations, music and expressive personal narratives. A consequence of this is that many images used in coverage produce a symbolic resonance by using the central iconography of the culture. They identified a powerfully associative, often metaphoric, level of meaning which was parallel to and sometimes in conjunction with the rational processing of information[24]. The respondents in this study admitted that the Chernobyl disaster had a powerful symbolic meaning for them. A couple of examples:

'[Chernobyl] has become a household name which we use for comparison ... it has become a kind of standard for ... for accidents.' (Male director, age 46).
'Because, before Chernobyl, then it was like you know whether and if and but — about these nuclear power station accidents, but now we have a name for it! You know ... now we are living with this 'before and after' Chernobyl-' (Female South Sami reindeer herder, age 34).
'... an accident which has made its way into the consciousness of the people and the history books as the great nuclear accident ... and I feel that Chernobyl, Hiroshima and Nagasaki will become ... synonymous terms ...' (Male director, age 48).

Different viewers will approach the same programme with varying frameworks of interpretation. Variation in such a 'frame' will produce different responses to the programme and different readings of what it means. The topic of nuclear energy and environmental news, resonates strongly within the terms of primary cultural classifications, such as nature, growth, dirt and death,

Corner and Richardson[24] claim. Reporting about nuclear energy combines this with technological terms (nuclear, fission, radioactivity) which have connotations to the global nightmare of mass destruction[24].

Moral issues make a radioactive risk an important policy matter. Justice and morality are discussed by philosophers but, according to Douglas[25], little is said about how moral principle affects the perception of risk. She argues that 'acceptable risk' is also a question of acceptable standards of morality and decency. A risk discourse must incorporate an analysis of the cultural system from which the moral questions take their form. This study sheds light on moral issues, matters concerning power abuse and metaphysical questions experienced by my respondents. These issues emerged from the data without any preceding questions.

THE RESEARCH PROJECT: CHERNOBYL NINE YEARS AFTER

The final section of the paper outlines the ongoing research project. The aim of the study is to examine how fifteen respondents, all involved in the Chernobyl disaster, experience and interpret TV news nine years after the accident. The aim is to discover how the news affects the recipients' interpretation of a disaster and what kinds of thoughts, reactions and associations the risk messages provoke in retrospect, in the present and in the respondents' beliefs about the future. This study is a qualitative reception study which attempts to gain new knowledge about the interpretation of risk communication from the receiver's point of view. A semi-structured theme interview of key informants has been carried out. Fourteen authentic news stories about the disaster in the main television news programme of Norwegian Broadcasting, were chosen from all news releases about the accident during the first two months after the disaster. The author, a previous TV journalist,

edited an extract consisting of a 40 minute videotape which was shown to the respondents. They were asked immediately after screening to explain how they interpreted the news stories, and if they recalled any thoughts or associations especially related to their everyday life. The interviews have been recorded in their entirety, transcribed as texts and will be analysed by a text analysis model. The programme analysis of the news will be combined with the text analysis of the interviews. The reception process will be regarded as an interactive process between the message, the social context, the cultural conditions and the communicative competence of the recipient who is an active interpreter and co-producer of the meaning of the risk message.

This qualitative study comprises 15 persons (7 females, 8 males), aged 34 to 56 years. The respondents represent three groups, consisting of five persons each: (1) authorities/experts, (2) the media, and (3) lay people. The lay people were recruited from groups which were especially vulnerable during the Chernobyl disaster (cf. Ref. 26): parents, pregnant women, farmers, Sami reindeer herders, fishermen and hunters. Their education ranges from seven years' obligatory primary/lower secondary school to university education to a Ph.D. level. By now all the interviews are on tape, have been transcribed verbatim and coded. The interviews lasted approximately $1-1\frac{1}{2}$ hours. The transcripts comprise about 400 pages and the condensed, coded version 150 pages. At present the project is in the analysis phase.

The main anticipation is that disaster news is polysemic, i.e. the symbols and images have many possible meanings and interpretations for the respondents. One also expects to find that the respondents' constructions of and interpretations of meaning are influenced by their individual communicative competence, their life-worlds and their horizons of expectations. Presumably, the respondents participate actively in the construction of meaning and some respondents choose metaphysical coping strategies to deal with threatening information.

REFERENCES

1. Rescher, N. *Risk. A Philosophical Introduction to the Theory of Risk Evaluation and Management.* (New York, London: University Press of America) (1983).

2. Nohrstedt, S. A. and Tassew, A. *Communication and Crisis. An Inventory of Current Research.* (Stockholm: Psykologiskt Försvar) report 163(1) (1993).

3. National Research Council (NRC). *Improving Risk Communication* (Washington, DC: National Academy Press) (1989).

4. Höijer, B. *Studying Viewers' Reception of Television Programmes: Theoretical and Methodological Considerations.* Eur. J. Commun. **5**(1), 29–57 (1990).

5. Burgess, J. *Making Sense of Environmental Issues and Landscape Representations in the Media.* Landscape Res. **15**(3), 7–11 (1990).

6. Burgess, J. *The Production and Consumption of Environmental Meanings in the Mass Media: A Research Agenda for the 1990s.* Trans. Inst. Br. Geogr. **15**, 139–161 (1990).

7. Anderson, A. *Source-Media Relations: The Production of the Environmental Agenda.* In: The Mass Media and Environmental Issues. A. Hansen (Leicester: Leicester University Press) (1993).

8. Otway, H. and Wynne, B. *Risk Communication: Paradigm and Paradox.* Risk Anal. **9**(2), 141–145 (1989).

9. Keeney, R.-L. and von Winterfeldt, D. *Improving Risk Communication.* Risk Anal. **6**(4), 417–424 (1986).

10. Fisher, A. *Risk Communication Challenges.* Risk Anal. **11**(2), 173–179 (1991).

11. Slovic, P. *Perception of Risk from Radiation*. Paper presented at the NOSEB Conference on Children and Radiation, Trondheim, June 1993.

12. Plough, A. and Krimsky, S. *The Emergence of Risk Communication Studies: Social and Political Context*. Sci. Technol. Human Values **12**(3&4), 4–10 (1987).

13. Dunwoody, S. and Peters, H. P. *Mass Media Coverage of Technological and Environmental Risk: A Survey of Research in the United States and Germany*. Public Understanding Science (1) 199–230 (1992).

14. Giddens, A. *The Consequences of Modernity* (Cambridge: Polity Press) (1990).

15. Haynes, V. and Bojcun, M. *The Chernobyl Disaster: The True Story of a Catastrophe — An Unanswerable Indictment of Nuclear Power* (London: The Hogarth Press) (1988).

16. Singer, E. and Endreny, P. *Reporting Hazards: Their Benefits and Costs*. J. Commun. **37**(3), 10–26 (1987).

17. Corner, J., Richardson, K. and Fenton, N. *Nuclear Reactions: Form and Response in 'Public Issue' Television* (London: John Libbey) (1990).

18. Wilkins, L. and Patterson, P. *Risk Analysis and the Construction of News*. J. Commun. **37**(3), 80–92 (1987).

19. Patterson, P. *Reporting Chernobyl: Cutting the Government Fog to Cover the Nuclear Cloud*. In: Bad Tidings: Communication and Catastrophe. Eds Walters *et al* (Hillsdale, New Jersey: Lawrence Erlbaum) (1989).

20. Lifton, R. J. *Imagining the Real: Beyond the Nuclear 'End'*. In: The Long Darkness. Ed. L. Grinspoon. (Binghamton, NY: Vail-Ballou Press) (1986).

21. Elliott, D. *Tales from the Darkside: Ethical Implications of Disaster Coverage*. In: Bad Tidings: Communication and Catastrophe. Eds Walters *et al* (Hillsdale, NJ: Erlbaum) (1989).

22. Günther, S. and Luckmann, T. *Are Secrets Immoral? The Construction of Secrets in Everyday Conversation*. Die Arbeitspapiere des Prosjektes Formen der kommunikativen Konstruktion von Moral. Nr. 16/1995. Fachgruppe Soziologie, Universität Konstanz und Institut für Soziologie, Universität Giessen (1995).

23. Nohrstedt, S. A. and Nordlund, R. *Medier i kris. En forskningsöversikt över mediernas roll vid kriser*. (The Media in the Crisis. A Research Summary of the Media's Role during Crises. In Swedish) (Stockholm: Psykologist Försvar) report 163(4) (1993).

24. Corner, J. and Richardson, K. *Environmental Communication and the Contingency of Meaning: A Research Note*. In: The Mass Media and Environmental Issues. A. Hansen (Leicester: Leicester University Press) (1993).

25. Douglas, M. *Risk Acceptability According to the Social Sciences* (London: Routledge) (1986).

26. NOU. *Informasjonskriser*. Norges Offentlige Utredninger (Information Crises. The Official Reports of Norway) (Oslo: Universitetsforlaget) (In Norwegian) (1986).

Radiation Protection Dosimetry
Vol. 68, No. 3/4, pp. 293–296 (1996)
Nuclear Technology Publishing

INTERACTIONS THROUGH THE NETWORK — UNDERSTANDING THE MYTHS TO CREATE NEW WAYS OF INFORMATION EXCHANGE

I. V. Zakharov
International Laboratory VEGA
Narodnogo Opolcheniya Street 34
123423 Moscow, Russia

Abstract — The introduction of open data networks in the former Soviet Union, even concerning nuclear matters, collided with Soviet myths of, for example, nuclear secrets, information prohibition and dangers of international communication. Moreover, it was considered very complicated. These myths share many of the features with perception of radiation risk, such as dread, fear and misunderstanding. The new opportunities for information exchange, created by modern telecommunications and computer networks, can dispel these myths and perceptions concerning radiation risk, provided proper consideration of the myths' origins is taken. New ways of information exchange, such as creating extensive, international information infrastructures, based on Internet, can create new conditions for presenting the social conditions related to radiation risk.

Radiation risk, both in the scientific sense, and particularly in everyday cognition, has turned out to be a strongly mythologised category. Ways and methods of receiving information, peculiarities of its perceptions and patterns of image construction, are such that understanding of this part of reality deviates from reality itself and moves toward myth.

What is a myth? Something that does not really exist but is actively cultivated. Each epoch, each political system creates its own mythology. Unlike rumours, myths are well regulated, lasting and stable. Rumour appears rapidly as a quick public response to some event (whether natural or political) and develops spontaneously, while a myth is created systematically and is long lasting, and with the concrete aim of the construction of an image. This image may be either profitable for the constructor, or rather simply and universally explain the phenomena which cannot be analysed seriously because of lack of knowledge, desire or time. The main advantage of a myth is that it does not require logical comprehension, because all its theses are primarily perceived as axiomas. Simplicity and the apparent probability of the myth promotes its fixation in mass conciousness and creates a corresponding stereotype of thinking. This stereotype is often very difficult to overcome, especially in cases of so-called social myths. Social myths are constructed for decades and are very stable to external conditions, like changes in the political situation or scientific discoveries that recover the things, for the explanation of which the myth was constructed.

It seems reasonable for us to pay attention to the mythologisation of reality in two areas: in the area of development of open telecommunication in the former USSR, and in the area of forming an adequate perception of radiation risk.

In the period of appearance and development of computer telecommunication in the former USSR (however, as it has turned out, in other countries as well) many types of social myths had to be met and overcome. Telecommunication was absolutely new and unknown in the USSR in the middle of the 1980s. A long time was required to explain its sense and purpose to people. This does not mean the technological part of the development of a network infrastructure in the country, nor the technical difficulties of creation and adaptation of communication software. It is first of all about the beginning of wide and open access to international networks for regular representatives of education, science and culture (mainly humanitarian). As soon as its essence as an effective, free and open way of access to information and contact with colleagues abroad became clear, difficulties with its perception and development began to arise. Myths of prohibition of such a kind of connection and communication were the hardest to overcome. For many years of 'stagnation', a stable stereotype notion of information as something closed to the public was composed. The first reaction of a person who learned of the opportunities of computer telecommunication was usually something like 'it's impossible, it simply cannot exist'. Immediately after demonstration of electronic mail and other types of communication, the image of closedness worked: 'It cannot be allowed, it is something that should be prohibited, we need a special permission for this'. This stereotype that had historical origins was transferred into a myth, the existence of which had other psychological and social implications. Still another myth existed parallel to this one and followed it in some sense: that computer telecommunication is dangerous. There were apprehensions of an ideological type (it should be taken into consideration that our work began in 1985–86), and fears of possible 'network diversion' and dread of opening some important secret evolved.

Another more widespread myth is that telecommunication requires special technical skill and wide experience of computer work. Often there are the reasons like 'we are humanitarians, we do not understand it and cannot work with this equipment'. Information about many non-technicians having successfully used telecommunication for a long time, causes astonishment, and in some cases even mistrust and suspicion.

Many Russian scientists work within strict budget frames and have a strong perception that 'it is very expensive, and we haven't money'. When we managed to convince them that it is either not very expensive or free, the following 'mythological chain' is built in many cases:

It's impossible → (after demonstration) → It's prohibited → (we calmed, that it is allowed) → It's difficult → (after explanation and examples) → It's expensive → (after explanation and figures) → It's impossible, it must be prohibited. And finally, in the case of free variant → It's suspicious.

This merry-go-round clearly shows the nature and vitality of social myths that were constructed over a long period of time.

In many cases, installed telecommunication systems were not used as they were supposed to be initially, which promoted the confirmation of these myths in consciousness. Images of something extra-complicated and important was artificially created, there was no openness and accessibility for all researchers and scientists, which was the main reason for installation and use of electronic mail. In simple words, the computer and modem are locked in the room of the director or other persons responsible for the mail, and other researchers are not allowed to use it. The aims of such things may be different, but myths are being cultivated this way.

However, despite all these moments, telecommunication in Russia continues to develop, and with our help too. Several computer networks have appeared in Russia during the past few years. Some of them are connected with nuclear energy in some way. Thus, one of the most mighty of Russian computer networks, RELCOM, was created and developed on the base of the Kurchatov Institute of Atomic Energy, the leading Russian scientific institution in this area. The scientific conference 'Research Networking in Russia and other NATO Partners', organised by NATO and with the active participance of the VEGA laboratory, was held in Golitzyno (Moscow Region) in October, 1994[1]. Among others, the system of computer telecommunication connections of the Joint Institute of Nuclear Researches in Dubna was presented at the Conference. This system (it is called JINET) began as a local network of the Institute and is now connected to the world computer networks via different channels.

Nuclear energy itself and related questions are also the materials for construction of different myths. It especially concerns the themes of security and human health influence. It can easily be observed, on the example of elucidation of events related to the Cherno-

byl accident, by media in different time periods (beginning and the end of 'Reconstruction' period at the end of the 1980s, at the moment of disintegration of the Soviet Union, and now). At every moment one can find several reasons for this or that interpretation of the facts, different presentation of data, i.e. reasons for myth creation. These are approximately the same reasons that we saw in the case of telecommunication perception: fear, dread of openness, someone's profit. The consequences are the same too: misunderstanding, misinterpretation, and in some cases, intentional lies. Unfortunately, the consequences of 'radiation myths' are often deadly.

There are several ways of using telecommunication in nuclear energy matters that can be mentioned.

One of them is the creation of different structures, like BBS or teleconferences, devoted to the problem. These things are important for the scientists working on the subject. Discussion of radiological topics through the computer network allows us to solve many problems connected with scientific elaborations, constructing the whole image of the subject in the regime of conversation. This direction can become more effective now with the help of existing Internet resources.

Elaboration of networks that link personnel of different nuclear objects is the other direction. Consulting activity is the main one here. Active interaction between systems of a similar type is possible, which allows common working strategies to be developed.

The third way of telecommunication application is closely connected with the concept of security. It involves the creation of radiological databases, i.e. original information about this or that nuclear object, and which can be used in case of emergency. Databases can contain many different components: technical, radiological, demographic. Assessment of the possible consequences of the emergency should be included. Databases of this kind should be connected to a centre, which serves as an information collector in this case. This information should be accessible not only to colleagues of nuclear energy facilities, but to other services as well. One of them is the disaster medicine service. Operative connection with medical centres, pharmaceutical suppliers and epidemiological organisations, sites of formation of special medical divisions and different governmental institutions is necessary here. At first this integrated data bank concept was developed in the form of the Russian distributed data bank of Chernobyl information. This data bank was organised for the purpose of data exchange between Russian scientific centres concerned with the scientific programme of the State Chernobyl Committee. E-mail communications were used for exchange of data concerning e.g. contamination, health effects, demography, agriculture, and source terms. The WWW (World Wide Web) technology is most convenient as a platform for a distributed information system which represents the integrated data bank by itself.

Telecommunication is also important as a method of

operative on-site connection in case of emergency situations. Computer, modem and each functioning telephone are required for reports from the site. This information, that comes directly from the place, allows the situation to be assessed sensibly and to solve the problems properly. This method can also be used for public information.

We participate (practically, analytically, methodically) in the organisation and support several 'logic networks' that aim to use telecommunication for the joint activity of specialists in the area of early warning of national conflicts, disaster medicine and other issues. It is obvious to us, that in spite of undoubted differences, there are some common features of telecommunication functioning in these areas.

It seems there are the following levels of circulation of radiological information that can be distinguished:

(a) operative (level of routine on-going functioning),
(b) scientific (expert level),
(c) governmental (level of decision making),
(d) social (public, mass level).

There are special types of information and concrete problems with its exchange at each of these levels:

(a) This is information for technical experts and operators. It should be as concrete as possible and deal with concrete objective matters. This information can give nothing to non-specialists, it may simply be incomprehensible to them. Misunderstanding will cause wrong interpretation, i.e. myth may be constructed, which may increase common fear and alarm.
(b) The widest circulation of information and opinions should be carried out among the scientific community. Otherwise, different and mutually exclusive conceptions appear in different countries and even in different institutes. Scientific achievements are often put in the first place, scientific discussions are being carried out to the public, which causes public misunderstanding and mistrust to the scientific community in general.
(c) The third way is particularly important because it should help to work out common concepts of security. There are different governmental approaches to this problem in different countries, but, in any case, these approaches should be known so that there is an opportunity to co-ordinate and to avoid myths about closedness.
(d) The psycho-social aspects should be taken in consideration when disseminating information to the public. Telecommunication can essentially facilitate the access to different information databases, but it should be remembered that these data vary greatly from country to country. Approaches to radiation risk and radiation itself are completely different in various regions of the

world, and in the case of a completely open network, some type of information noise appears. It is difficult to catch the right strategy in it and an impression of general confusion appears, in which no one knows what to do and no one trusts anybody. To avoid an increase of panic, psycho-social and ethno-cultural peculiarities of the population should be taken into consideration when working out systems of access to informational sources, including telecommunication.

New ways of information exchange, including opportunities and dangers of developing the Internet, can create new conditions both for appearance and destruction of myths in social perceptions, related with problems of radiation risk.

Related Internet WWW-sites:

"Polyn" database:
http://polyn.net.kiae.su

Chernobyl and its consequences:
http://www.physics.mcgill.ca/WWW/oleh/ukr-info.html

International Conference "One Decade After Chernobyl":
http://www.iaea.or.at/worldatom/thisweek/preview/chernobyl.html

Chernobyl — Ten Years On:
http://www.uilondon.org/chernidx.html

Chernobyl No More
http://www.t0.or.at/~C%2b10/

Chernobyl Facts
http://faraday.clas.virginia.edu/~ana4a/ChFacts.html

Chernobyl Organizations
http://faraday.clas.virginia.edu/~ana4a/ChList.html

SunSite exhibition of Soviet Documents related to Chernobyl
http://sunsite.unc.edu/expo/soviet.exhibit/chernobyl.html

Chernobyl — Ten Years On: radiological and health impact
http://www.nea.fr/html/rp/chernobyl/chernobyl.html

Information from Chernobyl and the Surrounding Area
http://www-personal.umich.edu/~bbusby/chern.htm

NIRS Web Site
http://www.essential.org/nirsnet/

A World Vision Home Page
http://solar.rtd.utk.edu/oldfriends/wvision/index.html

SIR-C/X-SAR image Chernobyl, Ukraine
http://www.jpl.nasa.gov/sircxsar/chernobyl.html

International VEGA Laboratory
http://www.glasnet.ru/~vega

REFERENCES

1. Proceedings of the NATO Advanced Networking Workshop. *Research Networking in Russia and other NATO Partners.* Golitzyno (Moscow Region) (Scientific and Environmental Affairs Division, NATO, Brussels) (1994).

2. *Real-time On-line Decision Support Systems (RODOS) for Off-site Emergency Management Following a Nuclear Accident.* International Scientific Collaboration on the Consequences of the Chernobyl accident (1991–95), Final report (Luxembourg) (1996).

3. Proceedings of International Conference. *One Decade after Chernobyl: Summing up the Consequences of the Accident*, Vienna, Austria, 8–12 April 1996 (Vienna: IAEA) (1996).

4. Khramtzov, P. *The Labyrinth of Internet. Practical manual.* (Moscow: Electroninform) (1996).

RADIATION RISK, RISK PERCEPTION
AND
SOCIAL CONSTRUCTIONS

Proceedings of a Workshop,
Oslo, Norway, October 19–20 1995

AUTHOR INDEX

Radiation Protection Dosimetry

INSTRUCTIONS TO AUTHORS

SCOPE: Radiation Protection Dosimetry covers all aspects of personal and environmental dosimetry and monitoring, for both ionising and non-ionising radiations. This includes the biological aspects, physical concepts, biophysical dosimetry, external and internal personal dosimetry and monitoring, environmental and workplace monitoring, accident dosimetry, and dosimetry related to the protection of patients. Particular emphasis is placed on papers covering the fundamentals of dosimetry such as units, radiation quantities and conversion factors. Papers covering archeological dating are included only if the fundamental measurement method or technique, such as thermoluminescence, has direct application to personal dosimetry measurements. Papers covering the dosimetric aspects of radon or other naturally occurring radioactive materials and low level radiation are included. Animal experiments and ecological sample measurements are not included unless there is a significant relevant content related to dosimetry in man.

Scientific or Technical Papers should be full papers of a theoretical or practical nature with comprehensive descriptions of the work covered.

Scientific or Technical Notes should be brief, covering not more than 4 printed pages (one page contains about 800 words or equivalent in figures) and are likely to cover work in development or topics of lesser significance than full papers.

Letters to the Editor should be written as letters with the authors' names and addresses at the end and should be marked 'For Publication'.

LANGUAGE: All contributors should be in **English**. Spelling should be in accordance with the Concise Oxford Dictionary. However please use dosemeter rather than dosimeter, for consistency within the journal. Authors whose mother tongue is not English are requested to ask someone with a good command of English to review their contribution before submission

TITLES should be brief and as informative as possible. A short title of not more than 50 characters for a running head should be supplied.

AUTHORS' names and addresses (with full postal address) should appear immediately below the title

ABSTRACTS containing up to 150 words should be provided on a separate page, headed by the title and authors' names.

SCRIPTS must be typewritten and **double** spaced. One copy must be directly typed and **three** additional (photocopies) should be provided for refereeing purposes to minimise the time required for refereeing. Headings should be given to main sections and sub-sections which should not be numbered. The title page should contain just the title, authors' names and addresses and a short running title. Manuscripts should be written in the third person and not the first. If your manuscript is prepared using a computer or word processor it would be helpful if you could also send a copy of the computer disc (please specify software).

FIGURES AND TABLES should not be inserted in the pages of manuscript but should be supplied on separate sheets. One high quality set of illustrations and figures, suitable for direct reproduction, e.g. black ink or good quality black and white prints of line drawings and graphs, should be provided with original typed manuscript. These should be approximately twice the final printed size (full page printed area = 19cm x 15cm). The lettering should be of such a size that the letters and symbols will remain legible after reduction to fit the printed area available. Tables should be typed. Tables should be lightly lined in pencil. All figures and tables should be numbered, using Arabic numerals, on the reverse side of each copy. Numbered captions or titles should be typed on a separate sheet. Figures and tables should be kept to the minimum consistent with clear presentation of the work reported. Half-tone photographs should only be included if absolutely necessary. Figures generated by computer graphics are generally NOT suitable for direct reproduction. Photocopies of all figures and tables should accompany each copy of the manuscript for refereeing purposes. Colour figures can be reproduced at cost.

UNITS, SYMBOLS AND EQUATIONS: SI units should be used throughout but other established units may be included in brackets (Note that cGy is **not** acceptable). Any Greek letters or special symbols used in the text should be identified in the margin on each occasion they are used. Isotope mass numbers should appear at the upper left of the element symbol e.g. ^{90}Sr. Equations should be fully typed. FOOTNOTES should only be included if absolutely necessary. They should be typed on a separate sheet and the author should give a clear indication in the text by inserting (see footnote) so that they may appear on the correct page.

ABBREVIATIONS which are not in common usage should be defined when they first appear in the text.

REFERENCES should be indicated in the text by superior numbers in parenthesis and the full reference should be given in a list at the end of the paper in the following form, in the order in which they appear in the text:-

1. Crase, K.W. and Gammage, R.B. *Improvements in the Use of Ceramic BeO in TLD*, Health Phys. **29**(5) 739-746 (1975).
2. Clarke, R.H. and Webb G.A.M. *Methods for Estimating Population Detriment and their Application in Setting Environmental Discharge Limits.* Proceedings of Symposium - Biological Implications of Radionuclides Released from Nuclear Industries, Vienna, March 1979. IAEA-SM-237/6, 149-154 (1980)
3. Aird, E.G.A.A. *An Introduction to Medical Physics.* William Heineman Medical Books Ltd (London). ISBN 0 433 003502. (1983)
4. Duftschmid, K.E. *TLD Personnel Monitoring Systems - The Present Situation.* Radiat. Prot. Dosim. **2**(1) 2-12 (1982).

All the authors' names and initials (unless there are more than 10 authors), the title of the paper, the abbreviated title of the journal, volume number, page numbers and year should be given. Abbreviated journal titles should be in accordance with the current World List of Scientific Periodicals. If all of this information is not available the reference should not be cited.

PROOFS will be sent to any nominated author for final proof reading and must be returned within 3 days of receipt using the addressed label which will be provided. Type-setting or printer's errors should be marked in red. Any other changes should be marked in green but if they are significant they may be charged to the authors. Authors' changes marked in red may not be accepted. The Editor reserves the right to make editorial corrections to manuscripts. An order form for additional reprints will accompany proofs.

SUBMISSION: All manuscripts (original and three copies) and correspondence should be addressed to Mr E.P. Goldfinch, Executive Editor, Nuclear Technology Publishing, P.O. Box No 7, Ashford, Kent TN23 1YW, England. It is *essential* that they are accompanied by six fully addressed adhesive labels addressed to the author nominated to receive proofs and correspondence. These will be used for acknowledgement of receipt of the manuscript, notification of acceptance, return of proofs to authors and supply of reprints. Papers will be considered only on the understanding that they are not currently being submitted to other journals. The Publishers, The Editor-in-Chief and the Editorial Board do not accept responsibility for the technical content, the use of that content or the views expressed by authors.

CORRESPONDENCE: Please ensure that you provide telephone, FAX and E-mail numbers if available. Please quote the manuscript number in any correspondence once receipt of your manuscript has been acknowledged.

COMPUTER MANUSCRIPTS: If your manuscript is prepared using a computer or word processor, publication may be quicker if you submit a copy of the disc with the manuscript copies. The following programmes can be readily accommodated: - Multimate, Wordstar, MS Word, Word Perfect, Displaywrite, ASCII files and IBM MS DOS Pro Dos Files.

COPYRIGHT: Authors submitting manuscripts do so on the understanding that if accepted for publication, copyright of the article shall be assigned to Nuclear Technology Publishing unless other specific arrangements are made.

GENERAL: In order to ensure rapid publication it is most important that **all** of the above instructions are complied with in **full**. Failure to comply may result in considerable delay in publication or the **return** of manuscripts to the author. In case of difficulty with illustrations and figures please consult the photo-reprographic section of your establishment. If illustrations of a quality high enough for direct off-set photographic reproduction cannot be supplied they may be redrawn by the publishers at the request of authors if all relevant details are provided. A charge will be made if requirements are extensive.

RADIATION RISK, RISK PERCEPTION
AND
SOCIAL CONSTRUCTIONS

Proceedings of a Workshop,
Oslo, Norway, October 19–20 1995

LIST OF PARTICIPANTS

Aanes, H.
Halliburton
Kokstaddalen 27
KOKSTAD
N-5061   NORWAY

Allen P.T.
University of Surrey
Robens Institute
GUILDFORD
Surrey, GU2 5XH   UK

Backe S.
Institute for Energy Technology
PO Box 40
KJELLER
N-2007   NORWAY

Ballangrud P.
Norwegian Armes Forces NBC - Defence School
Hvalsmoen
HONEFOSS
N-3500   NORWAY

Baverstam U.
Swedish Radiation Protection Institute
Head of Research Department
Box 60204, Fack
STOCKHOLM
S-171 16   SWEDEN

Bennerstedt T.
Nordic Nuclear Safety Research
PO Box 2336
BERGSHAMRA
S-76010   SWEDEN

Brenna M.
Norwegian Radiation Protection Authority
PO Box 55, OSTERAS
N-1345   NORWAY

Brenot J.M.
CEA, IPSN/SEGR
60-68 Avenue du General Leclerc
BP 6, Fontenay-aux-Roses
F-92265   FRANCE

Christensen T.
Norwegian Radiation Protection Authority
PO Box 55
OSTERAS
N-1345   NORWAY

Christiansen O.T.
Ministry of Health & Social Affairs
PO Box 8011 Dep.
OSLO
N-0030   NORWAY

Christoffersen C-E.
Norwegian Radiation Protection Authority
Grini Naeringspark 13
PO Box 55
OSTERAS
N-1345   NORWAY

Ehdwall H.
Swedish Radiation Protection Institute
STOCKHOLM
S-171 16   SWEDEN

Eijkelhof H.M.C.
University of Utrecht
Centre for Science and Mathematics Education
PO Box 80008
UTRECHT
NL-3508 TA   NETHERLANDS

Enander A.
Swedish War College
Jarnvegsgatan 6
KSRLSTAD
S-652 25   SWEDEN

Engoy T.
Norwegian Defence Research Institute
PO Box 25
KJELLER
N-2007   NORWAY

Eriksen G.S.
Norwegian Food Control Authority
PO Box 8187-Dep.
OSLO
N-0034   NORWAY

Gasemyr J.
University of Oslo
Department of Mathematics
PO Box 1053
Blindern, OSLO
N-0316   NORWAY

Gonzalez F.
Universidad Complutense de Madrid/CIEMAT
Avd. Complutense 22
MADRID
E-28040   SPAIN

Hellstrom T.
Norwegian Food Control Authority
PO Box 8187-Dep.
OSLO
N-0034   NORWAY

Henriksen E.K.
University of Oslo
Department of Physics
PO Box 1048, Blindern
OSLO
N-0316   NORWAY

Kelly G.N.
Commission of the European Communities
Directorate Gen. DGXII.F.6
Rue de la Loi 200
BRUSSELS
B-1049   BELGIUM

Kolstad A.K.
Norwegian Radiation Protection Authority
PO Box 55, OSTERAS
N-1345   NORWAY

Larsen A-K.
Norwegian Radiation Protection Authority
PO Box 55, OSTERAS
N-1345   NORWAY

Lindell B.
Swedish Radiation Protection Institute
PO Box 60204
STOCKHOLM
S-171 16   SWEDEN

Maerli M.B.
Norwegian Radiation Protection Authority
Grini Naeringspark 13
PO Box 55
OSTERAS
N-1345   NORWAY

Mardberg B.
Swedish War College
PO Box 27805
STOCKHOLM
S-115 93   SWEDEN

Matheson T.
Ministry of Health & Social Affairs
PO Box 8011 Dep.
OSLO
N-0030   NORWAY

Morrey M.E.
National Radiological Protection Board
Chilton
DIDCOT
Oxon   OX11 ORQ
UK

Natvig B.
University of Oslo
Department of Mathematics
PO Box 1053
Blindern
OSLO
N-0316   NORWAY

Nielsen T.H.
University of Oslo
Centre for Technology and Culture
Gaudstadalleen 21
OSLO
N-0371   NORWAY

Oughton D.H.
Agricultural University of Norway
Isotope and Electron Microscope Laboratories
PO Box 5026
AS
N-1342   NORWAY

Poffijn A.
Ministry of Public Health
Service for Protection against Ionising Radiation
RAC-Vesalivs 2/3
BRUSSELS
B-1010   BELGIUM

Prades A.
CIEMAT Instituto Technologia Nuclear
ED.1 D.113
Avd. Complutense 22
MADRID
E-28040   SPAIN

Reitan J.B.
Norwegian Radiation Protection Authority
Radiation Medicine Department
PO Box 55
OSTERAS
N-1345   NORWAY

Sjoberg L.
Stockholm School of Economics
Center for Risk Research
Box 6501
STOCKHOLM
S-113 83   SWEDEN

Skuterud L.
Norwegian Radiation Protection Authority
PO Box 55
OSTERAS
N-1345   NORWAY

Slovic P.
Decision Research
1201 Oak Street
EUGENE
OR 97401   USA

Stang E.
Centre for Technology & Culture UiO
Gaustadalleen 21
OSLO
N-0371   NORWAY

Stenmark B.E.
National Maritime Administration
Norrkopingn
SVERIGE
S-601 78   SWEDEN

Stephens S.
University of Michigan
Department of Anthropology
1020 LSA Building
ANN ARBOR
MI 48109-1383   USA

Strand P.
Norwegian Radiation Protection Authority
Osterndalen 25
PO Box 55, OSTERAS
N-1345   NORWAY

Tarabrina N.
Russian Academy of Sciences
Institute of Psychology
Laboratory for Traumatic Stress Studies
Yaroslavskaya Str. 13
MOSCOW
129366   RUSSIA

Thommesen G.
Norwegian Radiation Protection Authority
PO Box 55
OSTERAS
N-1345   NORWAY

Tonnessen A.
Ministry of Children & Family Affairs
Risk Perception Project Group
PO Box 8036 Dep.
OSLO
N-0030   NORWAY

Unhjem J.F.
Norwegian Radiation Protection Authority
PO Box 55
OSTERAS
N-1345   NORWAY

Van Bladel L.
Ministry of Public Health
Radiation Protection Department
Vesaliusgebouw 2/319
Quartier Vesale 2-3 SPRI
BRUSSELS
B-1010   BELGIUM

Van Nuffelen D.
Ministere de la Sante Publique et de l'Environ.
SPRI - Cite administrative de l'Etat
Quartier Vesale
BRUSSELS
B-1012   BELGIUM

Vanmarcke H.
SCK-CEN   Radiation Protection Research Unit
Studiecentrum voor Kernenergie
Boeretang 200
MOL
B-2400   BELGIUM

Vettenranta S.
Norwegian University of Science & Technology
Faculty of Social Sciences   Dept. of Education
DRAGVOLL
N-7055   NORWAY

Waldahl R.W.
University of Oslo
Department of Media & Communication
Box 1093
BLINDERN
N-0317   NORWAY

Weisaeth L.
University of Oslo
Division of Disaster Psychiatry
PO Box 39
Gaustad
OLSO
N-0320   NORWAY

Zakharov I.V.
International Laboratory "VEGA"
Opolcheniya Street 34
MOSCOW
129336   RUSSIA